Continental Shelves that Influence Tropical Storms

James M. McCanney, M.S.

PRINCIPIA METEOROLOGIA

THE
PHYSICS OF SUN EARTH WEATHER

Published By

jmccanneyscience.com press

Minneapolis, Minnesota

2nd Printing - 2004

ISBN 0-9722186-5-3

PRINCIPIA METEOROLOGIA

THE
PHYSICS OF SUN EARTH WEATHER

About the author and this text:

James M. McCanney, M.S. received a sound classical physics training at St. Mary's University, receiving a Bachelor of Arts degree with a double major in physics and mathematics in 1970. He was offered full scholarship awards to three major US physics graduate schools to pursue his graduate physics studies. However, he chose instead to postpone graduate studies for a period of three years while he traveled and taught Physics and Mathematics in Spanish in Latin America.

During this time he spent a good deal of time traveling to ruins of ancient cities and archeological sites, studying firsthand many times as the ruins were dug from under dirt that had not been moved for thousands of years. Also during this time he developed the basis for his theoretical work that would, at a later date, deal with the celestial mechanics of N-bodies and plasma physics. It was here also that he learned to appreciate the fact that the ruins and devastation he was witnessing had to have come from celestial events that were so devastating that they left the Earth and these stone cities in ruins, in some cases, leaving no trace of the inhabitants.

With this new understanding of archeology, astronomy of the ancients, physics and the world around him, Mr. McCanney returned to graduate school in 1973 and earned a master's degree in nuclear and solid-state physics from Tulane University, New Orleans, LA. He was again offered a full fellowship to continue on with Ph.D. studies, but once again he declined and returned to Latin America to study archeology and teach physics, mathematics and computer science in Spanish. He continued his work to explore the mysteries of celestial mechanics and its relationship to the planets, moons and other celestial bodies.

In 1979 he joined the faculty of Cornell University, Ithaca N.Y. as an introductory instructor in physics. It was during this time that he had access to NASA data returning daily from the Voyager I and II spacecraft as they traveled by the planets Jupiter, Saturn and beyond (as well as data from many other space craft). It was here he recognized that his theoretical work regarding the electro-dynamic nature of the solar system and universe had its signatures in the new data that was streaming in from the edges of the solar system. All standard science continued to look at gravitational explanations for the working of the planets, moons and other objects of the solar system, while Mr. McCanney was applying his electro-dynamic scientific theories, and ventured to say for the first time that comets were not dirty snowballs. His papers were published at first in the standard astrophysical journals, but soon he began to receive resistance from the standard astronomical community and within a short period of time, the journals would no longer publish his theoretical work. Mr. McCanney was removed from his teaching position because of his beliefs regarding the electro-dynamic nature of the solar system.

Contrary to the traditional belief that the solar system formed all at one time 4.5 billion years ago and has not changed significantly since, Mr. McCanney's theoretical work essentially stated that the solar system was dynamic and adopting new members on an ongoing basis. He pointed to the planet Venus, the Jovian moon Io, the Saturnian moon Titan and the small planet Pluto (which supports an atmosphere even though it is so distant from the warmth of the Sun and has insufficient gravity to hold an atmosphere for long) as being obvious new members of our solar system. He stated that all this was proof that the way this occurred was by "planetary capture".

His theoretical work additionally stated that comets were not dirty snowballs, but were large electrical "vacuum cleaners" in outer space. The comets were drawing in vast amounts of material by way of powerful electrical forces and there was potential for very large comets capable of disrupting the planetary structure that was already in place. His innovative theories on plasma physics and a new model for fusion in the solar atmosphere provided the basis for the electric fields and plasma discharge phenomena that have become the core elements of his theoretical models of the true nature of the solar system in which we live.

Upon being fired from the physics department for his radical beliefs, Mr. McCanney was rehired shortly thereafter by the mathematics department also at Cornell University, where he taught for another year and a half and continued to publish his papers in astrophysical journals. Once again astronomers forced his removal and he was once again blackballed from publishing in the astrophysics journals in1981.

During this time Mr. McCanney established himself as the originator of the theoretical work regarding the electrical nature of the cosmos for which he coined the term "THE ELECTRIC UNIVERSE", which today is being proven correct on an ongoing basis by space-probes returning data from outer space. Many of his predictions such as x-rays to the sunward side of comet nuclei, that comet nuclei would be found to have no ice or water frozen on their surfaces and that comets interact electrically with the Sun to affect Earth weather, have now been confirmed by direct measurements in 1986, 1996, 2001 and 2002 respectively. Many other more abstract concepts have also been verified.

There exists a rare combination of factors that makes Mr. McCanney a unique person who stands alone in the development of the scientific principles and historical perspectives summarized in this book. Some have tried to borrow and copy this work, but when observers consider the factors involved they too will agree that the extensive rewriting of standard scientific structures had to be accomplished by someone with a rare set of characteristics and circumstances.

He was always at the top of his classes in Mathematics and Physics and was always creating his own formulas and proofs. His education was soundly based in classical and modern physics. He was able to recognize that when the basic new aspects of the functioning of the solar system were understood and then verified in space probe data, he had the ability to extend this information and take it to all its logical conclusions. This all occurred while working in and around the top rated scientists of the day at Cornell University who were still at least 2 decades behind what Mr. McCanney was discovering and writing.

Another unique condition was that Cornell University offered a rare location since it was not only a Library of Congress (if it was in print it was there), but also it was a repository of data for NASA. Armed with his existing theoretical work and this incredible source of information, and with the timing that coincided with the daily arrival of new data from the Voyager and other space craft from the far reaches of the solar system, he was in a totally unique position to do what he has done.

An essential requirement of anyone who attempts to alter the fundamental propositions of a subject as complex as astronomy and astrophysics, is an in depth knowledge of the history of that and all related sciences. Mr. McCanney has studied the history of science extensively and understands where the theories came from that currently make up the structures of science. He studied archaeology and geology and was in the field in remote areas to witness ancient civilizations unearthed from a previous devastation,.

He has the rare ability to speak at many levels. He has taken a topic as complex as plasma physics and celestial mechanics (the study of rarified gasses and the motion of the celestial bodies) and simplified it in terms that the general public can understand. That is why his university classes always grew rapidly. He does not make an ego trip out of trying to impress his audiences with big words and unusual terms as do many university professors or the recent influx of internet hoaxsters.

There are few people who would have the tenacity to pursue and uphold their beliefs for as long as he has had to do in facing the odds pitted against him over the past decades, and to emerge in tact with as full a commitment as when he started that long ago. His personal philosophy states that he will not accept government funding on the principle that it has corrupted the scientific process.

These numerous and individually rare characteristics make the record clear that the important contributions made here combine both personal traits and a situation of "being in the right place at the right time" as the space craft data poured into Cornell University as Mr McCanney's theoretical ideas were solidifying.

In 1981 the Interdisciplinary Journal KRONOS agreed to publish what has since become known in inner circles as the "3 Part comet paper", which is republished in it's entirety at the end of the first book of this series Planet X, Comets and Earth Changes, along with other historically significant publications of Mr. McCanney. His work today includes many new significant insights into the connection between the Sun, comets, earth weather, The Sun-Earth Connection and Earth Changes. The results of that knowledge will become obvious when you read these books.

Mr. McCanney has also remained active and well known within the space science - astronomy community and within professional societies, and although standard astronomers still resist accepting his theoretical work, he is generally well respected amongst his peers in these communities when attending professional conferences. He is what some have called "the last of the independent scientists" who were able to work "on the inside" and still remain active to talk about it on the "outside".

In the mid-1990s Mr. McCanney's work was recognized by a

group of high-level Russian scientists who had measured but did not understand electro-dynamic effects around Earth and in the solar system. They translated all of his papers to date into Russian. These are being taught at the university level as the leading edge of research in this field. It is only due to the ongoing and intentional efforts of NASA that his work has received such little attention in the western scientific community and press.

It should be pointed out also that no new or bizarre fundamental laws of physics are needed to understand the electro-dynamic nature of the universe. This entire textbook is based on standard physics and simply introduces the principles of the working of our solar system based on a new understanding of how the Sun produces fusion and therefore electric fields (and magnetic fields) in the solar system. Once these fundamental principles are put in place, the rest is simply the logical conclusion of standard laws of physics being applied to the situation.

It is very interesting to note that historical records of the major disasters witnessed by the ancients are now understood in light of this new understanding of how our solar system works. A scientific basis and the "theoretical key" has now been introduced to give fundamental understanding of the Biblical references regarding the End Days, The accounts of the Exodus from the Legends of the Jews, the Mayan accounts of Quetzalcoatl (the plumed serpent god of the night sky whose heart became the planet Venus), the accounts of the Egyptian mythological planet Nibiru, the accounts and historical records and writings of the destruction of Atlantis as well as the writings of such world renowned authors as Casey, Sitchin, Velikovsky, Blavatsky, Donnelly and others who could see beyond the standard and incorrect explanations of where we came from and the true history of man and our planet.

This book is a summary of information that spans over 25 years of serious research and is needed on the international market to inform the public of the true nature of our past relative to celestial events, and additionally, of the dangers that stand before us as we deal with the possibility of new planetary members being adopted into the solar system.

The books in this series do not make any specific predictions of dates on the arrival of a new celestial object nor does it make any predictions or analysis regarding any particular planetary object(s) that might come into the solar system. Additionally, regarding the historical events, these books do not state definitive dates for past events … but only indicate the most plausible dating based on current information. Dating of events is a difficult area of study and many times taken too lightly by people who have done insufficient study to know what they are really talking about. The study of ancient calendars, for example, is probably one of the most complicated areas of study known to man.

The current text is the fourth in a series of books. The first book Planet X, Comets and Earth Changes defines the science behind the true electrical workings of the solar system and relates it to historical studies and modern space probe data. It is a treatise written for the layman on the 25 years of Mr. McCanney's theoretical work. ***It is essential that the reader understand at minimum the basic contents of that book to put the current book into perspective. The reader will not understand the current book and the science of the ancients without having a basic understanding of the true electrical nature of the workings of the solar system.***

The second book of the series Surviving Planet X Passage (a 60 page pamphlet), although not essential, covers an aspect of history that the avid reader may well wish to understand. This is the re-calendaring of our celestial clock after the Earth's orbital elements have been affected by a close encounter with a near passage of a massive celestial object as we know has happened in the past. This book outlines what the ancients performed to rebuild their calendars for survival so they would know the correct planting seasons.

The third book Atlantis to Tesla – The Kolbrin Connection takes the reader's knowledge to a new level and for the first time, defines for the general public the Physics of the ancient advanced cultures such as Atlantis. It links the past with the present, giving also a glimpse of the direction we must take to assure our species a place amongst the stars.

The current book Principia Meteorologia - The Physics of Sun Earth Weather is the culmination of Mr. McCanney's lifelong work which now details the effects of electrical conditions in the solar system on space weather and ultimately the weather systems of Earth. At present there are two more books destined to become part of this series that will be released at later dates.

a.s.

TABLE OF CONTENTS

PREFACE

Putting this book into perspective

Introductory note by a friend of the author

Throughout the history of man through legend and fable, by far the most dominant factor in everyday existence, and also the least understood, has been weather. Man has always known that the weather was driven by the sun. But there are also historical references from all civilizations past, that comets have caused immense destruction and devastation upon earth. Confirmation of Mr. McCanney's famous ***Plasma Discharge Comet Model*** now corroborates these historical records.

Even today scientists mistakenly believe that the visible light from the sun is the dominant force in shaping our weather. In the 1970s as spacecraft data began to return to earth from the distant planets, Mr. McCanney's theoretical work on the electrical nature of the solar system and universe began to synthesize into the foundation that has become his lifelong weather work, now culminating in this book.

Previous books in this series have created the base of knowledge that the reader must understand before complex weather systems driven by solar electrical energy can be understood by the trained scientist as well as the layman. The plasma electrical environment of the solar system is extremely complex, but the individual principles and systems can be described one by one and then put together like a giant jigsaw puzzle.

By the time you finish reading this book, which is written for the average person on the street as well as Ph.D. scientists, you will have a thorough understanding of the complex term we call weather. Unfortunately, meteorology has been stalled in archaic and outdated principles. This book will be the seminal treatise for understanding meteorology that will last for hundreds of years.

a.s.

Preface by the Author

In preparing to write this book, the most difficult part of all was looking over the enormous quantity of data that I have collected over the decades on all aspects of the solar system and Earth weather. The problem was not writing the book, the problem was how to condense all of this material into a book of under 300 pages. Many of the individual topics -- hurricane formation and control for example -- could take up 300 pages by itself without any problem at all. The complex workings of the solar atmosphere could equally take up 300 pages or more.

The multi-layer magnetic field of Earth with a high-energy Van Allen Belts and extended plasma interaction with the solar wind, for example, would be enough to turn most average people away from every attempting to read this book. This created the second problem, that is, how to take an extremely complex topic such as outer space plasma physics and reduce it to a level that everyone would be able to understand.

It seems sometimes that the more you try to describe things, the harder it is to understand, especially for people not versed in technical jargon. The physicists and scientists of course revel in their ability to create huge words and long equations that few people could even hope to understand. Over the years I have had the opportunity to teach these topics on many levels and to experience for myself the plight of understanding complex topics given the limitation of our language.

An additional problem in trying to present this material is the sheer quantity of basic concepts that have to be presented to tie all of the loose ends together into one theoretical composite presentation. That is why this book has been left to be the fourth in the series. Without first obtaining an appreciation and somewhat of a working knowledge for the first three books in the series, even well trained scientists (especially well-trained scientists of a traditional mindset) would have a hard time dealing with a range of the newly and completely different topics that they will be exposed to in this book.

Thus it is based on the many years of teaching at all levels, giving radio show presentations as guest, and conducting my own weekly radio show that I have gained the ability to present material of this nature for a wide and diverse audience. What is really very interesting about all of this is that many scientists with Ph.D.'s will have a harder time understanding this than a novice to this complex area of study. That's because the Ph.D. has a storehouse of preconceived notions and biases that would first have to be overcome and overturned in fact before they could begin to reassemble the information presented in this book. For this reason there is a well-founded statement that the old scientific guard must die off before the new guard can be established and take its place.

As I look back over the decades of progress in realizations that I've come to, it seems truly amazing now that all of this science once lay out their totally unknown. There was a time not to long ago when we did not even know that there was a solar wind rushing by us. At the time this book goes to press the general consensus amongst the core elite scientists of the day is that outer space is electrically neutral. This sentiment is slowly changing, but as I daily and weekly read the titles of seminars in talks and projects within the standard scientific community, I realized that they are just beginning to ask the questions that I already had answers for decades ago.

There is not a day or week that goes by even now when I do not come to some new and startling conclusion regarding weather or the subtleties of the physics of the solar system. I am many times amazed during question-and-answer periods when I'm a guest on a radio show on the insightful and thoughtful questions of the general public. It seems like deep within their psyche it is well known that all of these principles exist in that there is a basic electrical nature to us as human beings. One thing I've learned both scientifically and intuitively is that man has a link electrically to the universe we live in. It was during the 1990s as I worked with Russian scientists pioneering the weather work that you will now read about in this book relative to concepts such as tornadoes on the sun that we talked in the background about the electrical connection of humans to the environment of the cosmos.

The true understanding of the electrical nature of the solar system and its weather has only been possible due to the discoveries of satellites as they broadcasted data from the far reaches of the solar system in the past few decades. As many scientists attempted to remain with traditional ways of thinking, very early on I realized that there had to be a distinct diversion and entirely new set of principles to describe what this data was truly saying. Many times in science it is the key discovery that later seems so simple that was so very difficult before that key discovery was made. In the case of weather of the solar system and ultimately our planet earth, that key was the understanding that there was an excess current (electrical current that is) of protons in the solar wind.

I made this discovery as I searched for the primary source of electricity that powered what I was seeing in the solar system. Once this key was developed, the rest of the physics flowed forth giving me the insight into the workings of comet's true plasma nature. It allowed me to see it for the first time in theory the electron beam that emerged from the sunward side to meet every celestial object in what I later termed a solar capacitor. The electron beam, highly concentrated or pinched as it is called the physics, allowed me to predict that there would be x-rays to the sunward side far from the comet's nucleus. This prediction was made in 1979 in my published papers, but was not discovered until 1996 when a NASA satellite happened to lock into a comet's field of view with an x-ray detector.

Since, many comets have been observed to have this "x-ray signature" far from the nucleus and always on the sunward side as my work predicted. It is now accepted as standard feature of all comets.

This electron beam also became a source of energy that drives the aurora activity of the earth and other planets. As the Voyageur spacecraft flew past Jupiter and Saturn around 1980, it turned out that these so-called planets were actually small unlit stars that had their own proton winds. This told me that fusion, the energy source of stars, was occurring high in the atmosphere of the small unlit stars. I was able to see in the data coming back from spacecraft all of the properties of the electrically active star in what we used to believe we're just planets. This, along with many other factors both theoretical and observational, led me to conclude that the sun's fusion was not deep in its core as traditional theory would have told you, but the fusion, as with Jupiter and Saturn, was high in the atmosphere of the sun.

This meant that the Sun's atmosphere was now seen to be reactive to its environment. An entire host of new theoretical work emerged almost immediately, the only problem being that the traditional astrophysics astronomy and space science communities were not prepared to accept these radical changes in the way of thinking. It is almost comical now 25 years after the Voyageur passages of the planets Jupiter and Saturn that some of the same scientists are beginning to just barely ask the questions they should have been asking back then. As a result of this, literally all of the work that I developed was done on my own and without the ability to publish this in the prestigious scientific journals. My original papers were published in astrophysics journals as you have read previously, but the vast majority of the material had to be published via other channels.

One of the most bizarre aspects of this entire development of theoretical work was that I literally had no one to talk to about this as it was being developed. But from the very earliest stages I knew that everything I was doing was correct and that someday hopefully before I died, there would be an opportunity to present this to the wider scientific community. As it turned out however, even to this day they are reluctant to turn to the direction of radical change that is required to accept the principles involved in my theoretical work. In spite of the fact that I have attended many high-level scientific conferences and presented this work amongst the company of the most exclusive scientists in the world, the vast majority of presentation of this material has been directly to the general public through my radio shows, television appearances and in my books (which by the way have been banned from bookstores and libraries).

There is a very bright side to all of this however, and that is now the general public has the benefit of receiving a true scientific education before the standard science community receives that same education. Another benefit to me has been the already visible lead time that I have had which clearly sets this work apart as original and unique in this world of government supported monopoly of science where ideas can be borrowed without referencing the original author and the peer review system of publication prevents the original author from publishing his own material.

Before getting into the text of what you might find to be a relatively complex book, I'm going to go through just a simple example to give you to feel for how electrical energy from the Sun is transferred down to earth's surface to cause the weather we see as we look up through the clouds.

All of this will make a lot more sense as you get towards the end of this book and start to put all the pieces together that you will learn one by one in this book. But I believe it's something like showing someone how to drive a car, ride a bicycle or roller-skate. If you try to tell them in words and then expect them to do it, the results may not be what you thought you were describing in words. With that in mind, let us take a look at a real world example of plasma physics of the sun affecting earth weather.

Let us assume that the solar system and the earth and its weather are all in what we would call a normal state. There are always some storms around the earth and varying locations, but let's just say for example that the earth is relatively tranquil. Unknown to us a medium-size comet is racing into the solar system for close encounter with the sun. The comet is already discharging electrically the energy in the Sun's exterior electrical battery that I call the "solar capacitor". As it nears the sun, the electrical interaction via the comet at this time creates a fairly large solar flare. The comet acts as a "spark plug" so to speak to release the stored electrical energy in the solar capacitor ... directing via an electrical current passing down the length of the comet tail and invisible sunward electrical "spike" back into the solar surface fusion engine to create the surface fusion explosion that we see emerge as the flare. Remember that many solar flares occur without the ignition by a passing comet and this is due to ongoing dynamics within the sun itself, but I chose a passing comet to add another factor to this example.

The solar flare consists of the large burst of charged particles blasting out of the sun. Let's say for our example, that the solar burst is coming by earth but will not hit us directly. It takes approximately three days for this flare to reach us near earth but in that time, earth's protective magnetic field begins to compress. This in turn compresses localized electric fields around earth that had been stable up to that point. Already earth it is feeling the effects. Although satellite communications are not seriously disrupted, network managers of data stations begin to see the effect of corrupted data and poor transmission quality. Ham radio operators also begin to see their reception deteriorate.

As the bulk of the solar ejected material races by earth off to the side, electrical currents rush to outer space from our upper ionosphere (the boundary between earth's atmosphere and outer space) to balance this disturbance. The jet streams in earth's upper atmosphere respondent likewise, and the wind speeds increase in the upper atmosphere. The upper latitude jet stream begins to snake and dip causing some areas to receive colder air from the North, and adjacent areas to receive moist warm weather from the South. Standard meteorology states that the jet streams result from solar light, but they are missing the most important component … the invisible electrical component of the sun

Storm belts around the equator intensify as the electrical energy increases the flow of electrical current between the ionosphere to the upper cloud tops of the developing storm systems. This reaction and interaction continues over the next few days.

A factor never considered in standard meteorology is at work here. Electrical currents from the ionosphere attach to ground near shorelines, especially along the sandy shorelines and along the continental shelves which skirt much of our continental shorelines. Early Russian explorers noticed that even auroral activity could be found to follow the shorelines in the northern latitudes. The coastline of Florida of for example, is known to be the most lightning prone place on planet Earth. Underwater topographical maps of this area show that there is an extensive shallow shelf (the continental shelf) extending hundreds of miles out into the ocean. Therefore the underwater topography of earth becomes an important factor in understanding the electrical interaction on planet Earth, and even more important … when it comes to controlling storms, such as hurricanes, the knowledge of how the ionosphere electrical currents drive the storms and subsequently interact with the continental shelf as the storms make landfall, are important factors in the technologies which allow us to control these powerful storms

Going back to the example, the earth is moving in its orbit around the sun and even though the flare has passed, earth is now moving directly between the positively charged plasma that has already passed and the negatively charged region that extends millions of miles towards the sun. Now I will use an every day example that is useful to illustrate what happens next. The earth now acts as if it were a bug flying into one of the back yard bug killers sometimes called zappers that I use for example when I give lectures to the general public.

The bug flies between the electrically charged capacitor plates of the back yard bug killer (or zapper) and creates an electrical discharge sufficient to cause serious damage to the bug. Earth acts the same way but in the plasma electrical environment of outer space. So, even days after the plasma flare from the sun has passed earth, it is still causing electrical storm activity in our atmosphere. Standard science and meteorology would have told you that the flare missed us and therefore had no effect at all.

This simple example has included a brief overview of a few of the complex aspects of plasma physics. What you'll be able to do in this book is learn about each of these individual properties of plasma physics and in the end put it all together to understand all of the (currently known) factors that this book talks about that affect our weather. One of the most telling problems that I work out in this book deals with what our weather would be like if there were just solar light energy arriving in our planet environment. We would in fact have very bland weather with no major storms, no major wind or climactic storms. In fact, we would not even have clouds to any serious degree, since the biggest storm type clouds can only develop in a vertical electric field.

One of the most fundamental principles of physics is called conservation of energy. All physical systems must comply with this law of science. It essentially says that if you see an energetic system, then to describe this system you must identify the source of energy that creates the system. Looking at tornadoes, hurricanes and other violent storms, there simply is not enough energy in the local atmosphere (or ocean surface heating in the case of hurricanes) to create the amount of energy we see in these storms.

A tornado for example contains more energy than is received from solar light over vast surface areas of the earth. Additionally, there are many storm systems that develop during night hours when there is no solar light energy input at all. Clearly one can think of many more examples, simple examples that would prove to the average person that there must be some other source of energy that drives these incredibly powerful storms. Yet standard meteorology never considers these options. To be effective, this book first must convince the reader that standard meteorology has some serious problems and then make a convincing argument that the source for this energy is in fact in the invisible electrical energy coming from the sun.

When you begin to see the breakdown of traditional meteorology and the effectiveness of the explanations based on electrical energy of the sun, one can only wonder how thousands upon thousands of highly trained scientists could work around this problem for years and even decades and never ask this most fundamental question regarding where the energy comes from that power these incredible storms.

There is one last point to make before heading into the main body of the text. Once we understand what causes these incredible storms, we are then in a position to learn how to control and reduce their damaging effects. This has been one of the main goals of my personal weather work and as early as the mid-1990s I had developed a sound method for reducing the energy of hurricanes, which has the additional benefit of causing the damaging water to dump before the hurricane made landfall.

There is an adverse side to this also in that it is possible to control weather and increase the strength of the storm to steer it into populated areas thusly using it as a weapon of mass destruction. It is based on this realization that many foreign nations recently requested a moratorium on technologies such as HAARP and GWEN and energy beam control devices. If one looks closely there are many patents issued on whether control devices and many more must exist in the depths of secret black operations groups within the military.

I came to realize long-ago that there is literally thousands of times more energy coming from the sun in the form of electrical energy than arrives in the form of light or visible energy. The subtlety here is that we are shielded by many mechanisms including our plasma magnetic field from this incredible amount of energy that is passing by us every day. It is during times of change that this energy may break through that protective shielding barrier and arrive at our planet to cause severe weather and what we term natural disasters.

We see that the planet Mars is without an atmosphere although it has all the characteristics of a water planet in its geology. It is clear that Mars lost its atmosphere and oceans recently and the ancients from around the globe tell us via legends and tales that Mars lost this atmosphere to a large passing comet as they watched in horror from planet Earth. Modern scientists scoff at the idea and spend millions of dollars sending space probes to try and find some other reason for the missing water and atmosphere of our neighbor planet. Thus I included chapters on planetary as well as biblical weather.

jim mccanney

I. Planet X, Comets and Earth Changes

The following two paragraphs are the first statements of Chapter I of the first book of this series **PLANET X, COMETS and EARTH CHANGES - A SCIENTIFIC TREATISE ON THE EFFECTS OF A NEW LARGE PLANET OR COMET ARRIVING IN OUR SOLAR SYSTEM AND EXPECTED EARTH WEATHER AND EARTH CHANGES**.

News Flash! Comets are not Dirty Snowballs!

Introduction to: The Plasma Discharge Comet Model

If there were any phrase that must ring out loud and clear and dominate the pages of this book it is the above statement that "comets are not dirty snowballs"! With this basic realization, the standard theories for how the solar system came to be and how it works undergo the domino principle (one topples, then the next and the next until all have fallen).

In their place will go an entirely new set of principles and concepts that are essential to understanding how the solar system formed, but more importantly, that new objects (including some that are large and will become new planets and moons) may be adopted at any time.

The entire concept that traditional astronomical theories have been wrong, and that there is a deeper underlying mechanism that powers our universe, was the key to unlocking the true nature of weather. Without that basic understanding of the Physics of the Electrical Universe we live in, the view into the daily weather of earth would not have been possible. The significance relative to the current book on weather is that standard meteorology today completely lacks the tools and understanding to deal with this fundamentally more complicated view that is so integrally involved in our weather. This treatise on weather provides the correct basis to understand and even predict the weather based on measurements of solar electrical activity.

One can readily understand why very little if anything from the past did make any sense at all since the basic scientific framework was missing. With the Plasma Discharge Comet Model and the new reality of the electrical "Solar Capacitor" provided by our Sun, there is now a clear understanding of the source of electrical energy and the mechanisms by which it travels and provides our planet Earth with essentially an unlimited constantly renewed source of electrical power.

It is not clear whether ancient advanced civilizations knew about all of this, and to do what they did they may have only had an empirical knowledge. Much of ancient knowledge was of an empirical nature. Additionally they created mythologies that today many think are but erroneous legends of fanciful imaginations, however the pioneering work of Immanuel Velikovsky and others such as Ignatious Donnelly began the search for scientific explanations that are now coming to light in this book series.

Just a few short years ago we had no knowledge of the solar wind, the ionosphere, the Earth's shielding magnetic field or the van Allen Belts (high energy radiation belts that surround Earth). Today, however, we have far more information regarding the solar interaction with Earth and considerable data from space probes that give us detailed information on what is moving around out there. The thing traditional astronomers, space scientists and astrophysicists have been lacking is the understanding of the electrical nature of our solar system … in fact they openly denied that such electrical conditions could exist, let alone have any effect on our daily lives. The "magnetic" explanations given by traditional space scientists lack a first level understanding that is given in the first book of this series and which is essential to the understanding of weather.

I often tell people who have had astronomy courses that they have to unlearn what they were taught before relearning the concepts taught in the Plasma Discharge Comet Model and related theories, since the two avenues of thought are not compatible. Unlike many cases of science where a new theory modifies an older theory, this set of concepts replaces and shows the incorrectness of the other set of theories. Of course, the more astronomical education one has, the more difficult it will be to change the person's thinking patterns and someone with a Ph.D. usually becomes so defensive that they will not break down the mental barriers necessary to make the switch.

It has been interesting over the past 25 years since the Plasma Discharge Comet Model has been introduced that the "traditional" theoretical structures have "migrated" towards my theories every time a "new discovery" was made by space probes, while my theories have remained the same. This is why I reprinted in their entirety and in original form (in the first book of this series) the scientific journal papers that laid the foundation for my ongoing work that were published in 1979, 80 and 81.

I will now give a summary of the important concepts detailed for the layman in book #1 of this series Planet X, Comets and Earth Changes that are most relevant to the current book.

First the term "Planet X" has had a good deal of misuse in past years and was the cause of a large scale government lead internet misinformation program to make the topic of "Planet X" sound crazy to the general public ... so that when the REAL Planet X shows up and the public gets wind of it they would hopefully say "oh, don't mind that ... it's just those crazy Planet X people again". Luckily and thanks much to my constant vigilance and guiding of the public, the effect never came to pass. The true use of the term "Planet X" is that it has been used historically in the astronomical community since the middle ages to designate either observed or conjectured unknown or new planetary members of our solar system that have not been named.

In terms of my personal ongoing studies that I have been engaged in for over 3 decades is my "Search for Extra-Solar System Objects" ... that is, my ongoing search for objects that come into the solar system from beyond. These typically erupt into comets as they break the solar capacitor. Examples of such objects are occurring at all times and some are very large. Examples are the huge comets Hale-Bopp and the 2003 comet that has become known as Comet Neat V1.

Another part of the study is for example noticing patterns as with the spring of 2003 when we were (and continue to be as this book goes to print) barraged by comets coming in from the southern region of the sky. This can only mean that these are the beginning of a large entourage of comets that we will see in upcoming years as a new huge object enters the solar system from the south. Could this be the infamous Nibiru spoken of by the ancients? It is too early to tell as this book goes to print, but it is interesting to note that the US government (and also the Vatican) has placed many huge astronomical telescopes at the south polar region in Antarctica and oddly have placed NONE at the north polar region. Clearly there is a great deal of interest in the southern sky.

I wish at this point to be emphatic about a few topics relative to this point. First I do not project "dates of passage" and would not unless I had specific information that was concrete. The second is that even with specific data, it is impossible to tell exact orbits and "dates of arrival" since the big comets have their paths altered daily and many times a great deal because of the comet tail drag (as explained in the first book of this series). So even with supercomputers the erratic movement of big comets is unpredictable. That is why the ancients called them "The Lawless Ones", they knew that they did not follow the known patterns of celestial mechanics.

Also I wish to point out that you should avoid internet CHAT pages and other disinformation hubs spun out by the government and other people who have no training or knowledge of such things. These only tend to confuse the public and many times that is their entire purpose.

The last point I wish to make is that there is not just one Planet X, there are many … far more than we will know about with our best telescopes and equipment. And additionally we now know that the government has in place a program to keep this type of information from the people. It is a layer of filtering of data and space related information that comes from the very top of national and international security. Any scientist who works for these organizations is subject to such "gag orders" and cannot tell anyone or they will be immediately arrested and imprisoned. The scientists that work for the government have all been forced to sign non-disclosure agreements and this is not going to change.

So we may see at any time a large new object coming into the solar system and we know from history that it has sometimes been the ***companions*** to the big comets that have caused the damage to Earth by the process I call "action at a distance" … meaning they do not have to collide with Earth to cause damage. In fact many times they would be no where near Earth as they would interact electrically with the Sun and cause flaring that would drastically affect Earth. This is all explained in detail in books #1 and #2 of this series.

More importantly for the current book is not the topic of a "Planet X" type of object, but the ongoing daily activity of the Sun. The term "the vertical electric field" of the earth we will see dominates our ground weather, and this is controlled from outside our planet by the electrical power of the sun. That is, the Earth is constantly surrounded by solar wind passing by and this drives our outer magnetic field but also does something else … as the solar wind separates as it passes around earth's protective magnetic field that extends approximately 30,000 miles in the sunward direction, the positively charged protons go one way and the negatively charged electrons pass around Earth in the opposite direction. This causes a battery to form, and is just one of the many batteries that form around Earth as described by the Plasma Discharge Comet Model.

Yes, Earth is discharging the solar capacitor and this capacitor harbors more energy than you could imagine. This is the source of energy used to constantly replenish our "Local Environmental Batteries" which I will now call "LEBs" throughout this book for short. From this point on you will start to see information that comes directly from my personal science diaries and which has brought me to the state of writing this book to disclose the science weather. There is an entire chapter on LEBs in this text since there are so many and they all affect us either directly or indirectly.

The following is the core on which the rest of the book is based. It is an extension of the first book of this series and you will not understand what this is saying without having at least a rudimentary understanding of the first book Planet X, Comets and Earth Changes. Themes from that book are woven throughout this book and is required reading for anyone who attempts to understand the current book or future books in this series.

The LEBs are constantly around the Earth and are the result of the solar electrical power system. The Sun on a daily basis pours out far more electrical power than it does in the form of visible light (the light energy that reaches us at the surface of the Earth). It is amazing that after watching the solar data for decades that traditional astronomers, space scientists and astro-physicists have no clue that this exists. Additionally it is amazing that the weather service we call NOAA (the National Weather Service) has no clue of how this affects our weather and there is no use of it in the weather prediction software that is used to predict our weather.

The reason I mention this is because one of the primary visible effects of the LEBS is the severe weather systems that are directly powered by electrical currents that arise out of the changing conditions of our Local Electric Fields (LEBs) and these are directly the result of solar storm activity which arrives at Earth sometimes days after the storms occur on the Sun (many times the result of interactions with passing comets).

One of the beneficial side effects of tapping into the world-wide system of LEBs is that we would reduce severe storm activity. There is enough electrical energy in an average summer thunderstorm to power a state for a month. Yet we continue to ignore this source of free energy and burn fossil fuels, oil and even worse nuclear fuel that then can be a bio-hazard for millenniums to come. Much of the history and significance of these topics will be described later in this book.

The primary LEB is called the vertical electric field and is the result of the charged capacitor that exists between the surface of the Earth and our ionosphere. The structure of this LEB is quite complicated and depends on what latitude you are located. Additionally the field is constantly changing at the mid northern and southern latitudes due to the snaking of the jet streams.

The more stable of the ionospheric jet streams is the westerly flowing equatorial jet stream, which remains fairly steady. I have discovered that it migrates to the north of the equator slightly during the northern hemisphere's summer months and migrates to the south during the summer months of the southern hemisphere. This is due to the interaction of the Earth as the northern and southern magnetic poles interact with the solar wind and an incoming electron current sheet as the Earth moves around the Sun in its orbit. The northward and southward migration of this central westerly moving equatorial jet stream has dramatic effects on the seasonal weather of the tropics, especially hurricane formation and the hurricane season itself. The causes of this migration are detailed later in this book.

The traditional concept that the jet streams of earth's upper atmosphere are formed as heat from light from the sun hitting earth's surface somehow rises up and creates bands of winds moving at up to 600 miles per hour contradicts the second law of thermodynamics (you cannot form an organized energy system from a dissipating energy system ... and secondly there us simply not enough energy available in the meager allotment of solar light energy. That is why I began early in my career to look for alternative sources of energy not only for the formation of the jet streams but for the creation and sustenance of highly energetic storms such as hurricanes and tornadoes (there is simply not enough energy in the solar light hitting earth's surface to cause the weather we are seeing on a localized let alone global scale).

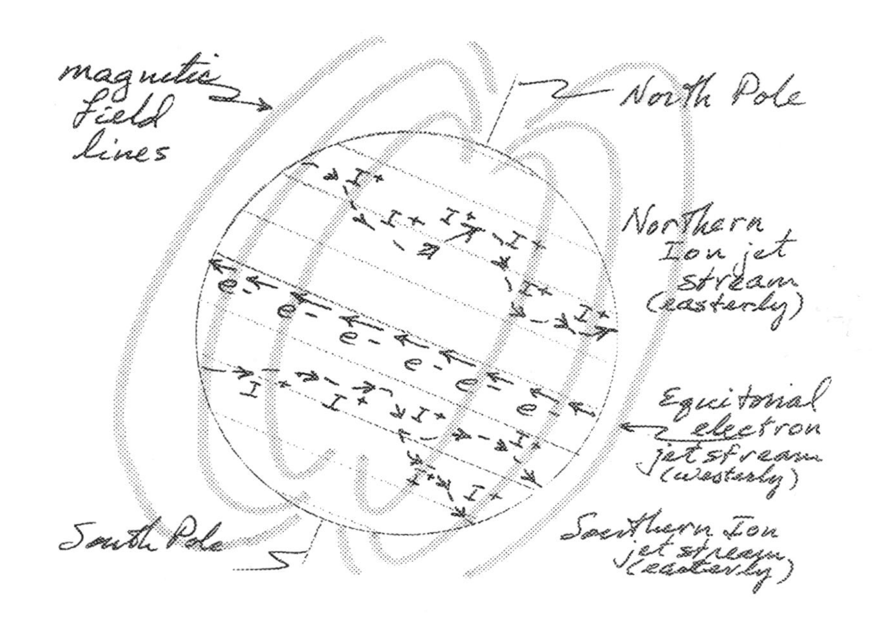

Figure #1. Earth's jet streams and local magnetic field.

Figure #1 attempts to draw a picture of the Earth and its jet stream systems. These are driven by the many layers of outer magnetic fields that are in turn driven by the passing solar wind and other electrical current sheets that occur as Earth discharges the solar capacitor. Additionally the movement of these "ion belts" is the source for one of the layers of Earth's magnetic field and is the source for the vertical electric field that is shown in Figure #2 that was tapped by the Atlantians and Tesla for an unlimited source of electrical power as noted in the third book of this series entitled **ATLANTIS TO TESLA – THE KOLBRIN CONNECTION**. A detailed description of the mechanisms involved are beyond the scope of this book, but I now have planned for an upcoming book the design and implementation of a Tesla power system including the household adapters necessary to build a nation wide working system. I have enough detailed descriptions of these to offer a 2 year advanced graduate level Astrophysics course in just the topic of near Earth electric fields alone.

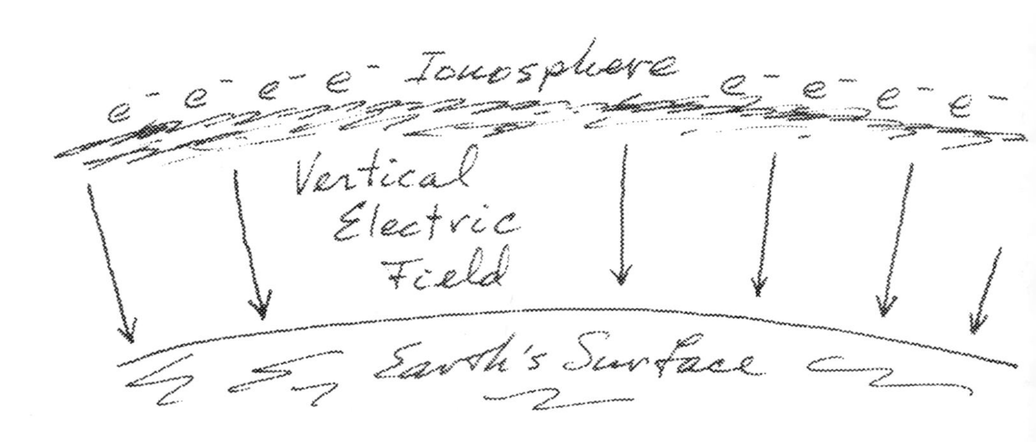

Figure #2. The ionosphere to Earth's surface vertical electric field.

Another important factor in the use and understanding of tapping into the vertical electric field is that the atmosphere contains what is known in Physics as a dielectric. These are molecules that contain a small charge pair that enhance and increase the amount of energy that can be stored electrically in the ionosphere without it discharging to the Earth's surface and dissipating as would occur if we had no atmosphere (or an inert atmosphere with just a gas such as helium for example which would not create a dielectric effect). It is this dielectric effect that increases the "capacitance" or capacity to hold electrical charge that is the key to drawing on this unlimited power source.

As the ancients and Tesla discovered, if you induce a condition into the atmosphere to reduce the dielectric in a vertical path to the ionosphere, you then induce a "path of lesser resistance" to ground (the Earth's surface) and current naturally begins to flow. Once this flow begins, it will maintain until the dielectric condition returns to "normal" or until the entire capacitor or battery has been drained. This is the source of unlimited electrical power and there are good examples that we see every day to prove this.

Since this capacitor is constantly being replenished from outside by the immense electrical power of the larger solar capacitor which spans and powers the entire solar system, we are not in danger of depleting the energy source. This is understandable also by virtue of the fact that this energy is constantly coming down to earth in the form of major storms and atmospheric electricity … we would be simply using energy that is coming down in the major storm systems. There would be a dual benefit in that we would reduce major storm damage and use this energy in a useful manner to replace the polluting fuels that we are currently utilizing.

Electrical storms are powered by this same energy source. The way this works is that clouds begin to form (clouds in fact would not form if it were not for the vertical electric field) and they act as a "finger" pointing upwards towards the ionosphere. This initiates the electrical current flow and the power we see unleashed in a thunder storm is being powered by this energy source. Additionally the cyclonic storms are directly powered when electrical current sheets go all the way to the ground or in the case of hurricanes, to the surface of the ocean. What happens in this case is that the ground air becomes ionized and rushes inwards to the current sheet and UP the vertical electrical column forming a vortex (the reverse of water running down a drain causing a vortex motion). These processes will be described later in this book.

This is the power source for cyclonic storms from tornadoes to hurricanes. My weather work has also shown that the low pressure cells that exist in the lower regions of these storm cells are in fact connected electrically to regions in the ionosphere that are then connected electrically into outer space and form comet-like tail structures attaching to Earth as giant invisible serpents. It is through these regions that water enters the ionosphere on a regular basis during the ongoing development of large storm systems on Earth. Hurricanes and typhoons (pacific hurricanes) likewise are formed in this manner and move westerly with the westerly moving equatorial jet stream.

So the first source of electrical power and the specific LEB essential to understanding weather is the ionosphere to Earth surface "vertical electric field". In the central equatorial jet stream the negatively charged electrons are in the ionosphere whereas in the temperate regions the positively charged ions are the dominant charged particles in the ionosphere. The equatorial region is more stable (it does not snake around as do the mid-latitude current sheets), it provides a greater source of energy and the electrons flow from above whereas the electrons (the primary charge carrier in the free energy system) comes from the ground (a much less efficient process from an engineering design stand point).

The second LEB that is essential to understanding weather is outside the planet and in the solar system environment itself. It is the source of electrical fields that cause the inter-planetary electrical currents to flow, and these are the "rivers of electrical current" spoken of in these books.

The electrical currents that flow in the solar system are a direct result of the planets discharging the solar capacitor. Although comets in their highly elliptical orbits discharge the solar capacitor to a greater degree, all of the planets are doing this also. This creates an electrical current sheet connecting each planet to the Sun and it extends outward in the anti-Sun direction for millions of miles. As I generally say, the electrical sizes of the planets are far larger than their physical sizes.

This is further enhanced by a region of the solar system through which we pass every August ... what I have termed the "August return current sheet from the solar capacitor" that is required to keep the solar system in electrical balance. This sheet is centered on the August region ... but we enter this region sometimes as early as June and exit as late as November. Many times this sheet moves like a swinging snakelike plasma electrical current and affects our weather as it combines with the electrical current sheets associated with the planets or passing comets (even small comets have affected our weather when they passed in association with other electrical current sheets). The reason this is in the August direction is related to the larger electrical formations of the solar system. There are most certainly other return current sheets near the poles of the Sun but which do not affect us directly as does the August return current sheet.

The August sheet is where the current returns to the Sun on an ongoing basis from the outer solar system and the far reaches of the solar capacitor which I now estimate is many "Pluto distances" from the Sun. When the planets align ***electrically*** with each other and the sun, these electrical current sheets become attached and augmented, and this is when increased solar activity occurs as the planetary currents feed back into the Sun's surface to cause increased solar fusion and flaring. When many planets align this greatly enhances the solar flaring and this in turn increases the electrical flow to the planets and increases their discharge of the solar capacitor. This is why we have the greatest Hurricanes, tornadoes and auroras centered on the month of August. There are other factors of course and this is but one of the main sources of energy.

The ancients knew this and used it to enhance their power usage, and formed the basis of their knowledge of astrology (the precursor to the modern science of measurement we call astronomy). As already noted, the ancients did not necessarily need to know everything about the sources and Physics of the processes. All they needed was the thousands of years of development and they were far more capable of understanding this free unlimited energy source than we are today. Thus the first book of this series sets the stage for further information as a completely new set of logical and scientific principles are presented. The dominant comment I receive from people who have read these books is that finally they have a basis for understanding everything from the history of man to ancient weather and the true origins of the solar system. People are thankful that at long last the incorrect theories of astronomy, astro-physics, geology, and other branches of study are being replaced ... there are other people who are not so happy to see this material reaching the public eye.

II. SURVIVING PLANET X PASSAGE

The second book of this series (a 60 page pamphlet) **<u>Surviving Planet X Passage</u>** speaks directly of the Earth-Changes events that we know from the historical record occurred in the past and could occur again (depending on many factors) if a large new comet would come into the solar system. Of importance to the current book is the portion on re-calendaring the Earth, that is, rebuilding the calendar after a pole shift or other changes in our orbital elements. The reason this is important here is because after the destruction of the ancient world, the mathematical systems and knowledge of the stars and calendar were passed on and became essential for the survival of those that remained once the aftermath of the cataclysm had cleared. Since the calendar had changed then so did the growing seasons.

An essentially important point was made: there are two distinct types of pole shift … 1) the first is a shift of the mantle over the core that physically changes the celestial north and south pole of Earth and an internal core pole shift that directly affects the inner rotation of the planet's core and 2) the shift of the north and south magnetic poles and subsequent migration as it attempts to regain a true northerly position on the planet. These two distinct types of pole shift are related, but very different. The biggest point is to dispel the rumor that somehow the Earth does this by itself. The second point is to dispel the rumors that magnetic pole migration causes the earth itself to "flip". The process similarly does not happen when an asteroid or comet collides with the Earth, but only when a large comet nucleus (planets sized) passes by or near Earth, which would likely also alter our orbit around the Sun, the length of our day and many other orbital factors including our weather. You will see why these events are the most likely candidates for the push needed to drive earth into the ice ages and to account for the many other accompanying activities such as mountain building and changes to the landmasses.

Part of this short book is dedicated to answering FAQs (frequently asked questions). These are included primarily to show that there are dedicated groups of people in the world today whose sole purpose is to destroy and change the true historical record through preconceived misinformation campaigns carried through the major news media and especially on the Internet. Part of our ability to move forward in our society and in cases of stress ... to survival ... is in the understanding of the past. Without that understanding, your chances of survival in a worldwide cataclysmic event would be extremely small to nonexistent.

The middle chapters of this pamphlet are dedicated to that time when the Earth struggled for survival and the races of man ascended from the ashes and tried to rebuild a new existence. Every race that survived did so because it was able to quickly rebuild the planting, growing and harvest seasons. After the ancient cataclysm the growing seasons were quite different from the old ones due to a shift of the celestial poles as a massive gravitational wave of a large passing comet wrenched the earth's mantle from its rotating core. There were many that survived the initial devastation but were unable to cope with the long term rebuilding. Weather that was far more severe than anything we can imagine today was a dominant factor in daily and long term survival.

We find that these ancient cultures put a significant value on the priests and "wise" men who were able to understand the motions of the planets and stars and direct their civilizations accordingly. This of course is also the origin of the universal worldwide concept and science so to speak of astrology (something modern astronomers talk about with disdain even though their very own science of astronomy, the measurement of celestial positions, historically was a derivative of the earlier science of astrology).

If one takes for example, the Mayan civilization of Central America, in many cases they rebuilt their cities upon the bases of much older cities that were destroyed in the cataclysm. This insight is a direct result of my surveying on-site at many of these ancient cities and in fact identifying the location of the old North Pole, that is, the location of the North Pole prior to the pole shift that occurred as the tremendous gravitational wave from a large passing comet threw the surface mantle of the Earth ajar from the co-rotating inner core. This pamphlet presents the physics of how this took place and discusses the physics (and misconceptions) of pole shifts. In many of the ancient cities, this interesting universal result shows that many of the cities were not built on what we would call true north-south east-west meridians. We also find in many of these locations that primitive rings of rocks, such as the ancient celestial ring of Zimbabwe, were dedicated to tracking the celestial sphere, and primarily the planet Venus. What is most interesting about all of these ring rock patterns is that they are set out in a full 360° pattern, indicating that Venus was very much not in the orbit in which we see it today.

Other early celestial sites in Peru, Central America and other places around the earth follow the same pattern … all were set up to track the ever changing movements of that huge comet whose planet sized nucleus eventually became the planet Venus, devastating Earth on two separate occasions and removing the atmosphere and oceans of Mars during a close passage as recounted in legends from around the world.

There have been discovered in the Chaco Canyon area of Arizona, no less than 150 such rock ring circles, all dedicated to providing the local residents with information relative to harvesting, planting and possibly religious ceremonies. Similar rock circles have been discovered all over the world, and currently I am personally studying some in the upper Midwest and other areas of the world.

Some people who have read this information in the **Surviving Planet X Passage** pamphlet have called it the most significant information relative to survival that they have ever seen. They have suggested that anyone who is serious about survival would necessarily need this information and without it they would be completely unable to provide the most basic necessity, that is food for the survivors, in the aftermath of such an event, even with out the rapid pole shift.

As mentioned, mixed in with these celestial calendars to determine the planting and harvesting times of year is the fact that all of these sites in ancient times were tracking the movements of the planet (comet) Venus. As we know from the Mayans, they did this because they believed that every 54 years Venus (which they called Quetzalcoatl … "the plumed serpent god of the night sky whose heart (the comet nucleus) eventually became the planet Venus" according to the Popul Vuh … their religious "bible") would return to destroy their existence and they would have to rebuild their temple cities again.

As we now know, modern archaeology, geology, anthropology, astronomy, and meteorology (as you will find out in this book) are all completely inundated with incorrect theories and concepts regarding the true nature of man in our solar system and the history of the planets. In most cases, the scholarly fields simply ignore or downplay and write off as mythological trivia the information that passes down to us the most important and glaring message that comes to us from these ancient civilizations, that is, that their immediate ancestor's civilizations were destroyed by a gigantic extra solar system event caused by a massive large comet (actually group of comets) raging through the solar system with some of them passing very near Earth. Ancient severe weather was one of the main descriptions we see repeatedly in the ancient texts.

Much of the archaeology that we are uncovering today is from post cataclysm civilizations, and one of the great mysteries is the source of their myths, writing and mathematical systems and the links between them and to the pre-cataclysm civilizations. Many of the words used to name places (such as the word Mu in the eastern cultures and root word ATL in the meso-american cultures) are clearly remnants of the past civilizations that went down during past events of celestial origin (and had nothing to do with anything colliding with Earth). These events were all caused by what I have termed "action at a distance" as the severe events were caused by close encounters with large comets and their massive nuclei as detailed in the first two books of this series.

The main point I wish to make here is that we do not know and are unable to sort out at this point how many catastrophes there were in relatively recent history, and which ones caused which civilizations to go under. There is evidence that there was severe devastation of early civilizations during the Venus event which some place as little as 3650 years ago, while there is other evidence suggesting that older civilizations went down much earlier. We may never be able to sort out completely, which events were responsible for the downfall of which civilizations. The real question is whether we will learn from these events to save our species or let it be destroyed by similar events while being kept in ignorance by the "seats of wisdom", who refuse to understand and admit what our true history is trying to tell us.

The entire issue of survival comes down to one simple word, and that is "knowledge". The entire issue of surviving the passage of a large planet newly forming (by way of a massive comet as described in legends that come down to us from all corners of this planet by the survivors who witnessed the devastation firsthand) is one of knowledge of the processes involved as the solar system adjusts to adopt this new member. It is for us to either accept this or in the case of many traditional astronomers, to deny it. As already mentioned, if man is reduced back to the cave age then survival means using what is at hand such as a pilot rocks to make a calendar for planting and harvesting. That would be just one issue that could make the difference between survival and extinction.

I often look around when I'm in public and as I look at other people to imagine who are the survivors and who are those who would certainly be extinct after the first few hours or at most the first few days if there were such a catastrophic event. Many of the richest and loftiest of our citizens today would not last 10 minutes in a true catastrophe. Part of the knowledge mentioned above includes the knowledge of how to stay calm and react intelligently under such stressful conditions. As with people who have lived through a major earthquake, they will tell you that no matter how much preparation you may make, you could never be prepared completely for that moment when the Earth begins to tremble under your feet. Imagine an earthquake of 20 on the Richter scale where mountains are forming and oceans are washing across the land. Are you prepared for such an event?

I am always amazed that people want to know a date for when such an event may happen. I ask them what they would do at that point, make a quick run to the grocery store and buy an extra can of tuna? Would they begin to exercise on that particular day? And would they start to read a book like the survival book, or order survival gear by mail order? If one is not prepared many years in advance both mentally, physically, spiritually and with the current knowledge, any hope of survival would be minimized quickly.

The second book of the series, the "Surviving Planet X Passage" pamphlet is an essential key to putting the mysteries of the past in line with modern scientific theory. Once these subtle points have been identified, it becomes obvious what the ancients were doing and why. It also clarifies their obsession with astronomy and celestial following of Venus and the identification of the correct growing seasons … as their very survival depended on it.

III. ATLANTIS TO TESLA - THE KOLBRIN CONNECTION

This book entitled **ATLANTIS TO TESLA – THE KOLBRIN CONNECTION (THE SCIENCE OF ATLANTIS AND TESLA ARE REDISCOVERED, GIVING A UNIQUE UNTOLD VIEW OF LIFE ON THE LOST CONTINENT, ANCIENT SPACE CRAFT DESIGN, UNLIMITED ELECTRICAL POWER AND THE SECRET SOCIETIES)**, the third book in the series, is unique in that it covers such a wide range of topics. From ancient archaeology to the most advanced electromagnetic propulsion systems, from the destruction of the Earth by ancient catastrophic events to the emergence of secret societies who currently are in control of almost every aspect of modern society. The KOLBRIN, which I consider to be the true Old Testament, gives us a shocking revelation that has been edited out of more modern versions of that great book. It provides the critical lost link between the ancient past and present that so many groups are trying to suppress and keep from the masses whom are trying to wake up to some basic reality of man's true history.

Few people that have read the **Atlantis to Tesla** book have walked away unaffected. After its initial release it generated a huge amount of interest in these areas of study and generated a plethora of Nuevo experts in related fields. But most of all it was greeted with shock from the groups that thought they had been successful at keeping a lid on the information that it exposed. And last but not least it released information of the overall connection from the advanced ancient civilizations to the man we call Tesla ... with the most interesting revelations providing the guiding light on the fact that, through my research on the electrical nature of the solar system, the physics of Tesla's inventions have finally been uncovered including the source of energy that he tapped into to produce his amazing energy devices (which included his full scale Tesla Tower which he used to extract unlimited electrical energy from the ionosphere via the vertical electric field of Earth).

It is interesting to note that even Tesla never truly knew or understood the energy sources that he was dealing with (e.g. he knew about and could measure the vertical electric field of earth but had no clue how it formed, that there was a solar wind coming from the sun that ultimately powered this field and that this was indirectly the source of the power he was able to tap into via his tower).

Out of these amazingly varying topics emerges as a central theme the electrical concept of weather. One has only to look at the electrical lightning patterns over a volcano at night in the South China Sea to realize that the ancients looked at this vast source of energy and learned how to tap into it. There is clear evidence also that they may also have learned how to build simple electromagnetic propulsion systems and ride the "electromagnetic rivers" that flow out of our planets and into the solar system and beyond to explore the planets and possibly neighboring stars (the Atlantis to Tesla book gives a full engineering description of one of these propulsion systems). For these electromagnetic paths I coined the term "Electro-magnetic Highways (or Rivers) to the Stars". The use by the ancients of vast arrays of sea water batteries was another revelation that showed that these groups that have been lost under the invisible veil of time had far more going on than we ever have given credit.

There is also emerging clear evidence that our neighboring planet Mars may have been inhabited or at least visited by some ancient advanced cultures prior to having its atmosphere and oceans ripped off by a large passing comet as recounted to us by the ancients. On top of all of this exists a clear pattern of deception and a highly effective misinformation campaign to keep correct historical information from the public by the secret societies and the psychologically disturbed scientists who work for them.

One question that time will only answer is … has NASA discovered remnants of advanced civilizations on Mars and has it been investigating them while leading the public on a wild goose chase with their mini Mars Rovers that landed in the middle of remote desert regions of the central waste lands (certainly not the place you would send a space craft if you were going to explore for traces of water). If this is the case then it is my personal opinion that there have been numerous secret missions to Mars to investigate these "ruins" for the controlling "secret societies" which, remember, have the Intelligence agencies of the world working for them. Once again "weather", in this case the weather of another planet, becomes instrumental in understanding our past and the electrical nature of the solar system is at the center of these issues.

Writing the ATLANTIS TO TESLA book was a fascinating experience as it covered the many topics that bonded the ancient past to our modern culture and the future. It also gave the public a detailed look into the intricate past of much of my research. This book was prompted by friends who encouraged me to write the book after listening to me talk about these topics on a regular basis.

Regarding the location of the central ringed city of Atlantis, there are ongoing disinformation campaigns to try and locate it for example in the Mediterranean Sea (and just about every other place on this planet). This of course is intended to draw attention away from the true location in the South China Sea (I am talking about the mother continent of Atlantis and not one of its world wide colonies). The keys to understanding where the true location of Atlantis used to be prior to the catastrophe that took it under the ocean are many. These are described in the ATLANTIS TO TESLA book. One, for example, is that to the ancients the pillars of Hercules were two tall columns of smoke rising from twin volcanoes, one being Krakatoa which lies off the South China Sea in the Sunda Straight between the islands of Java and Sumatra … this was the famed entry point of the main continent of Atlantis. Another fact is that to the ancients the Atlantic Ocean covered the entire volume of water that we have many names for today (e.g. the names Pacific Ocean, Indian Ocean, etc. only coming in modern times after they were rediscovered). To the ancients the entire world ocean was called the Ocean of the Atlanteans … or the Atlantic Ocean. The ancients never considered the Mediterranean part of this Atlantic Ocean.

The **Atlantis to Tesla** book describes how the South China Sea location was identified by a South American Physicist in the mid 1990's and was subsequently explored by the US Navy since that time (out of a secret submarine base located in Northern Australia).

It was very clear that Atlantis had many colonies around the world, but the main continent of Atlantis lay in the South China Sea. This has significant implications for the use of naturally occurring electricity that the Atlantians were well known to have been able to derive from the vertical electric field. This is due to the fact that the South China Sea both then and now was and is well connected to the ionosphere and beyond in what is currently called in the scientific world an "anomaly". Whenever spacecraft fly over this area in low Earth orbit they experience electrical difficulties much the same as they do when they fly over the region known as the Bermuda triangle.

As noted in the Atlantis to Tesla book, living in this area without learning to use the naturally occurring electricity would be like living next to the ocean and not learning how to swim our sail. The Mediterranean Sea has no such significant connection to the ionosphere in fact in this respect it is relatively tranquil. The list of reasons for why Atlantis lies in the South China Sea is extensive and as noted is described at length in the Atlantis to Tesla book. It is also described in detail in the literature associated with the person who discovered this fact, a physicist from South America. There have been many claims regarding the location of Atlantis throughout history with none of them bearing fruit because of the many factors that would have to be true for a place to in fact be the ***main continent*** of Atlantis (and not one of its colonies).

One must also understand that weather was a significant factor for the continent of Atlantis is it lay in the South China Sea. The equator lay in a different region of the Earth at that time and to understand this, you need to take the globe, which is a model of the Earth, and remove it from its stand. Place one finger just north of the State of Michigan in Ontario Canada. This is the location of the old North Pole prior to the pole shift that occurred as a large planet sized comet came by Earth many thousands of years ago as explained by the ancients. Then place the finger from your other hand on the exact opposite side of the globe and you should end up somewhere just east of an island in the South Indian Ocean called McDonald Island, this would be the location of the old South Pole. Now rotate the globe around these to axis points and you will be able to locate the old equator (this line that is midway between these two points that encircles that globe as you rotate it on the new polar axis).

Note that this places Siberia at about 25 degrees north latitude where it then supported a tropical climate with mastodons ranging the vast regions. As the pole shift occurred the mastodons were flash frozen over night with the fresh tropical plants still undigested in their throats as they died still standing on all four legs. These were discovered in the 1900s as the trans Siberian railway was built. The meat was so fresh (even after thousands of years in cold storage) that it was shipped to France where it was served as a delicacy in the finest restaurants and the railroad workers ate the meat also as they worked their way across the Tundra.

It was Immanuel Velikovsky who made the issue of the frozen mastodons commonly known in his famous books in 1950's along with many other earth signs that indicated that Earth went through a significant catastrophe just a few thousand years ago. It was generally accepted up to relatively modern times that earth went through a significant disaster … this was only reversed by modern astronomers who wanted to counter the success of Velikovsky. It was the modern astronomer who insisted that no such event could have occurred as they promoted the incorrect idea that the solar system is static and without any change since the alleged "origin". This of course I have shown to be incorrect as the solar system is ever changing and dynamic. It can and is adopting new members all of the time as we are now modern observers to this fact as comets of medium size like Hale Bopp are now captured into the solar system and someday will become permanent members … although possibly in odd orbits (not to say that the Planet Pluto does not have an "odd" orbit).

Note also on the globe that you are rotating around the old poles that the region of Antarctica that is closest to the tip of South America (the region we today call Patagonia) was also out of the arctic region and would have been without an ice cap … it was said to have been inhabited by mastodons and a vast civilization. Recall that the Piri Reis map that Columbus had in his possession as he searched for the trade route to the east was handed down from ancient Phoenician traders who had the map from the ancients and it showed a perfect outline of Antarctica that was only later confirmed to be accurate by modern satellite imagery that could see through the ice cap. This was the region of Antarctica that the mariners passed as they traveled to and from the mother continent of Atlantis that lay in what we now call The South China Sea.

Now rotate your globe with the old polar regions at your finger tips as noted above to the South China Sea and note that Atlantis lay just south of the old equator and to the East lay the vast expanse of what we now call the Pacific Ocean. But remember that the ancients called this the Atlantic Ocean along with all the other ocean waters of the world, that is, they only recognized one vast ocean covering the earth (the Atlantic Ocean). This area was called the Atlantic Ocean during the time of Atlantis, being lost from modern reckoning until Balboa and Magellan rediscovered and named it thousands of years after the great catastrophe that took Atlantis under the ocean.

The reason this vast ocean lying to the east of Atlantis is significant is because the large storms such as hurricanes would have built up and moved across this vast expanse prior to arriving at the eastern shores of the continent of Atlantis. Even today this area is so electrically active that volcanoes in the area at night can be seen from a great distance due to the electrical activity above the volcanic calderas as they connect electrically to the ionosphere above.

This is an area so rich in natural electrical energy flowing from the ionosphere down to the surface of the Earth that the ancients could hardly help but learn to tap into this and eventually develop the many ways of using this electricity. So one sees that there is a tremendous integration of ideas, concepts in physical science that go together in understanding the ancients, their weather and therefore their cultures.

As described in the **Atlantis to Tesla – The Kolbrin Connection** book, the ancients' vision and use of technology was far different than what western man has developed today. The greatest thing I learned personally from this study was at one does not need a complicated equipment, computers or vast chemical rockets to go into outer space (in fact these all introduce complications and limitations that are not necessary to go into space as we have witnessed these limitations with our own space program).

The KOLBRIN, and other ancient texts described that horrendous weather inflicted on Earth as a number of very large powerful comets found their way through the solar system. It talks specifically of the ancient advanced civilizations and their demise at the hands of the "sky monsters". It was clear also that the tragedy was NOT ONE OF AN ICY COMET CRASHING INTO EARTH, but of fiery hot comets (multiple comets of a vast powerful nature) that polluted Earth with foul smells and choking fumes as the seas rose up and lands were destroyed FROM A DISTANCE by a powerful gravitational wave from an electrically active comet (the descriptions of the huge lightning events are also clearly described). This was the cause of the great flood also with the deluge pouring in from outer space from the vast comet tail. Here too we have seen with modern satellite data moisture arriving into our atmosphere to fuel large storm systems … confirming in miniature what the ancients saw with the disastrous flood of the entire earth, which was both 40 days and nights of torrential rains as well as a huge tidal bulge of the earth's oceans. The weather book will also describe how there is a good possibility that the ancient atmosphere was quite different from our own, being altered drastically but a close encounter with this massive comet. There are historical legends and writings as well as scientific corroboration to support this possibility.

Mars lost its atmosphere and oceans to one of these powerful comets as the ancients looked on with horror. Today's scientists are sending space probes to Mars scratching their heads trying to figure out how Mars could look like a water planet yet have no water or atmosphere. The ancients clearly tell us what happened but modern science will not listen.

Much of the understanding of our own climate, atmosphere, oceans and weather come from our understanding of what happened to the ancients. The hurricanes we see today and the tremendous storms over land that occur when the jet stream dips down and touches the Earth providing us with incredible straight-line winds are just small samples of what the ancients described. The ancients are very clear on these events ... the Earth-wide devastations that they experienced on multiple occasions were caused by massive comets that fought and raged in the sky's above them ... altering our solar system on an irreversible path. We see the destruction of these events all around us in the solar system today if we only open up our eyes and look.

The trouble with modern science as I have pointed out many times before, is that they proclaimed theories to be true prior to sending out spacecraft to test those theories. They were so adamant regarding the correctness of these theories (an unfortunate situation which they maintain today) that they are locked in their own gridlock and unable to see the light of day or allow anyone to understand the true nature of our past.

Weather is more than just something to tell us if the sun will shine tomorrow are not, it is a link with our past and future and links us indelibly to the bright yellow ball we see every day in the sky called the sun. The inability of modern meteorology to predict weather on a consistent basis is due to the fact that they have failed to include the very essential electrical nature of the solar system. What I have learned through my decades of research regarding the weather of the solar system is that mostly we are protected and buffered from the tremendous electrical energy flowing by us on a daily basis.

What I also have learned is how to identify the triggers and mechanisms by which this energy can come pouring in to the surface of the earth and create effects for Earth weather systems. It has also allowed me to understand the weather of the planets and larger moons of the solar system. And last but not least, it is allowed me to read ancient writings and identify in terms of scientific principles what our ancestors were talking about as they spoke figuratively of events surrounding them that were so vast and powerful that they could only use meager words that they had available at that time.

It finally gave me the ability to look into the prophecies of the ancients that we would once again see the same events in some future time. Interestingly enough along with these prophecies that came from the true profits (not the many phonies we see today) it is clear that "of that date no man knows the time". They were also very clear there would be many people that would come to make false predictions and lead you astray. This prophecy has certainly been fulfilled many times. This is why I personally do not pick dates for future events and would not do so unless I had very specific scientific information.

IV. REVIEWING STANDARD METEOROLOGICAL CONCEPTS AND NASA/NOAA PROGRAMS

Today from every news media outlet viewed by the public, one can see the descriptions of the underlying concepts of the modern meteorological community. We daily hear of supposedly "accepted" topics such as global warming, The Greenhouse Effect, EL-NINO, that hurricanes form from warm water and tornadoes form when clouds rub together. We're told that lightning comes out of clouds and even that it rises up out of clouds somehow being generated by wind turbulence in the cloud itself (in other words the cloud is somehow internally generating the energy to create lightning).

Scientists with NOAA and the National Weather Service work in conjunction with scientists at NASA to coordinate measurements from satellites and through computer simulation in an attempt to predict our weather. Many people would be surprised to find out that all of the basic concepts in use today in meteorology are totally incorrect and that the satellites used to measure and coordinate data gathering are incorrectly designed for the task they are intended. So before getting into the varying topics of the electrical nature of the solar system it is imperative that the reader understands the current condition of theories and understanding in use today by so-called weather experts.

Part of the problem that has led up to this situation is that many of the theories still being used have been in existence for decades. Not that there is something inherently wrong with old ideas, but in this case, the old ideas do not include the essential ingredients of the electrical nature of the solar system. That is why weathermen can be correct with their predictions one day and so totally wrong on the next day as the electrical conditions only manifest themselves under certain conditions.

That is why I intend to describe one by one the various theories that are in use today and describe why each one lacks theoretical backing. Later in the text I will deal with more general concepts to highlight the myths such as global warming, the ozone hole, and even the fact that the word "climate" is a modern myth. As it turns out we are dependent on a minute-by-minute basis upon the **electrical** energy of the sun in addition to the electromagnetic radiation (visible, infrared and ultraviolet light as well as x-rays) pouring out of the sun. If for example the sun were all of a sudden to turn off and stop emitting any form of energy it would be simply a matter of a few short days until the Earth plunged into a deep freeze never to return again.

This is easily understandable when you look at the fact that as the earth turns on a given day between day and night, the average temperature drop at the surface of the Earth is between 10 and 20° Fahrenheit. This occurs in no less than a 12-hour block of time. Additionally the earth has a tremendous ability to release energy from the surface of the Earth up through the atmosphere and out in the space in a very short amount of time. This occurs more rapidly in a dry atmosphere than one that contains water (high humidity or rain-conditions) because of a simple chemical principal called heat content (and has nothing to do with what meteorologists have been calling the greenhouse effect). From this point alone one can easily see that the word climate has very little meaning since that implies that temperature and weather systems are stable over decades if not hundreds (or even millions) of years and additionally that it is some sort of inherent property of Earth itself. What we should be really talking about is the total energy output of the sun (both light and electrical) and its short and long-term stability!

The modern theoretical sentiment is that our climate has been stable in fact for millions of years and that even the dinosaurs lived in an atmosphere somewhat similar to the one we see on Earth today. Nothing could be further from the truth. One of the great mysteries of modern meteorology, something you really don't hear people talking about in the scientific community that any length, is the cause of the ice ages, one of which occurred on this planet a mere few thousand years ago. The date really is not very important, what is important is that didn't happen millions of years ago, but only a few thousand years ago.

Data on the age of the Antarctic polar cap or example has forced many investigators to believe that the ice age occurred no less than 4000 years ago (this is from data collected from the ice cap itself ... whereas astronomers try to put that date out much farther since they otherwise have no explanation for how it could be so recent). Once again it is not the length of time in the past that is important, but simply the fact that geologically it formed in extremely recent time.

The other point regarding the Antarctic ice cap is that the land underneath is warm, which is causing the cap to slide off into the ocean at an unprecedented rate ... certainly not commensurate with a cap that would have been there since the formation of the planet. The numerous open lakes that exist under the ice cap including the large Lake Vostok are clear indicators of the very recent laying of the Antarctica polar cap.

Another major point is that the Earth has seen these events many times and to the non-casual observer it is apparent that large civilizations existed on this planet prior to those events (something also that modern science tends to refuse to acknowledge). What makes us think that we are so special that such an event could not possibly happen to us? Did the Earth create these worldwide disasters all by itself as many modern scientists would want you to believe? Or were their external forces far greater than anything that Earth could produce by itself? Clearly there are combinations of factors that create these situations and we are just beginning to discover and research the many "trigger mechanisms" that throw earth into these devastating conditions for life on earth.

So the simple topic of climate and the belief that there is something called the global warming that happens slowly and somehow you produce this by breathing or driving your car is pure folly. Before you jump up and down and throw this book down, because you are totally convinced that global warming and greenhouse gases are terrible threats to mankind, let me add a statement that I always include, that is, we should not be burning fossil fuels (as they are incorrectly called) simply because they pollute the Earth we live on.

Interestingly enough for those who are really seriously interested in saving the planet, the entire political football that has become legislation in government negotiation over the global warming issue has been stalled because of bickering over whether global warming is truly an issue are not, to what degree it will affect us and in what far future date it will begin to take its toll. It has ultimately removed the real issue to set behind the counter and take a back seat to the superfluous issue of global warming. As long as the "global warming – greenhouse" façade is present there will be no real progress to curb the flow of pollutants into our fragile environment ... and the first to recognize this should be the throngs of people who have waged the political battles on the front lines only to see no real results after decades of effort.

THE TRUE ISSUE IS ...
WE SHOULD NOT BE POLLUTING THIS PLANET BECAUSE WE LIVE HERE AND THERE IS NO OTHER PLACE TO GO ... WE MUST PRESERVE BOTH THE PRISTINE NATURE OF THIS PLANET AND ITS RESOURCES (ESPECIALLY ENERGY RESOURCES) FOR FUTURE GENERATIONS ... MANY THOUSANDS OF FUTURE GENERATIONS ... AS WE ARE HEADED RIGHT NOW, A SINGLE GENERATION IN JUST A FEW COUNTRIES WILL USE UP THE MAJORITY OF THE EARTH'S ALOTTED ENERGY RESOURCES, NOT TO MENTION DUMPING CONTAINERS OF NUCLEAR WASTE IN THE OCEANS DEEPEST CREVICES ... THIS IS UTTER INSANITY ... AND IN PLACE OF TALKING ABOUT THESE REAL ISSUES WE ARE LETTING POLITICIANS BICKER OVER THE LONG TERM EFFECTS OF GLOBAL WARMING WHICH IS AT MOST A SECONDARY ISSUE ... IF AN ISSUE AT ALL !!!!

The real issue is simply that we should not be polluting the planet we live on. If pollution of its own right and preserving the resources for future generations were the issues, we would probably be much farther ahead in the international arena than we are today with politicians bickering over hypothetical effects of global warming ... with one scientist saying one thing and another scientist saying another, and with one politician interpreting this information based on his constituents' need for short term corporate profits.

This subtle logic has escaped most people, so when I make a statement that global warming is ridiculous idea it tends to bring out negative reactions from the environmentally conscious populace. The people in the pollution (energy) industries love the global warming issue because it takes them out of the limelight and allows endless meaningless "research" to go on for years while they pollute our planet into oblivion. Scientists love it because it provides them with an endless flow of grant money in years so they can fly around to conferences all over the world at taxpayer's expense ... and lastly, politicians love it because they can spout about all they are doing for the environment to "curb global warming" while allowing the pollution industries to proceed unabated.

There is another theoretical aspect to this entire issue. I use the following example to make my point. Imagine that every 12 hours someone hits you over the head with a giant club ... sometimes harder and other times a bit softer ... and along with this someone else taps you on the head with the smallest lightest most fragile feather. Now convince yourself that the greater long-term damage is going to be due to the light fragile feather. This is what scientists are expecting you to believe when they talk about global warming. As I have already said, the energy input to the planet Earth on a daily basis from the sun is like the giant variable giant club, whereas the alleged greenhouse effect (otherwise called global warming) due to greenhouse gases is like the feather.

With the Earth having the ability to rid itself of all of the energy it receives from the sun every day which is billions and billions and billions of times more than the total amount of trapped energy that could possibly be due to greenhouse or global warming gases, one can see readily that the greenhouse or global warming effects are irrelevant in the overall scheme of things. Global warming scientists always use the magic word "computer modeling", but their models reflect the programming that is put into the computer. So in this case if I wanted to program a computer to say that all your hair will fall out in one month based on my theoretical model of hair falling out of your head every day, I could predict that you would be bald within a few short weeks. So it is with the computer models of the highly paid scientists who tout the theory of global warming. It is their computer programs and not reality that is speaking.

The other issue with global warming is that there is a great deal of funding at stake. What I have learned about funding from government sources is that ... where there are funding sources, there are scientists who will say whatever it takes to get that funding. The research results will confirm the expectations of the funding agency because remember that next year there will be follow-up grants and the next year after that there are more follow-up grants and the next year after that there is a bigger follow-up grant.

There was recently a large body of scientists who signed essentially a petition stating that 98% of all the respected scientists in the field of climate research agree with the concept that we are sending ourselves into global warming. The other issue here is that the scientists who disagree have long since been pushed out of the field and simply have no voice. So is it any wonder that the majority of scientists who remain on the inside are all in agreement. Because next year, guess what, their paycheck depends on the governments providing more funding for global warming "research". This is just "good business".

This entire issue will be taken up again and future chapters since I think it is so incredibly important to contain, isolate, identify and dispose of these ideas that dominate the weather and meteorological concepts of our day. However, one last point here is that as we move to a warming trend coming out of the last ice age, this is the true cause of what we're seeing today in our atmosphere and weather. The cause of this will become clear when you realize that the cause of the last ice age was initiated as Earth plunged into a deep freeze with a great influx of water as we passed through the tail of an extremely large comet. Two effects occurred at the same time. The first was the great influx of water otherwise known as the great deluge. The second was the lack of sunshine that the ancients talk about explicitly which robbed our planet of the much-needed daily energy from the sun … this was the cause of glaciations in the beginning of the last ice age, which included a shift of the earth's mantle over the core thusly moving the celestial north and south poles … this being caused by a large gravitational wave of a massive comet nucleus passing at close range.

As Earth began to come out of this deep freeze the recovery was very slow. There is even an indication that the sun itself lost a good deal of energy during this time after the great comet passing. Since we don't have good satellite data of this period of time we will never know the true story, but we do have a clear record of the warming of the Earth. The warming began very slowly and has taken thousands of years. We are just now entering the upward trend at the end of the warming cycle, and this causes a much more rapid increase in global temperature. This is what we're seeing today as "global warming".

Many scientists that have studied the global warming issue for years and are in fact honest about the situation conclude that what we are seeing today is far too rapid and advanced in part to rapid for any global warming that might be due to greenhouse effect by greenhouse gases. At any rate these topics will be taken up in a future chapter in more detail.

The failure of standard astronomy, space science and meteorology has been so complete that recently they have added the ultimate "swance" factor ... they have introduced the idea of "chaos" and "randomness" into climatology and meteorology (and even celestial mechanics) so that when their models and predictions do not work out, they can introduce the concept of randomness and then they can retain their grand positions and funding!!! "Swance factor" was a term we joked about in science labs when experiments did not work out and rather than redo them properly some students chose the method of fudging data ... somewhere in the middle between theory and experiment, if you looked closely, was the "swance factor" ... that magical number that made it all work out. Unfortunately some professional scientists have taken this method into their careers after graduating. The concepts of "chaos" and "randomness" are the officially accepted conceptualizations of the "swance factor".

One of the greatest myths of modern meteorology is propagated by the measurement of temperatures and then indicating that this implies "global warming". The trouble with relating temperature to heat content is that there are so many mechanisms that the earth has to retain heat energy. Also temperature is not a measure of other stored energy as in the vertical electric field. There is a myth that temperature is related to heat content of the planet, which is a totally different quantity. If the air has more relative humidity then the drop in temperature as night falls will be less than if there were less relative humidity. So why do scientists not relate temperature to relative humidity rather than the alleged global warming? ... because there is no grant money available to do so.

Temperatures are more related to the direction of the jet streams than they are to solar energy input. As the sun's light energy comes down to earth on a daily basis, if there were no jet streams then a given latitude would all have the same temperature around the globe. Minneapolis would have the same temperature and "climate" as Seattle. So why is it 40 degrees below zero in Minneapolis and 45 degrees above zero in Seattle on a given day? Because the jet stream brings the cold air from the north in the usual winter pattern whereas Seattle receives its jet stream wind and ocean currents from the south and west. Then on a hot summer day in Minneapolis the temperature might by a steamy 98 degrees while Seattle is at 55 degrees. Clearly the measurement of temperature cannot be used to determine overall global heat content as is being done by climatologists. The determination of the overall earth heat and energy budget must include all sources and sinks (sinks are mechanisms that harbor energy) which must include the electrical sources of energy that can turn into heat energy if released to the surface of the earth as is the case with the phenomenon known as El Nino, or the heating of the surface water of the Pacific Ocean by electrical currents from the ionosphere.

The picture that has been presented to the public has been so distorted and with such unbelievably bad science that it requires a good part of this book to dispel these myths before correct material can be presented.

There is little doubt that the heat content of the planet is increasing, however this is due to the fact that we are emerging from an ice age and we are on the final upswing to return to normal and secondly there is ever increasing data that the sun itself is emitting more energy. One must understand that the glaciated state of earth during the past "ice age" was caused by the encounter with a large comet just a few thousand years ago. The legends of the ancients all talk of the tremendous cold that accompanied that event and this was caused as the earth took apparently about 40 days to emerge from the comet tail … all that time missing its daily dose of energy from the sun. After earth emerged with its polar caps flipped by an estimated 30 to 40 degrees, the earth began the long slow warming process that we are finishing today. Later chapters actually will chart this along with many other earth changes so that the myriads of effects are related to our long recovery. Yes the planet is warming, but this is just the natural result of warming after the ice age. Glaciers covering half of North America are not our natural or normal state and to many of us it would seem that getting back to normal would be a welcome event as opposed to something to cause alarm … and most of all it is not something caused by man's efforts. For those who have read too many newspapers and science magazines this will come as a shocking statement, however there are many scientists with no voice in this matter who agree with everything I am saying here. There is an entire chapter devoted to this topic and I suspect that many people will have their eyes opened after reading that information.

The least scientific information being propagated today comes from the National Weather Service and the associated National Hurricane Prediction Center. The misinformation involves incorrect theories for the creation of tornadoes and hurricanes and is further complicated with the annual "predictions" of storms that come out of these centers … and finally, once a storm forms they attempt to predict the path based on regression statistics and incorrect meteorological models. The end result is a disaster with the public paying the bill for this fiasco, and also paying when the predicted paths of hurricanes are incorrect and the lives of millions of people are destroyed without so much as an apology from these government supported agencies.

It is with great hesitation that I even include the following incorrect information so please be advised that the following is quoted from NOAA information and is NOT my concept for the formation of tornadoes and hurricanes.

The standard meteorological "theory" for tornado formation states that (as quoted directly from NOAA model) 1) tornadoes are extremely violent storms of rapid rotating winds … they form when cool, dry air clashes with warm humid air, creating huge thunderstorms 2) a thunderstorm creates updrafts of warm humid air, and more warm air rushed in to replace it 3) upper level winds create suction above the storm.

The standard meteorological "theory" for hurricane formation states (once again quoted directly from NOAA) 1) in a mature hurricane wind picks up warmth and moisture from the ocean, circling inward ever faster from the outer cloud bands to the inner eye wall, where winds are the strongest and where it finally rises rapidly and is pushed out the top. 2) in the beginning a disturbance forms in the atmosphere, developing into an area of low atmospheric pressure. Winds begin to move into the center of the storm seedling from surrounding areas of higher air pressure. 3) warm water heats the air and it rises at it nears the center. 4) higher salt content is said to increase the hurricane strength 5) the ocean feeds warmth and moisture into the storm, providing the energy that causes the warm air in the center to rise faster. 6) hurricanes dissipate when high level winds blow the tops off the hurricane causing it to drop its water.

Remember that the above is the NOAA standard story which is totally incorrect and in neither case is the one calculation made that any model must contain … that calculation is called "conservation of energy" and there is simply not enough energy (by a factor of thousands) for either of these models to account for the incredible energy locked into these storms!!!!

Current meteorological models do not include the one factor that in fact is 100% responsible for these tremendous storms ... there is NO inclusion of the electric conditions of earth or the solar system yet they include a myriad of other incorrectly applied factors.

When NOAA makes its annual hurricane prediction, it once again uses a myriad of factors unrelated to the real cause of these storms such as the strength of the Pacific Ocean heating, the water temperature, global warming, ocean salt content, positions of the jet streams that they believe help dissipate the storms and a host of other factors. They do not make a prediction as to dates or even weeks when they expect hurricanes to form, but make a seasonal prediction (with monthly updates) and give general numbers such as so many named storms, so many severe storms and so many land fall storms in a given season. They base the numbers on regression analysis of past years data for storms and then attempt to extrapolate into the future to get an overall number of storms.

This to me is something like taking the winnings over a season at Las Vegas and attempting to extrapolate this coming year's winnings. It will be about the same with some modifications, but this is a very broad-brush stroke approach and does not really tell anyone anything about a specific day or time. Furthermore, since the numbers are updated every month, they can "adjust" the numbers to make them fit the outcome. I have seen another trick they play at NOAA and that is that in a season with too few storms, anything short of a breeze is named a storm, and in years with too many storms as in 2004 they do not name storms that should be named storms... One of my many contentions in this book is that the scales and classification schemes used to classify storms is grossly inadequate to account for all the conditions and variables in these storms and secondly the scales can be used in as arbitrary way (they are open to interpretation by the viewer).

By contrast when I have made hurricane predictions in the past, I specify specific dates when the solar electrical conditions would be correct for the triggering of conditions that would then spawn hurricanes. This is because these factors are in fact the causes of hurricane formation and they are predictable. Going into past years one can also apply these same principles to determine what the true causes of storms were at that time based on solar electrical conditions. An entire chapter is dedicated to the art of storm prediction. This eventually may become a more exact science once the solar electrical conditions are properly measured with satellites that have been properly designed for this purpose. So until that day I continue to interpret data from satellites that were not designed to detect or monitor electric fields.

There are two major programs within NASA. These programs were initiated up in approximately the year 2000 as their basis for all other research programs. The first was called "The Sun Earth-Connection", which was an umbrella title under which all programs regarding solar system weather and Earth weather would be housed. The second program was called "Living With A Star" which was a fancy title for "how do we live in outer space" and more immediately, "how do we get through the Van Alan belts" which surround Earth. But oddly enough, this second program should not even be necessary since supposedly NASA sent astronauts to the moon passing through the Van Allen belts with no apparent problem in 1969. Clearly there is a problem even today in understanding the technology necessary to move safely in outer space with man-made spacecraft.

Very few people have a real idea of the amount of equipment that has been applied to studying outer space. We see very little of this in the public domain. For example there are no less than approximately 50 solar research stations supported by the United States government sprinkled throughout the world. But rarely if ever do you hear even the slightest amount of information from any of these. They were designed to provide research information, which would ultimately be used to forecast Earth weather for the benefit of mankind.

Likewise there are hundreds if not thousands of earthquake sensing stations sprinkled around the Earth with their data continually being broadcast back to central computerized locations to process this data. In past years all the information from these arrays of sensors, satellites, computer processing systems and government supported research laboratories has been taken off-line so that only a few elite scientists have access to this information and ultimately certain controllers who are able to control this incredible amount of information, yet keep it from the public. Most people in everyday life did not see the several changes occurring (that is, where this information is becoming more and more restricted). But to those of us that watch this daily and depend on this information to provide daily updates to the public, it is glaringly obvious that the research facilities that we all paid for are becoming extremely restrictive with the information that they pass out. The term we use for this is "sanitized information".

One great example of this is how they attempt to convince the public that man causes all of the damage that is being done to earth. As mentioned above, pollution is the real issue is being averted here. But secondly and more importantly, our solar system is very dynamic and ever changing. It took me a long time to understand why the controllers, the people who control the governments of the world that is, are so afraid of letting the public know that there could be vast natural disasters in store for us.

The answer turns out to be quite simple. If all of a sudden the people of the world would one day look up into the sky and see a vast comet with an entourage of companions all wildly filling the day and night sky, this would be the one thing that would cause the general public to drop their attention from the controlling hand of the controllers. It would be immediately obvious to every person on Earth that there is nothing that could be done by the so-called people in charge. Their control would be loosened since the public would turn to another source for direction, realizing immediately and universally that the controllers are powerless to do anything about this situation. All of the militaries, all of the guns, all of the big ships of war would all of a sudden be rendered useless and insignificant in light of the approaching celestial catastrophe. What would create serious havoc within the ranks of the general public would be if they discovered at this very same time that the controllers and their scientists had known about this for a long time and in fact had absconded with the resources of the many to stock up and prepare to save themselves and a select group of friends, while letting the public hang out to dry so to speak.

So it is for this reason that all of the true weather information all of a sudden is being withheld from the public. It is also for this reason that a tremendous amount of misinformation is being passed off by government planted imitation scientists to every media outlet … this is what we have come to call the "misinformation crew" … withholding real information while transmitting totally incorrect and fabricated or filtered information. Many of these front people are in fact of the opinion that they are part of the "in crowd" and have a ticket waiting to enter the confines of the protected areas when the other shoe drops.

Many of these people are actually dupes and will find the doors closed and the lock combinations altered when they attempt to enter the caves that were prepared for the "select entourage".

This all goes on behind the scenes and has a very specific purpose. It is designed to keep the 95% of people (who get their primary source of news from major news media) from having a clue of the real truth of what's going on around them. This is also done to "condition" people to accept whatever they are told no matter how ridiculous or far fetched that may be. This is required by the controllers so that when the real news occurs, they can transmit almost anything and the public will buy it hook line and sinker. Understanding the subtleties of news and misinformation is as important in understanding the weather, as understanding the weather itself.

"The Sun Earth Connection" program is an umbrella that covers over all of the programs within NASA aimed at investigating solar conditions and weather in the solar system as well as Earth weather. All of the dozens of satellites that monitor the Sun and solar conditions fall under this one umbrella. Once again it is imperative to understand that there are numerous levels of scientific endeavors occurring within this construct. I have numbered these as tier 1, 2, 3 and 4. Tier 1 includes an upper-level un-named and never seen a group of scientists and Secret Service controllers who have ultimate control of all of the scientific equipment and data. These scientists can go into any facility or data center at any time and takeover so that all the other scientists must leave or work on their projects under the control of the Tier 1 group based on their security clearances.

These groups truly know all of what is really going on (for example the true story about Planet-X and extra-solar system objects coming into the solar system that may affect Earth). Information from this group moves up the chain of command to the overseeing controllers. Either this information is kept from view of lower Tier 2, 3 and 4 scientists or in fact many times misinformation is generated and sent down the Tier chain along with corrupted or incomplete data. This is then distributed to the news media for public consumption.

In many cases incorrect theories are allowed to be propagated amongst the Tier 2 and lower scientific groups to keep the information that is "sensitive" within close circles. This is all part of the misinformation cycle. This is true whether we are talking about earthquake data, satellite weather data, volcanic eruption data, spacecraft data from distant planets, solar eruption data from solar monitoring satellites, etc. ... In today's so-called information age, nothing could be further from the truth. If you know people who work in an astronomical observatory they may or may not tell you that on a given night certain people walk into the facility and everyone has to leave that normally works there.

The tier 2 scientists are the ones you may see visibly working for NASA, attending scientific meetings or writing articles in journals and possibly even interfacing with the public in newspapers when scientific questions are asked of NASA. Everything that comes to the public from this group is filtered and sanitized through one of two NASA outlets or media centers. The first is Goddard Space Flight Center in Greenbelt, Maryland. The second is located within the Jet Propulsion Laboratory (JPL) in Pasadena California. These are the primary outlets for scientific types of information. NASA learned a long time ago that it has to sanitize and monitor its information output because scientists unfortunately usually unwittingly tell the truth, or in many cases, do not understand the history of the political correctness or incorrectness of what they are saying. NASA has learned it is not always good to let the truth out to the public.

So the division between Tier 1 and 2 scientists is very clear to those of us who have seen this on the inside at work. Good information always moves up the chain of Tiers but not always down the chain. Many of the Tier 2 scientists have no idea that there is a complete layer of scientists, the Tier 1 scientists, hard at work above them ... monitoring and controlling their work and information flow.

What we have learned from observing this charade that has gotten less respective of public rights and more restrictive over the decades, and especially in recent years, is that the one thing they want most to keep from the public is an event that would turn the public's attention and let them know that the people "in charge" wear no clothes. It is already noted this would be something like the Sun being out of normal cycles and affecting our weather, an extra solar system object traversing our solar system that may affect weather or other conditions on Earth ... natural catastrophes beyond anyone's earthly control.

The typical misinformation article released to the newspaper or evening news may typically have some scientists predicting doom and gloom, this is to get the public's attention. But in the typical misinformation article and actual doom and gloom is actually negated at some point, usually by putting it out millions or billions of years in the future or by placing it in some remote star system unrelated to our own. Many times these are released at the same time as real events to take the news media away from the real events. Or sometimes these articles are released much in advance of known events to sensitize the public to the misinformation. Remember that there are people who get Ph.D.'s in misinformation, and how to manipulate the public sentiment and opinion. This is all part of the daily affairs of the Tier 1 group of scientists and controllers.

Tier 3 scientists would be those teaching out of textbooks that are standardized in colleges, universities or high schools around the country. There also are groups of scientists who are flown around the country regularly on what are known as "outreach programs". Their job is to bring the standard fare NASA party line into the high schools and grade schools of this country. Even thought their way is planned and paid for by NASA, they claim to be "independent" and somehow doing this out of the goodness of their hearts. Generally these are well-meaning well-intentioned people but also generally poorly informed and without a real knowledge of the true structure of science, especially the Tier 1 layers of science that are stationed above the umbrella of government-supported science.

One of the primary motives behind this entire effort is to bring a standard party line to the public showing that all scientists are in complete agreement on the theories of how the solar system works, where man came from, geology, and weather. This gives the illusion of oneness and correctness. This is even necessary and required by law in some states before such information can be placed in textbooks for grade school and high school students. It also helps to keep the money and grant flow into the pockets of the scientists to play the game.

So you see this well greased machine is necessary for the ongoing smooth operation of the scientific community as we know it today, and the hub of this of course, at least in the public eye, is the Tier 2 group of scientists visibly working at NASA (what many people consider to be the top tier of scientists in this country).

The reason I've spent so much time integrating this particular structure into this book is twofold. The first is so the readers of today truly understand where information and misinformation come from and what they look like, because these readers will have to deal with this on a day by day basis, especially if we ever experience a large-scale solar system natural disaster such as the extra solar system object coming in and affecting other planets or Earth.

The second reason is historical. Hopefully in a far distant future people will read this text and want to know the true condition of man in the days when this book was written. Many times it would be this kind of subtlety that would be lost to the changing history books as mainstream science grapples to adopt these principles, such as those described in this book, as their very own.

As of the writing of this book, the Sun Earth Connection Program is just beginning to ask the questions that are answered in this book and in previous works. Many of the facts that were predicted early on in my work decades ago relative to the electrical nature of the solar system are being measured daily by satellites circling the Sun and our own planet Earth. The drawback for the government supported scientists however is that they have an albatross around their neck by way of archaic outdated theories which I have enumerated before.

I call them the axioms of astronomy. They are 1) that all planets and moons formed at one time 4.5 billion years ago; 2) that there is no electrical activity in outer space; 3) that comets are harmless little dirty snowballs and could not possibly affect Earth (unless on an extreme rare occasion one collided with Earth); 4) that the universe began in a colossal Big Bang (currently estimated to be 12 billion years ago by mainstream science) that has been expanding ever since.

None of these concepts are true as already discussed in previous books. So how could the scientists who are now measuring and realizing the electrical nature of the solar system possibly come to correct theoretical conclusions when they're strapped with the underpinnings of their theoretical structure as listed above. This is what creates such a convoluted unadulterated mess in the modern scientific journals. The most recurring theme that is seen to try and account for this discrepancy is the "magnetically induced" concepts.

One example is that somehow fluids flow in the center of our own Earth to cause a magnetic field that would last for millions and billions of years. There is no law or principle of physics that would suggest one could create a magnetic field from swirling molten lava deep in Earth's core. In the first place at the depth and pressures involved in the Earth's core there is no such thing is flowing molten anything. We are tricked into believing this because we see flowing molten lava coming out of holes in the Earth's surface that we call volcanoes, but deep in the core of the Earth such movement is not occurring.

The theories regarding electricity and magnetism are very clear and simple. One is either dealing with a permanent magnet that could only form all in the presence of an already existing external magnetic field, or with a magnetic field that is generated by the flow of electrical current. In either case one needs electrical current to flow on a continual and ongoing basis (not just for a few hours or days or even years, but for countless millions of years). In the case of the permanent naturally occurring magnet, there must be a long-term stable external magnetic field present as the molten iron and nickel cools to become solid (cooling through what is known as the Curie temperature of the metal), thusly locking the magnetic field strength and direction into the solidifying material. On a forming planet like earth this would take 100's of millions of years, so the external "plasma" magnetic field would have to be present and oriented in the same direction during this entire cooling process. This requires a constantly occurring flow of electrical current, which in turn requires a constant voltage in outer space to maintain this electrical current. It is easy to calculate that any charged area or naturally occurring voltage in outer space would be quickly dissipated ... so this implies that the source of the electric field must be constantly re-supplied and this can only be caused by conditions set out by the controlling star. It is this kind of simple logic that has escaped the standard models of astrophysics for the formation and ongoing operation of the stars and planets.

The second simple fact is that electrical current does not flow without a voltage, and in this case for continual electrical current flow in the same direction to maintain what we're observing in the solar system ... this additionally requires a voltage that maintains with the same polarity, and over extremely long periods of time.

This voltage may vary or change with time and in fact it does change with time, and sometimes even in direction as we see regularly with our sun's magnetic field that we receive daily that is locked in the solar wind ... but the dominant recurring direction is the same. So the belief that you can have magnetic activity in a free-flowing plasma within the solar system, Galaxy or universe at-large without electric fields is theoretically impossible. This is the quagmire that sets in front of the scientists now grappling with how to create theories to explain electrically active solar system data but without admitting that the solar system is in fact electrically active.

All of this goes back to the 1950s when the scientific community rose up to defend itself against Immanuel Velikovsky who stated that the ancients in their writings had seen enormous electrical activity in the heavens. Traditional astronomy denied that any such activity could be possible, and reaffirmed this in the 1970s in their final attack against Velikovsky. Interestingly enough many of the young scientists and astronomers recently donned with Ph.D.'s know little or nothing of this history because they were protected from it throughout the graduate school careers.

That is why it was almost comical to listen to certain young astronomers as they attempted to describe the newly found planet Sedna (a small Mars like planet recently discovered three times the distance from the Sun to Pluto), stating that if this planet ever were to come into the inner solar system it would be a comet of such colossal proportions that it could render severe damage to Earth and "would be the largest comet that anybody would ever have seen". Within hours the older traditional astronomers were cringing in their boots as they tried to backpedal and cover the tracks of their younger peer.

The following is a list of theories based on impossible magnetic explanations that permeate the astronomical, astrophysics and space science journals today. These concepts are impossible because they do not get to the root cause of magnetism in the solar system, but assume that magnetism is an entity of its own and exists of its own without any root cause... that is ... electric currents which require electrical voltages to exist for long periods of time and aligned in the same direction.

Note: the following text is extremely tedious as these bullet items numerate the difficulties specifically with certain modern astronomical and astrophysical theory. The more casual readers may wish to skim the first part of each bullet items to get the concept and then skip to the next chapter. At some point, after understanding more detailed explanations in the book regarding the electrical nature of the solar system and electrical weather, you may wish to return here and reread these sections for further clarity.

- Magnetic reconnection … this is a term that came into use possibly decades ago to explain the seeming contradiction in the measurements a magnetic field strengths in outer space. In theoretical physics, magnetic field lines loop (sometimes in strange contorted patterns) but always rejoin each other at some point. In measuring the magnetic field of the Earth's tail, which extends far to the anti-sunward side of Earth, scientists came to believe that the data was telling them that the magnetic field lines were not closed. Once again they were treating this situation as if the magnetic field lines were an entity all to themselves, not being caused by a primary mover, which we know has to be electrical currents in outer space (something they deny the existence of). So there had to be an explanation of the strange behavior of the magnetic field, an explanation that was purely magnetic in nature and did not delve into the more subtle nature of the electric currents or electric fields, which ultimately generated the magnetic field. Thus the more than magical term magnetically connection was invented to account for this anomaly.
- Magnetic bubbles … my theoretical work has shown that the fusion of the sun is that the surface of the Sun and not deep in the core as stated by traditional theory, however when scientists discovered immense energetic phenomenon occurring at the surface of the Sun, they needed an explanation. Enter once again the magnetic explanation. For decades scientists involved in high-energy research have been attempting to contain fusion with magnetic bottles (man-made magnetic fields that contain moving charges in the laboratory). So it was somewhat of a natural offshoot of this idea that gave scientists the belief that possibly the Sun might be doing this also. Remember that prior to this, based on calculations of the core fusion model of the sun, the solar surface should have been a very smooth 6000° glowing ball with very little if any surface activity. This model of the Sun stood for many decades until finally it was observed that the solar surface was immensely active. So scientists conceived of the idea that possibly magnetic bubbles (with magnetic fields that were so magical they occurred all by themselves) existed in the solar surface to contain immense amounts of energy that were

pouring up from the solar core (they did nor realize that the reverse was happening). Once again there is no understanding of what created these magnetic bubbles other than the fact that scientists measured their existence but without again searching for the direct cause of the magnetic fields (e.g. localized electrical fields at the surface of the sun). Remember that once a concept like this is in place in so-called respected journals, it never leaves. It only can be added to by an unending list of papers, equations and supportive work. Never will it be allowed that someone could enter this arena and state that the magnetic bubble concept is incorrect and replace it with something different. That something different is the simple fact that the Sun's fusion is that the surface creating the immense amount of energy that we see there and the resulting "electrical fire" is in fact creating the observed magnetic fields (not visa versa).

- Magnetic tails of the planets and comets are actually electrical tails that are part of the larger overall electrical discharges of the solar capacitor ... the magnetic fields are secondary effects
- Solar pick-up ions (ions are inexplicably accelerating after they leave the sun, so magnetically induced accelerations are introduced ... this is an impossible situation in a free flowing plasma but is used extensively in spite of the fact that it contradicts Maxwell's equations for free plasma situation)
- Magnetic field induced dynamo ... claims that the planetary magnetic fields exist in and of themselves as molten material allegedly moves within the interiors of planets
- Magnetically induced electrical currents between moons and planets (the moon and our planet interact electrically but the most striking example is the moon Io of Jupiter which passes a one million ampere current between the planet and moon ...once again space scientists have the story backwards imagining that electric currents are induced by magnetic fields rather than seeing the root cause which are the local environmental batteries (LEBs) within Jupiter's fusion capacitor ... One must realize that Jupiter is a small star
- magnetic acceleration of auroral electrons (last but not least the auroral electrons are accelerated as they pummel earth and

create the auroral displays at the north and south poles ... all of the planets with magnetic fields have such auroral displays ... yet once again magnetic fields can only direct plasma beams in a free plasma environment, they cannot introduce energy into the electrons ... this can only be done by electric fields

There are likewise non-electrical concepts, which try to explain such phenomenon as spacecraft charging. In this case, in trying to identify an effect which was noticed very early in the space program, spacecraft charging, the currently accepted theory is that electrons somehow burrow into and under the skin of the spacecraft and stay there are thusly causing spacecraft charging. As explained in detail in the first book of this series, all objects moving in a non-uniform plasma will charge negatively due to the higher mobility of electrons. If you have forgotten this very important result from the first book (or never read it) be assured that this is the primary concepts that you must carry into this book to understand the details of electrical weather.

It is what causes comet nuclei to charge and draw in the vast tail that we see from Earth. It is what caused the space shuttle to glow as it went slightly above lower Earth orbit and into the Van Allen belts on one of the early space shuttle missions. It is what caused electrons to accumulate to the sunlight side of the dust cloud of barium let out of a satellite that space scientists observed to better understand the nature of dust particles in a plasma. And last but not least is the cause of spacecraft charging.

The effects of this are readily seen in for example SOHO data (a satellite that orbits the Sun between Earth and the Sun continually collecting data on solar conditions and taking pictures of the sun in many different wavelengths). During periods of very high x-ray generation at the satellite, even though the electron stream is very intense in the area of the satellite, the electron meter of the satellite actually shows the electron count going down to zero.

This seeming contradiction actually is telling the true tale. Since the satellite is involved in the discharge of the non-uniform plasma, it becomes negatively charged as stated in my theoretical work. It then repels electrons from hitting the spacecraft and maintains the electrical potential of the spacecraft at such a level that electrons cannot reach the detector. This condition is maintained throughout the solar flare or burst that is causing the non-uniform plasma in the vicinity of the spacecraft, eventually to subside after the flare has passed and local conditions have returned to normal. At this point the electron count seen by the spacecraft detector goes up in spite of the fact that the actual electron count moving by the spacecraft is lower than before. It is thus a complete lack of understanding of such subtleties that has filled the scientific journals with endless meaningless equations and hyperbole.

In addition to the above stated facts, it turns out that the x-rays being generated that are also being detected by the same satellite are not being generated by the Sun at all ... but are in fact being generated in the local environment of the satellite by the same process that causes x-rays to generate far to the sun side of comet nuclei (which are also negatively charged by the same process just described). Notice that traditional science needs two separate and distinct theories to describe what is in fact the same process at work ... one around the spacecraft, and one around a comet nucleus. In actuality, to the sun and the solar wind, they see both objects as exactly the same ... they are both inert objects setting in the non-uniform plasma that is rushing out from the Sun at all times which we call the solar wind.

The following is a list of criticisms, which do not necessarily involve magnetism or magnetic concepts as with the bullet items above. They however point to flaws in concepts that have been integral parts of traditional astrophysical theory for a very long time. Once again, scientists are trying desperately to get away from these, but as with any albatross they remain hanging around the neck of those attempting to explain electrical observations of the solar system by traditional astrophysical theory. The following observations are listed as observations that contradict modern traditional theory (this is by no means a complete list that would also deal with planets such as Jupiter and Saturn which exhibit a vast array of electrical properties). The following statements are the true nature of the sun and solar system ...

- The sun is not long-term stable and it interacts with its environment including when comets come by
- The Sun's fusion is not at the core but is in the atmosphere ... fusion is ignited by energetic lightning bolts in the electrical storms in the solar atmosphere ... the surface features of the sun are reacting to the localized fusion fire

- There is no contained source of energy to provide relativistic electrons for the solar Corona unless you understand that the sun is a "super atom" with the interior positively charged nucleus surrounded by the shell of relativistic electrons … when the solar surface emits streamers of positively charged particles they stream outwards accelerated towards the corona … these open magnetic "holes" and the positive streamers pour into the solar system as the solar wind (with its excess current of positive charge that supports the solar capacitor)
- There is no recognition that Jupiter and Saturn have fusion and their atmosphere and are in fact small stars in standard theory yet the proton winds emanating from their atmospheres was measured directly by the Voyager space craft as early as 1980
- There is no recognition of interstellar electrical currents (and therefore electrical voltage) as recognized by Russian researchers
- There is no explanation for observed tornadoes on the Sun
- American scientists have never reproduced the Russian experiments proving that the Sun's core is cooler than its exterior surface … these are very simple experiments (and will be detailed later in this book)

V. IN THE BEGINNING THERE WAS VOID AND DARKNESS

At this point you have gone through the drudgery of putting the past behind you but have gained an essential understanding of the problems that exists in currently "accepted" ideas. So get prepared to change the way you think about our origins, the planet we live on, the atmosphere and oceans, the concept of what we call climate, the chemistry of our oceans and atmosphere, the magnetic fields that surround our planet, and the true meaning of the term "weather".

To truly put the concept of electrical comets, weather, planet formation, lunar capture etc. into perspective, it is necessary to put limiting set parameters on the formation of the solar system of which we are just one small member. In my astronomy classes I used to draw a model of the solar system on the board to give students a perspective of size and distance in the vast emptiness of outer space. There are more molecules between us and the edge of our atmosphere (a mere 60 miles vertical) than there are in the emptiness of outer space all away to the farthest galaxy or quasar. Remember that the majority of our atmosphere lies within the first one to two miles of this 60 mile distance to the "edge of space".

I would draw the sun as a 1 inch ball on the left side of the long lecture hall blackboard, and beyond the right side of the blackboard some 50 feet away would be the small distant planet Pluto (a microscopic ball of chalk dust on this scale). On this scale Earth was a tiny speck of dust about 8 feet from the 1-inch tall Sun and the giant planet Jupiter was a mere 10th of an inch in diameter about midway on the great blackboard. The point of the whole discussion led up to the fact that the next star system (our closest stellar companion) on the same scale would be some 300 miles away.

Our Sun and solar system lie at the edge of our Milky Way galaxy and if you look closely in the night sky in the northern hemisphere you can see our nearest galactic neighbor The Andromeda Galaxy which is actually larger than the full moon in relative size as we gaze up into the starry night sky. Astronomers have photographed thousands of galactic structures and the most predominant characteristic of all of these structures is that they all contain a central massive nucleus but secondly and most importantly, there is tremendous symmetry in the spiral structure of the galactic arms.

The modern "accepted" theory for evolution of the galaxies and galactic arms is known as the "density wave theory". There is a good deal of theoretical work that has been done around this model to account for rotational velocities of the stars as they move about the central galactic nucleus. Some models estimate that a near collision with another galactic structure in formation caused the so-called density wave of matter to begin thusly forming the galactic arms. The one problem that all of these theories have in common is that they cannot explain the incredible symmetry that is observed in all galactic structures. In a computer model with one perfectly scripted encounter one might get the galactic arms to appear with symmetry ... but in the random movements of objects in outer space you would rarely if ever see such perfectly planned collisions or encounters between celestial objects. You might be able to computer model this once under ideal pre-planned conditions, but this would not happen billions of times in outer space to repeatedly give us the tremendous symmetry found over and over again in ALL galaxies. In other words, how did one arm forming on one side of the galaxy know to leave a void or to produce stars in exactly the same density and in the exact same spot as in the other arm hundreds of millions of light-years away? The answer is that the density wave theories simply cannot account for the symmetry observed in galaxies.

The symmetry is such an essential property of galaxies that it in fact must be the starting point of any galactic formation theory. It was with this in mind along with a thorough understanding of what are known as velocity curves of stars that have been measured in distant galaxies, that I derived the model for galactic formation that is presented in the first book of this series (in the appendices). It is a reprinted article that was published in the refereed scientific journals in 1980.

About that time it was discovered that the measured velocities of stars moving around the galactic nuclei of many galaxies did not match the theoretical expectations based on Kepler's and Newton's Laws of gravitational motion. Not only did my new model (new in 1980) account for the great symmetry of galaxies but it also resolved the issue of the velocities of stars moving around the central galactic nucleus. The new model showed why the velocities of the stars in the middle of the galactic arms seemed to be going faster than they should relative to the outer and inner stars of the galactic arms. Prior to this astronomers had to invent "missing mass" ... that is mass that supposedly was in the galaxy but invisible to us ... the eventual problem with this was that the amount of missing mass turned out to be more than the mass of the galactic nucleus which once again created an unreal scenario that needed more convoluted theories to account for this stranger than before situation.

My new model showed that as the rotating dust and gas clouds collapsed inwards on the central massive galactic nucleus, an incredibly hot fluid was produced and out of the inner region of this collapsing fluid cloud was forced out two moving streams of hot stellar material ... one on each side of the galactic nucleus. If there were voids (diminished amounts of stellar material) on one side of the galactic nucleus ... then there would be a void in the other side also. If there were a rich dense mixture on one side of the nucleus then there would be a rich dense medium on the other side of the nucleus ... as this was all happening in the same confined region around the compact galactic nucleus. I applied fluid flow dynamics to this problem and determined that only on very rare occasions would there be more than two fluid flows coming out of the nucleus and generally coming out on opposite sides of the galactic nucleus. There was a probability of a three-armed galaxy (or four or five armed) but the probabilities were extremely low.

This outward moving stream or spray began to condense into stars of all different sizes moving radially out from the galactic nucleus and with a slight forward motion (due to the already spinning collapsing dust and gas cloud) that put the out-flowing streams in very long elliptical arcs around the galactic nucleus. The effect is much like a rotating lawn sprinkler that throws out two streams of water in opposite directions as it spins under the pressure of the water coming out of the nozzles. The only difference is that, in the galaxy, the central core has a gravitational field within which the stream will move during the lifetime of the evolving stars.

The reason the concept of galactic formation is so incredibly important is because it tells us that in the original stellar systems that emerged from this galactic arm, there would only be two (or possibly three at most) stars orbiting each other in the beginning of each star system life cycle. This meant that all the future planets, moons, asteroids, comets etc. all had to be captured one by one a later dates. The Russians had already done extensive statistical studies of this type of system and the result was very clear. If there were any smaller objects in these initial solar systems with just one or two small companion stars, the smaller objects would have been expelled from the system ... again leaving only the original pairs of the star system. This leaves us with a simple exclusive mechanism for the formation of solar systems and that mechanism is called "capture".

The standard "accepted" theoretical concept for the formation of solar systems claims that all at one time ... some 4.5 billion of years ago according to standard astronomy ... the sun and a large cloud around it all coalesced at one time and all planets, moons, asteroids and comets formed and were in place in nice neat orbits (with the planets in neat circular orbits). The only problem is that as we look out into the solar system, none of the planets, moons, asteroids or comets appears to have anything in common with each other let alone their ages. The adherence to this "axiom of astronomy" by traditional astronomers has forced their hands to develop dozens and dozens of ad hoc after the fact concepts in attempts to explain why none of the planets and moon's look or act alike if they all supposedly formed at the same time ... the most striking of these being Jupiter and Saturn with their families of comets and moons. None of these moons look anything like any of the other ones in spite of the fact that they supposedly formed within inches of each other in outer space.

Venus shows characteristics of being a young hot planet that can only rationally be explained by considering that it must be a new member of our solar system. Venus has no tectonic plates as does the Earth, yet it has extensive mountain ranges (that were formed from recent volcanic activity). The volcanic activity on Venus is so recent that as the Magellan probe passed over Venus the second time in a few year period, the surface mountain features had already changed dramatically. This is not the earmark of a 4.5 billion year old planet.

So from the beginning of galaxy formation to the never-ending ongoing adoption of new members into a solar system, the picture that is emerging is one of constant change and adoption of new members. New major planets do not form everyday which is clear from the fact that we only have nine major planets in the solar system to date. There are about 40 large moons in the solar system and possibly no more than a hundred large asteroids.

Almost daily, with the advent of new large telescopes and automated search programs in the astronomy community, new planet-sized objects are being discovered at the far reaches of our solar system. Astronomers did not expect to find these new objects and they don't fit theoretically into the normal structure of a solar system that formed all at one time. The orbit of Sedna, the new Pluto sized planet, has its closest approach to the sun at nearly three times the distance of Pluto (previously most distant planet) and has its farthest orbital distance from the sun at a whopping 80 times the distance to Pluto.

This discovery brings out an entire new possibility ... that there are many planets out there that we have never seen before because of the limitation of our optical equipment in addition to the limitation of the time we have been spending in the past looking for such objects. Some of these may be quite large and some of them may have paths that bring them into the solar system and possibly even the inner solar system. Some of them may have extensive moon systems such that when they do come into our solar system we have an entire entourage of objects, some of which may be torn away from this parent object and adopted by the capture process within our own solar system to become new members. These would be the huge comets.

This is like a giant celestial billiards game which in a sense has predetermined outcomes ... except for the fact that we now know that the orbits of new comets (especially the large comets) change dramatically as they move out into the solar system due to the comet tail drag as explained in the Plasma Discharge Comet Model. All of this would work under the force of gravity if it were not for the charge separating ability of the stars and small stellar objects undergoing fusion reactions in their atmospheres. ***This is where the electrical nature of the universe comes into play.***

Any object with fusion in its atmosphere (which in the case of our own solar system would include the sun, Jupiter and Saturn) will create the non-uniform charge distribution around it by way of what I call the solar or fusion or proton wind capacitor. Any object moving within that solar (or fusion) capacitor will discharge the capacitor, causing the object to become negatively charged, with objects in elliptical orbits creating a greater discharge of the solar capacitor than objects in near circular orbits. By definition, all of the objects within a fusion capacitor are comets ... including the planets in stable circular orbits and their fleets of moons. So comets are solar system objects with the large ones being planets or moons in formation as determined by their size. One of the main results is that ***the planets and moons never stop evolving and are subject to change ... including sometimes radical change ... throughout their lifetimes as members of a solar system.*** Thus as we see weather come in from outer space this may include water and electrical energy ... and may at times include influxes of chemicals or molecules and atoms that are drawn into the planetary atmospheres from our local space environment. Our weather is dynamic - our planets are not stagnant never changing hulks of rock isolated in outer space from the beginning of time.

Additionally the planets with their electric fields interact with each other and the solar environment ... and interact with comets as they pass by ... being affected more by the larger comets than the small comets (e.g. earth passed through the tail of comet Halley in 1910 with little noticeable interaction ... but then again we did not have sophisticated weather and orbiting space satellites at the time so if this were to happen today we might get a very different picture of that historical close range encounter of earth with a comet).

Since the galactic nucleus is undergoing fusion also, objects that pass within its fusion capacitor would also discharge its electrical storage capacitor ... so in the strictest definition of the word, our sun is a comet relative to our galaxy and its galactic nucleus. The Sun in fact has an elongated tail and it is known that the solar magnetic field interacts with the intergalactic "wind" just as the planets and comets in our solar system interact within our own stellar fusion capacitor.

When a discharge of one of these fusion capacitors occurs, the object that creates the discharge will become charged to a negative potential (because of the higher mobility of electrons relative to the other positively charged material) and begin to draw in positively charged dust, atoms and ions in its vicinity like a giant cosmic vacuum cleaner. So it is within this extremely complex environment that gravity is mixed with electrical discharges that we find ourselves ... floating through the universe hoping for another peaceful day as unimaginable amounts of power are flowing around our planet.

When one examines the meteorites that fall to earth's surface from outer space, you see that these objects contain metals, crystalline structures and dense materials that must have formed under tremendous pressures. I have never been able to figure out why astronomers claim that this material was somehow formed under feeble gravitational conditions as a nebulous dust cloud collapsed billions of years ago. Some of these objects contain remnants of magnetic field's indicative also a formation under high-temperature and pressure deep in a stellar or planetary core. It is likewise curious that astronomers expect comet nuclei and asteroids to be similarly loose composite material rather than dense rock and metal.

It has always been my impression that these materials came from tremendous explosions of which we can readily identify a few sources. The first being the stellar nova where a star completely explodes into a billion pieces that are blown off in outer space in all directions at high velocity. The second source would be a planetary collision or possibly a collision between larger celestial objects such as stars. The simple mechanics of such a collision or explosion would produce the spectrum of sizes of objects that we observed moving around our solar system. There are countless small dust grain sized objects, fewer objects of baseball size, and progressively fewer objects as we go to larger and larger sizes, and their shapes and composition would reflect their formation deep in a celestial object's core and a violent "birth".

And so it is with comet nuclei that we see coming into the solar system, the majority of which are small and will never grow into large comets because they simply do not have enough gravitational attraction to hold a matter that they are drawing in by the Plasma Discharge Comet Model. The bigger comets however will have enough gravitational attraction and therefore will continue to grow in size and additionally will have their orbits change much more rapidly because of the tail drag imposed by the attracting comet tail ... otherwise known as tail drag.

The greatest mistake the traditional astronomers have made is in assuming that all comets must be little in addition to the fact that comets are not dirty snowballs which they claim would be melting away. So when they finally discovered objects larger than what were expected by standard theory, they were left with no explanation for the presence of these newly discovered objects.

If earth and the other planets with surface features would have formed in the environment where nothing ever came close to them after they were formed and became planets, they would have perfectly smooth billiard ball surfaces with very few if any surface features at all as they would have cooled in the confines of outer space from the molten state to solid state. Furthermore, the only divisions in the landmasses would be separating on all plate boundaries rather than having the plates moving towards each other as is observed. The only mechanism to get plates to move towards one another is to have an outside force from a passing gravitationally large celestial object.

From looking at the earth objectively, just from the point of view of mountain building, it appears that earth has had at least 20 to 30 major encounters with foreign celestial objects during its geological history (close passages and not simply collisions) and probably more given the fact that much of the geology of the earth is hidden deep beneath the ground. Earth has seen many encounters and probably has had many different atmospheres and chemical compositions of its surface … more than we are fully aware. It has had many surface, ocean and temperature changes and possibly even may have lost its atmosphere at time of two in its past … only to regain it as it is steadily drawing in dust and gases from its environment in the solar system. The earth is obviously an extremely old planet and would have looked much like Venus in its early days after it also raced through the solar system as a huge bright comet during its own fiery birth billions of years ago.

Some scientists believe that we have lost planets in the solar system due to major collisions. What I find amazingly interesting is that these same scientists deny the possible existence of an object like the so-called Planet-X or Wormwood planet of the ancient Bible. Some of the same scientists even spent decades of their life in government-supported searches for large extra-solar system objects, which were thought to be affecting the orbits of the outer planets. With such glaring contradictions in their belief systems one can only believe that they are being told what to say.

Scientists have often speculated that possibly our moon was not with earth when it was formed and therefore it was either blown out of the earth during celestial explosion of cosmic proportions (caused by the intrusion of a large celestial object) or that it was captured. As with all "standard" theory, every time you turn the corner there is an exception to the rule that it simply does not fit … and so for these cases only (selectively and arbitrarily) they be grudgingly allow just once the idea of planetary collisions or the necessity of capture as a mechanism to account for certain members of our solar system.

There is a good deal of evidence to indicate that our moon in fact had an atmosphere at one time … complete with water in sufficient quantity to cause flows and rivers and to create other geological features not explainable by any other mechanism. I always find it interesting that the United States spent so much time examining the alleged moon rocks … with the amount of material falling on earth from outer space and with no atmosphere at the moon to alter the condition of these rocks, it would only make sense that any rocks picked up at the surface of the moon would have nothing to do with the original lunar surface but would be simply a collection of material that fell to the moon's surface over the eons of time that the moon has been moving through our solar system in outer space.

Planetary atmospheres is a topic that could take up a volume by itself. Mars has the exact same atmospheric composition as does Venus (although Mars has a far thinner atmosphere), and both are very different than Earth's atmosphere although earth is situated between them. This is because Venus and Mars had a recent close encounter by which Venus withdrew the atmosphere of Mars and left a faint trace of what Venus had accumulated as it passed as a large comet in historically recent times as recounted by the ancients. There is a basic physics problem that will determine the minimum size for a celestial object to maintain an atmosphere. An atmosphere is required by a planet to hold liquids in place (especially water). So is it not interesting that the moon and Mars show signs of water erosion yet have no water. In the case of Mars the erosion had to be in recent geological time since the surface features are still crystal clear and with the ever present Martian winds and dust storms, the features would have long ago been eroded. The Earth gained its initial atmosphere from its early life as a comet but there is evidence that this has changed many times in its history … and it may change again of we have the misfortune of being approached at close range by a large celestial object. Remember that any large objects coming into our solar system will not be viewed as a circular roving planet but will be in the form of a huge comet, since it will be discharging the solar capacitor. Some of the greatest disinformation being circulated today is that an incoming planet would be big and visible as a planet … however on this point the ancient legends are clear … they speak of the giant comets that stretched from one end of the sky to the other that preceded the days of destruction on earth.

There are moons and planets within the solar system that are large enough to sustain atmospheres yet have none … and there are small asteroids that have exhibited signs of having a faint atmosphere yet are too small by theoretical standards to maintain an atmosphere. The great moon Titan of Saturn has an atmosphere many times denser than our own and I have predicted from the beginning that Titan will be discovered to be a hot Venus like object … totally out of character with its size and location in the solar system … unless you consider that it is a NEW object in the solar system.

Other interesting aspects of atmospheres, now that we understand that they change, is that the earth had epochs when it had no polar caps and may have had much thicker denser atmospheres say during the time of the dinosaurs than we have now. The composition may have been quite different, and even man may have evolved in a very different atmosphere than what we have today (possibly much thicker with much higher moisture content and possibly more oxygen, etc.).

Regarding the number, size and distribution of large extra-solar system objects *of which we know nothing*, it is safe to say that there are more than we will ever imagine … and no matter how many we discover in the future, there will always be the chance that there is yet another with an uncharted orbit that has our name on it so to speak. The unknown object that could come and devastate earth and its inhabitants and leave our legacy to be dug up out of the remnants by some future civilization and wonder what life was like and what kind of atmosphere we had at this time in earth's history and … why this technologically advanced society never used their resources wisely to make it into outer space to preserve their future generations and their species. They would see that we scoured the earth for resources and pursued earthly pleasures at the expense of all resources while the time clock ticketed away as the approaching object ever so surely reduced our wonderful planet to a smoldering ruin in a single brief passage.

There are many unknowns in our ever-changing solar system. For example, in times of extreme energetic discharges of the solar capacitor … could Jupiter or Saturn ignite and burn as a fusion star for a brief period of time? The ancients claimed to have witnessed such events … should we now believe them? Could a massive new comet come into the solar system and become a planet in the same orbit as our current earth-moon system … causing us to become a double moon of the new planet? Or might we witness Jupiter or Saturn someday adopt a new moon … it might be quite the show from our vantage point on earth much as the ancients tell us they saw.

VI. ABOUT THE COVER PHOTO

As this book went to press I had been pouring through my volumes of storm photos for a cover photo that would present the image I wanted to portray in this book. This represented my life long work on weather and as with the cover picture on the previous books, I wanted something dramatic to tell a visual story. It was then, when Hurricane Frances on September 9, 2004 was making landfall on the Bahamas and Florida, that I saw the cover photo and it said everything I wanted to say. Florida had already been devastated recently by other storms and this was already turning into a record season for hurricanes and tropical storms. Hurricane Charlie had hit Florida on August 13 as it took a dramatic sharp turn from its "predicted path" and headed into the unsuspecting laps of Floridians of the southwestern bays and islands who already were celebrating as they thought the storm would go farther north according to the incorrect "predictions" of the National Weather Service.

One of my pet peeves of course is that the National Hurricane Prediction Center has always been playing a game of Russian Roulette with the public in their predictions of hurricane paths. In the first book of this series I describe the 1999 incident when category 5 hurricane Floyd was charging within 150 miles of the Florida coast and at 9 AM school children were still in school. They did not want to "alarm" the public and there were even estimates made of lost revenues if they called for an evacuation. Floyd turned north and eventually devastated the entire northeastern seaboard of the United States all the way to Nova Scotia. Florida was spared in this deadly game … this time.

In spite of any claims, using computer models based on the past paths of hurricanes even when coupled with so called computer models of atmospheric conditions … is like trying to bet on a Blackjack game at the casino based on yesterday's winning hands. Eventually your luck is going to run out … and on August 13, 2004 with Hurricane Charlie their luck ran out … one can argue about the "reasons" … but this remains one of my pet peeves that this group is still playing god with the lives of coastal residents as guinea pigs.

Stories emerged quickly that the death toll was enormous as tornadoes ripped through trailer parks during evening hours and with no one evacuated. We may never know the true death toll of this devastation as government FEMA and military personnel blocked entrances to the devastated areas until they had been "cleaned up". The official death toll was claimed to be something like 74 dead ... but from visual reports of a few people there were thousands dead in single trailer parks alone. We will never know the true death toll from this and other storms. The under reporting of death tolls in storms (and other natural disasters) on a worldwide basis began in the 1990's and continues today. It is as if there has been a preplanned decision to keep the public from knowing about any serious natural catastrophes that are caused by events outside of the control of the controllers.

The 2004 hurricane season also was the first in which it appeared that possibly there was serious evidence that these storms were being manipulated to alter their paths. At this point it would be impossible to prove conclusively, but the shapes of some of the hurricane eyes indicated possible alterations by possibly beamed energy devices that are now in orbit around the globe.

The east and west coasts of Florida have provided an amazing testing ground for the theories presented in this book. As the vertical electric field of planet earth "searches" for paths by which energy can flow from the ionosphere to the earth's surface, it turns out that the coast of Florida is one of the most prolific lightning sights on Earth. I have seen this first hand while flying along the length of Florida from north to south at night with the range of thunder storms lined up like soldiers along the Florida coast line ... with lightning so prolific that you could read a newspaper in the cockpit of the airplane with the light. The reason for this is due to the shallow continental shelf that extends outwards to the Bahamas on the east coast and another two hundred miles to the west of the Florida peninsula. Like the Great Salt Lake in Utah which has proven to also be one of the attachment points for the currents from the vertical electric field ... it has become obvious that this is due to the shallow salt water basin adjacent to dry land. Other connection points of the vertical electric field are in the South China Sea (another shallow salt water basin) and in an area known as the "south Atlantic anomaly" ... otherwise known as the Bermuda Triangle.

The reason this is important is because in the early days of my weather work in searching for the reason why these tremendous storms would lose energy upon landfall, I began to associate the areas of storm dissipation not with land, but with the conditions under the ocean near land. Clearly the dissipation of these storms was not due to the wind encountering trees or hills or buildings. There was some more fundamental process at work. Understanding what this process was would be the key to learning how to control and reduced the energy of these incredibly powerful damaging storms. The final result was that the storms literally short out electrically (just as you a short circuit and electrical circuit) as the storm's powering source (the vertical electrical connection to the ionosphere) shorted out to these regions of high electrical activity off shore in these shallow salt water basins.

When the hurricane is out over the ocean, the electrical currents from the ionosphere connect electrically to the ionized air that this above the surface of the ocean. Over the ocean this is the path of least resistance for the electrical current flow and this is what causes the hurricane to draw the incredible amount of air into the central vortex and up the eye … this is the energy source which keeps these tremendous storms growing and building as it passes over the ocean. When the leading edge of the storm begins to encounter the electrical current path to the shallow continental shelf region, two things happen. The first is that the power mechanism that continues to drive the storm is shorted out and the wind speeds begin to reduce. The second thing that happens is that the storm begins to drop its water. Any hurricane expert can tell you that the water damage is generally far worse than the wind damage.

It was here that it occurred to me that if one could begin to short the hurricane electrical current farther out at sea, then you could effectively cause the damaging wind to cease or at least diminish and the storm to drop its water harmlessly out over the ocean. I then attempted to conceive of the many methods of doing this. The first was thought was to fly over the hurricane with B-52 bombers and drop spools of conductive wire that would unroll as they dropped through the hurricane and with a balloon at the top of the wire. I later determined at this may not be a very good idea as it may in fact *increase* the energy of the hurricane by creating more conductive paths to the ionosphere.

It was then that I conceived of the idea that finally I believe is the best solution to mimic nature's own method of diminishing the energy in a hurricane. This method is safer, less expensive, and most of all is reusable. It requires an integral knowledge of the undersea topography offshore from landmasses and islands around the Caribbean (or around the pacific islands and landfalls in the case of Pacific typhoons). Prior to the hurricane coming towards the shoreline, ships would pass along the continental shelf contour dropping off buoys that would be grounded to the ocean bottom. Attached to the top of the buoy would be once again conducting wire tethering a weather balloon filled with helium (also I considered the idea of using kites). The idea is to short out the hurricane farther out along the continental shelf ... vastly reducing the energy and causing the water to dump offshore. In most cases if you could simply reduce the energy and water content of a hurricane by 20 to 40%, 90% of the damage would be prevented once the storm finally made landfall.

The buoys could set at sea for the duration of the hurricane season and then be collected for repair to be ready for the next hurricane season. Smaller Caribbean islands with lower budgets could possibly share systems that could be moved as hurricanes moved through the area during the hurricane season. The point is that this method requires an initial investment but the cost of installation and maintenance each year after would be minimal ... at least when compared to the damage of a major hurricane.

A second benefit would be that eventually we might even learn how to tap into this electrical energy source to place this huge amount of free energy to good use on our electrical grid system.

/II. THE ELECTRICAL SOLAR SYSTEM WEATHER

This chapter will begin to define in earnest the essentials of the electrical solar system. The previous chapters have presented a large number of concepts without the central unifying theoretical structures. The future chapters will build on what is presented here. Remember that many of the sentences here could be further expanded upon to give many hours of deeper explanations. One must also incorporate the many chapters of the previous books as a base for the complex weather material.

Starting with the sun's interior and working outwards, the early work that lead me to understand probably the most important discovery was that the solar fusion is at the surface of the sun and not in its core. The last chapter of the book shows a correspondence early in my involvement with the Russian scientists where they were amazed at my theoretical work resolving this not so obvious fact. The reason that they were amazed was because they had just measured the same condition with x-ray photographs. The Russians were experimentalists primarily. The diagram on the next page shows how they performed their experiments after initial x-ray photographs were taken of the sun. Their initial simple photographs showed the opposite of what one would expect based on the traditional core fusion model of the sun. Initial photographs showed they central part of the sun to be cooler and there be it appeared to be a central circular core that they said was about half as large as what we see is the outer visible ring of the solar atmosphere.

An x-ray camera with a narrow field of view was scanned across the disk of the sun. Each pixel was recorded across the full spectrum of x-ray sensitivity of x-ray camera. The first pixel, since it was only at the very left edge of the disk of the sun, represented x-rays that were generated in the very top layer of the solar atmosphere. Moving into the next square or pixel, these x-rays included a source of the deeper portion within the sun and also x-rays from the surface that were recorded on the previous measurement. The third reading in the third box from the edge of the disk of the sun would include x-rays that

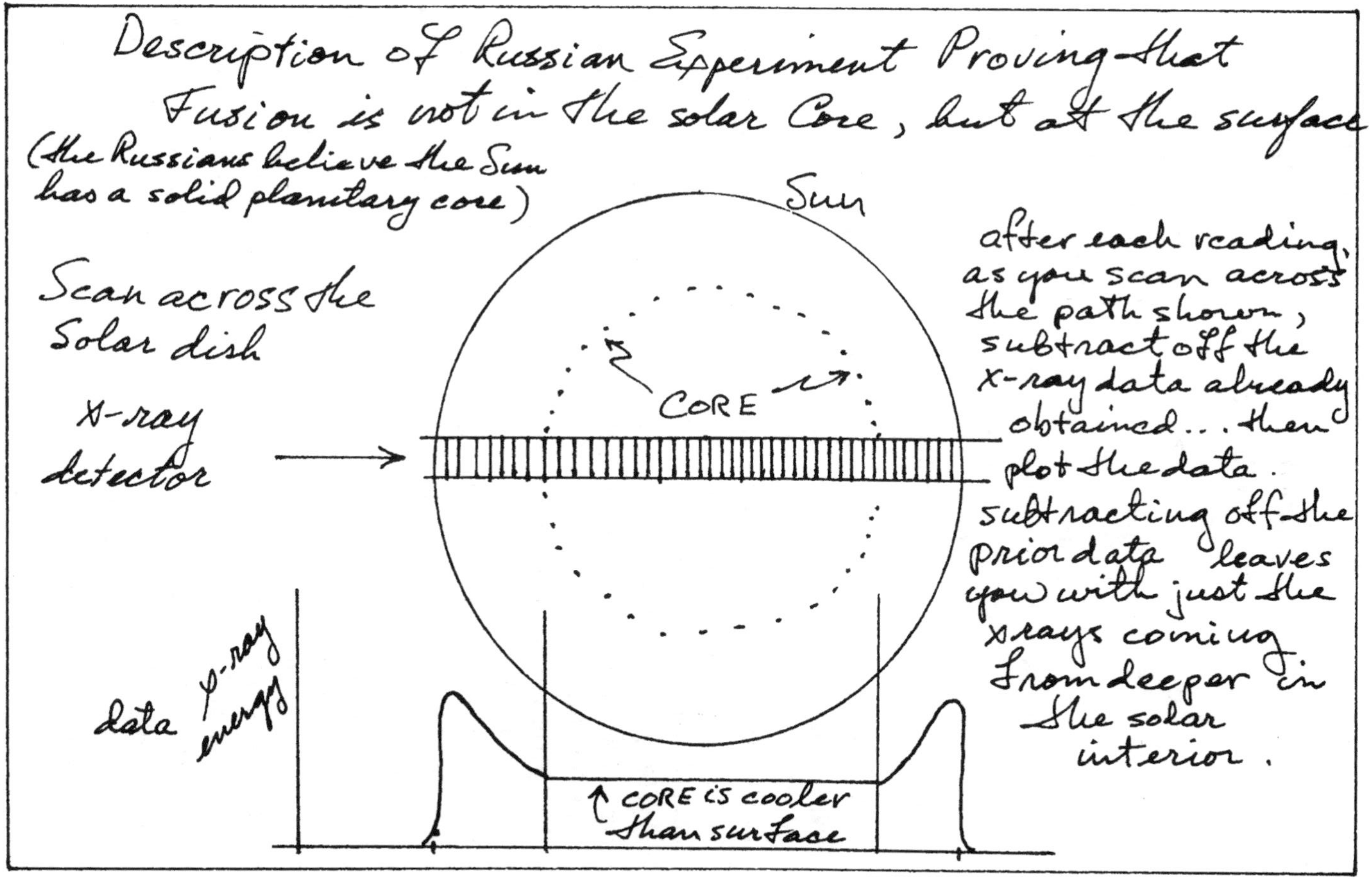

Description of Russian Experiment Proving that
Fusion is not in the solar Core, but at the surface

(the Russians believe the Sun
has a solid planetary core)

Sun

Scan across the
Solar disk

X-ray
detector

CORE

after each reading,
as you scan across
the path shown,
subtract off the
X-ray data already
obtained... then
plot the data.
subtracting off the
prior data leaves
you with just the
xrays coming
from deeper in
the solar
interior.

data X-ray
energy

↑ CORE is cooler
than surface

were generated deeper in the core of the sun. So by subtracting off the x-rays that were known to be coming from the exterior part of the sun from the first two readings, this left in the data for only those x-rays generated from that third level deeper in many atmosphere of the sun. This process continued as they scanned across the disk of the sun. The end result of this very simple experiment that could be reproduced by any high school students today showed clearly that the core of the sun was cooler than the surface. In addition as they reached a certain level within the core of the sun the x-ray signature became flat. In other words there was a solid core like structure in the sun that had a cool and constant x-ray signature, implying that this was in fact a solid cool core or planetary type of core within the center of the sun. Their data showed that this core was approximately half of the size of the sun that we see.

This has incredible ramifications for our solar system and everything that happens to our planet Earth. This means that the concept that fusion is created by tremendous pressures within the deep core of the sun, although these calculations seem feasible on the surface, the reality is that the experiment shows that the solar interior is cooler than the outside atmosphere of the sun.

There are now many new reasons why he we must look to the solar surface for the fusion engine of the sun, not the least of which is the fact that the solar surface is anything but docile and uniform. Even in the 1979 to 81 era when my papers were originally published concerning this topic, it was firmly believed that the fusion of the sun had to be contained within the core, a concept that still is firmly adhered to. As a result of this theoretical concept there were standard physics problems that were applied and gave a very specific result. One such result was that they believed that the core of the sun was very small, was composed of a solid metallic-like hydrogen and was surrounded by a tremendous atmosphere. When one calculated the movement of heat from the central core to the solar atmosphere, to reach the solar surface one used a mathematical model called the "random walk problem". In the dense confined regions of the solar interior after a single fusion reaction, the distance that this energy moved and was carried in the form of x-rays was extremely short, on the order of subatomic distances. The primary result, as the energy migrated slowly outwards from the core by the random movements of xrays being transmitted then absorbed and retransmitted etc., showed that it would take an estimated one million years for the energy being created today in the core of the sun, by this model, to reach the surface. The end result of this model was that the surface of the sun would have to be extremely uniform in temperature and structure. A great deal of effort was made to assure the uniformity and constant 6000° temperature of the solar surface.

When close observations were finally made of the solar surface, the surface was anything but normal and uniform. Tremendous flares coupled with extremely complex magnetic fields at the solar surface and massive explosions were occurring all the time that were totally unknown prior to close observations. Solar flares, C. M. E.'s (coronal mass ejections where literally the entire surface of the sun exploded into space), and the solar wind were concepts that were literally unheard of if not just in their cradle days in the year 1979.

But I'd come at this problem from a totally different direction. I was searching for the source of the electric fields that powered the solar system. There were other factors that pointed me in the same direction. For example, the fact that planets had internal magnetic fields that were locked in their solidified surface mantels and interiors indicated that there had to be a sustained plasma magnetic field in the vicinity of these planets as they solidified and cooled. I was already convinced of the electrical nature of comets and was searching also at this time for the charging process that now is clearly defined in my work.

The Earth exhibited auroral displays at the north and south poles and there was a need to understand where the charged particles came from to provide the concentrated sheet of current that impinged on the polar regions 24 hours a day and seven days a week. Other planets with magnetic fields experienced the same situation, so this was not simply a situation peculiar to Earth and was a common characteristic of all planets with magnetic fields. Clearly the Earth had no energy source of its own so once again one has to look towards the sun for the source of the electric fields that caused the movement of charged particles in outer space.

In a 1999 newsletter sent out by the American Geophysical Union, one of the main unsolved problems of astrophysics was the source of particles and cause of the acceleration of the charged particles that create the auroral displays on Earth and the other planets. In 2004 to question in the standard astronomical community remains the same. If you understand that Earth is in fact discharging the solar capacitor and it has inherent in this process the sunward electron beam just as do comets or any other object that is discharging the solar capacitor, then the source of the particles as well as the source of the energy is explained by the single concept. It is very interesting that in the mid-1990s scientists even began arguing over observations of comets that showed that they in fact generated their own light rather than simply reflecting light from the sun. This would imply an auroral type of display. Recall that the ancients talked extensively about the bright comets, that is, the huge comets like we have not seen in modern times that were so bright they illuminated the planet in the daylight sky. The following picture is of the auroral display as taken in ultraviolet light by and earth circling satellite. These displays vary in intensity and respond to solar flares and other electrical conditions in the solar system.

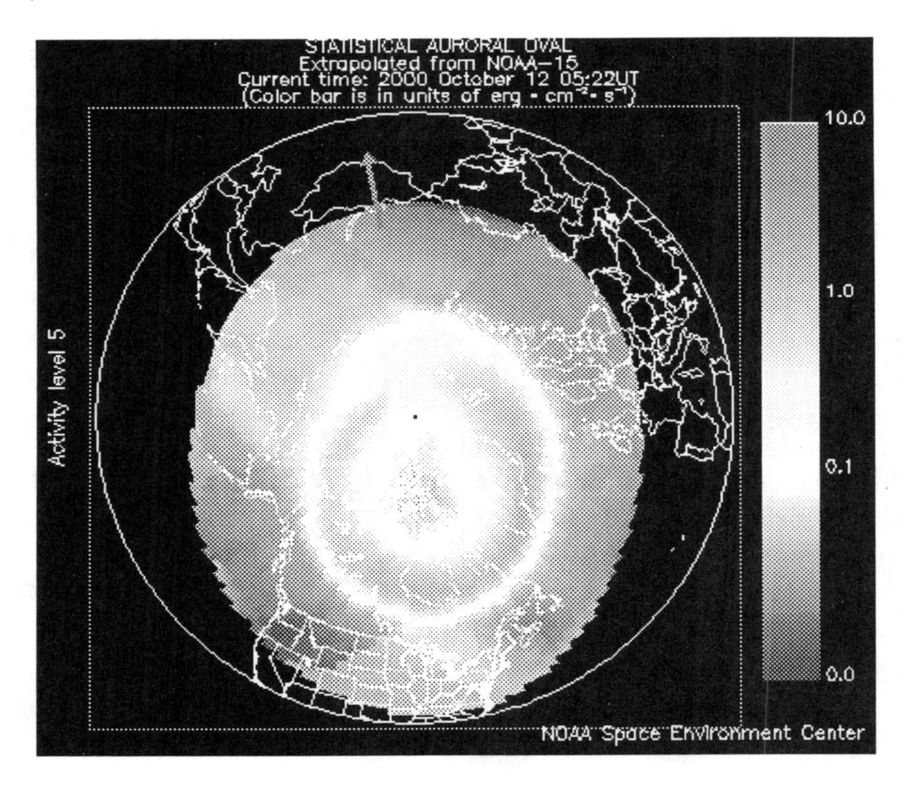

A bright auroral ring at the north polar region … the south polar region has a similar auroral ring … these respond to solar conditions

The following two diagrams define the classification of x-ray solar flares. The classification of x-ray flares is B, C., M. and X class flares. The X class flare was added to the list in the late 1990s since prior to that time no one had ever observed a flare of greater magnitude than the M class. This was quite an unusual event at the time, however today, with the advanced state of solar energy that is occurring at this time, X class flares seem to be quite common these days.

Class	Peak (W/m^2) between 1 and 8 Angstroms
B	$I < 10^{-6}$
C	$10^{-6} < = I < 10^{-5}$
M	$10^{-5} < = I < 10^{-4}$
X	$I > = 10^{-4}$

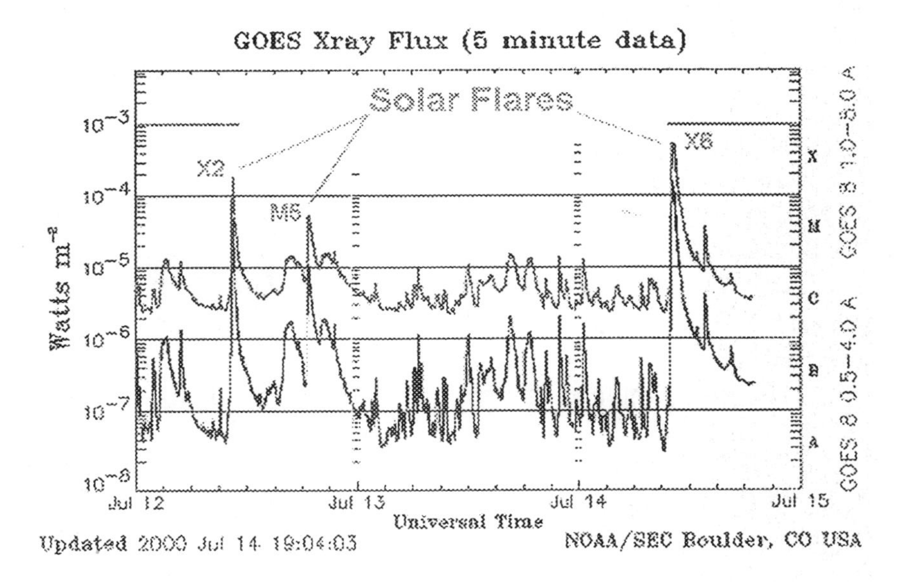

Classification of X-ray Flares of the Sun

It appears that the classification of solar flares, just as with the classification of hurricanes and tropical storms, is in need of revision and expansion due to the fact that there are so many more parameters that will define the solar storm than simply the x-ray generation from the storms. Additionally, I have discovered that many of the x-rays recorded at the sensors of satellites are in fact generated locally due to high currents of electrons that occur around the satellites as they also are discharging the solar or other local capacitors during the solar storms.

There are two primary sources of charging of objects in a non-uniform plasma (plasma with non-uniform charge distribution), and once again this is possibly one of the more fundamental and more important concepts when dealing with the electrical solar system. It is a concept that has eluded literally all of the plasma physicists that have ever worked around this problem from its inception. Although spacecraft charging has been known about since early in the days of the space program, and electrical anomalies where astronauts cannot radio to Earth over certain portions of the Earth, what actually caused this has always been a mystery even until today.

The current belief in the industry is that somehow electrons floating around in outer space get trapped under the spacecraft skin or the surface layer of metal on the spacecraft thusly causing the spacecraft to charge. But if this were the case then the spacecraft would charge to a certain voltage and just stay there. That's not what is observed. Additionally some spacecraft become charge to extremely high potential's (always negative implying electrons are doing the charging) and in a few hours completely lose the charging phenomena.

Clearly something else is at work. One also observes inanimate objects with no metal at all such as asteroids or comet nuclei charging to extremely high potential's (always negative once again). The space shuttle charge is similarly and creates a phenomenon known as "space shuttle glow" when it enters certain regions of outer space where NASA has learned it should not go. Interestingly enough this is near the Van Alan belts slightly above the rated orbital limit of the space shuttle.

The true cause of spacecraft charging, and charging of objects in space in general, is illustrated by the diagram on the next page.

2 methods by which objects become electrically charged. in outer space.

#1

object moves from one region of charge concentration to another. it will be "charged" relative to the new region of space that it will be entering. As a result, current will flow.

#2

Both methods cause negative charge on the object.

e⁻

object charging as it discharges plasma.

While discharging a non-uniform plasma - current flows. - electrons dominate due to lower mass.

The first charging process involves an object moving in a non-uniform electric field, also called a non-uniform plasma. The plasma is a region of outer space with extremely rarefied gas of electrons, protons, ions, dust particles in general the majority of these materials are charged. The key to all of this is to understand that there are non-uniform charge distributions that occur in plasmas ... I have identified dozens of these regions and the sources of energy that create the charge separation. Ultimately they are all powered by the solar non-uniform electric field (there is a future chapter in local electric fields or LEBs). As the object moves from one region of charge density to the other, the object will attempt to drag the electrical potential from one area into the next, so the object will be charged relative to the new area and electrical current will quickly flow in an attempt to neutralize the charge in this object. This is the beginning of the breakdown or current flow within the non-uniform plasma.

There are simple calculations that one can make about non-uniform plasmas and in theory they should not exist in outer space at all according to traditional theory. But this is like the theory that claims that bees cannot fly ... there is something else going on here and there is a rational explanation. Remember as you are reading this, you understand more about the electrical nature of outer space than all the NASA scientists put together.

Due to the fact that charged objects have great mobility (no resistance to move) in outer space, any charge accumulation would be quickly neutralized typically in a matter of minutes. This is what has always held astronomers, astrophysicists and space scientist back from a true understanding of the electrical nature of the universe. They never considered that the charged plasma was being created continually by an outflow of the excess of positive charge from the solar wind emanating from the sun, which was always considered to be electrically neutral (one of the "axioms of astronomy") which no one could ever violate. Remember that you could not get a PhD until you learned and bought into this incorrect science hook line and sinker.

In actuality, as their stated before, there is far more energy in the flow of electrical energy coming off of the sun than there is in the light energy that we consider to be the main source of energy coming from the sun. Furthermore this energy then becomes stored in the solar capacitor in the form of a non-uniform electric field that permeates the entire solar system all the way to the donut shaped plasma nebula far beyond the most distant planet Pluto.

The second method of charging is the one that is of utmost importance in outer space. It begins where the first charging process leaves off. Once the electrical current flow begins to neutralize the object's charge which was charged by the process already mentioned above, in a free plasma in outer space the electrons produce the majority charge carrier in the discharge. Compared to protons, electrons have 2000 times greater mobility or ability to move in the electrical discharge, therefore they are the dominant charge carrier in the discharge (and also invisible to us).

As the discharge precedes the electrical size of the discharge increases and spreads throughout the non-uniform plasma. In the case of the solar capacitor this turns out to be a radial line with the sun in the center, the object in the middle and the nebular plasma at the far reaches of the solar system on the far side. Generally the localized discharge is more regional in nature but the discharges all have the same exact characteristic. In the case of the solar capacitor with the sun in the center that is charged negatively relative to the rest of the solar system (due to the out flux of positive charge in excess in the solar wind) the electron discharge comes from the sunlight direction to strike the object. The final piece of the puzzle comes in the simple understanding that as the discharge precedes and grows, the object's charging increases and as such it becomes the attracting center for everything positively charged in the vast area of space around it ... essentially becoming a giant cosmic vacuum cleaner in space. The physics of this as explained in the first text of this series and as explained in my original papers in 1979 shows that the characteristic comet shape forms around this object. One last point is that in experiments in the laboratory an interesting phenomenon occurs and is repeated in outer space. The electron beam stays "locked on" the object so to speak and thusly assures the constant building of charge.

Small objects such as spacecraft (and objects up to the size of small asteroids and comet nuclei) have insufficient mass to hold the materials they draw in and this material eventually is blown away or in some cases literally baked onto the surface of the object by the intense electron beam. Larger objects begin to retain the material and in fact grow ... with the very large objects becoming even planet or moon sized and these then hold the possibility of becoming captured as new planets or moons of the solar systems.

The one effect that occurs is that the ion and dust tail actually creates a "drag" effect that alters the orbit of the object and contrary to the incorrect dirty snowball model of comets, which states that small comets alter their orbits by a process called "jetting" and only could e effective for the smallest comets, the Plasma Discharge Comet Model shows the opposite in that the "tail drag" has the greatest effect on the LARGER objects such as large comets ... this has been verified with the large comet Hale Bopp that had its orbit changed on a daily basis over a period of 6 years such that its orbit went from a 4200 year orbit to only 2600 years in this short a time. Jetting could not be the cause of this as the nucleus was as large as our moon.

Two processes can cause the charging to diminish ... the first is that the object passes out of the solar of local non-uniform plasma and the second is when the "tail drag" causes the object's orbit to become circularized. Objects in near circular orbits (such as the planets) do not discharge the solar capacitor to the same degree as do objects in elongated elliptical orbits. Planet Earth for example is still involved in the discharge of the Sun's capacitor and this is the cause of much of our weather, however it is not as much as even a small comet. That is why the electrical alignment of a small comet can affect our weather when coupled with other electrical alignments such as happened with comet LEE in 1999 when it coupled with planetary and other electrical solar system alignments to spawn 5 major hurricanes in the Atlantic Ocean at one time.

The sunward side electron beam which is characteristic of all of these discharges is the source of electrons that creates our auroral displays at the north-south pole of the Earth and is also the cause of x-rays that form to the sunlight side of comets.

This process was described in my original works which were published in the 1979 to 81 era, and are the premises of the first book of this series and was reiterated in the text of that book and is being summarized again in this book since it is such a fundamentally important concept with respect to the entire topic of the electrical solar system and Electrical Universe. Without understanding this concept, you would not understand why the Earth has local electric batteries (LEBs) or how this could possibly come down to the Earth's surface to affect our weather.

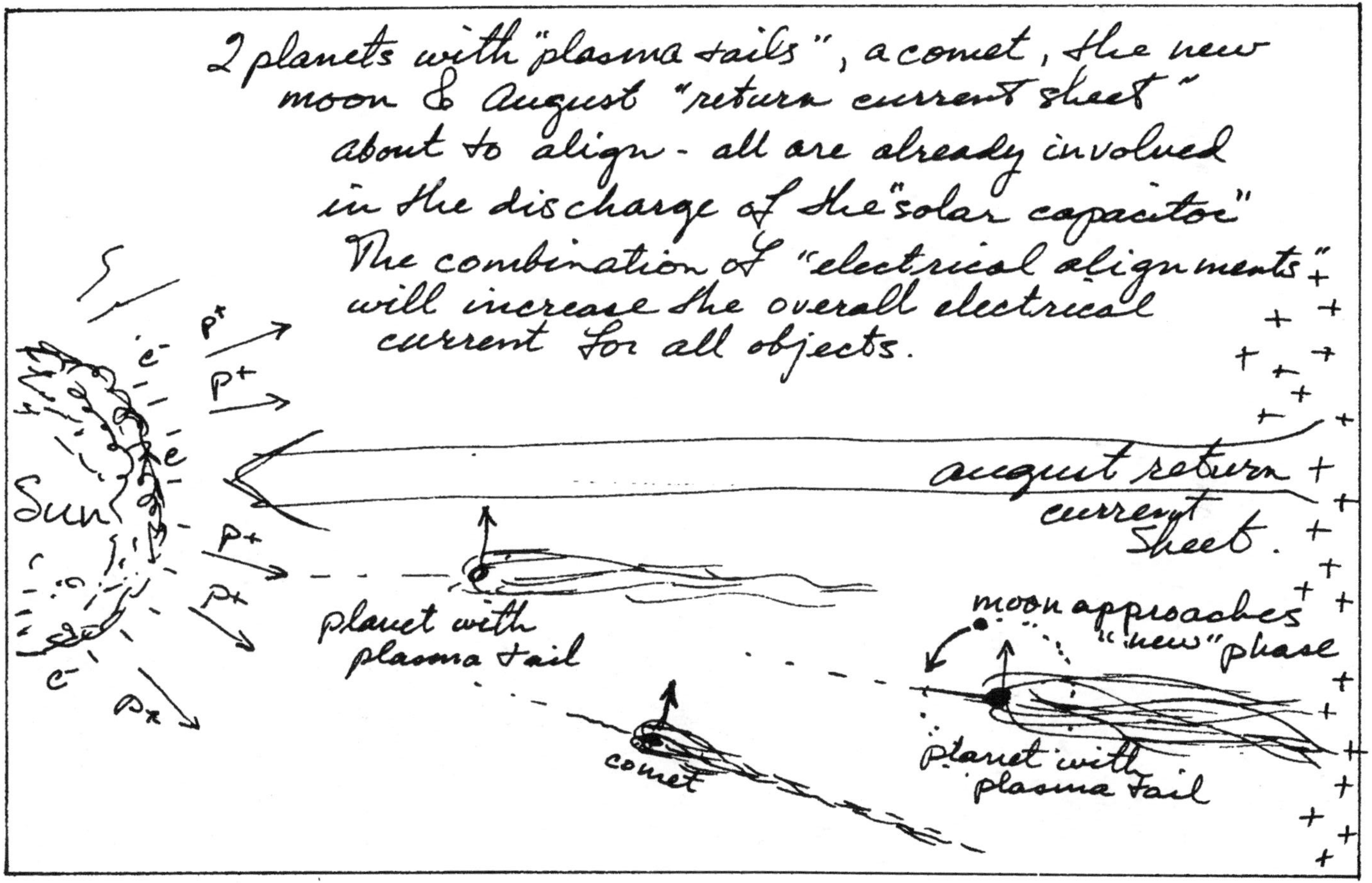

2 planets with "plasma tails", a comet, the new moon & August "return current sheet" about to align - all are already involved in the discharge of the "solar capacitor".
The combination of "electrical alignments" will increase the overall electrical current for all objects.

Sun

e^-

p^+

August return current sheet.

planet with plasma tail

moon approaches "new" phase

comet

planet with plasma tail

The above diagram shows two planets with plasma tails, a comet, with the new moon and the August return current sheet all about to align electrically (do not confuse this with gravitational alignments as there were many hoaxes in the past regarding gravitational alignments of the planets). All of the objects in the diagram are already involved in the discharge of the solar capacitor. The combination of electrical alignments will increase the overall electrical current for all objects. This is an illustration to show that these are electrical discharge current flows, which combine to create a greater effect in the plasma discharge of the solar capacitor. All of the planets have discharge tails (incorrectly termed "magnetic tails" by standard astronomy) and all have electrical currents of electrons entering their " nose" side from the sun. The "electrical size" of the objects is far greater than the physical size. All of the discharge activity is an attempt to neutralize and drain the energy stored in the LEB, but since this is a vast store house of stored energy and continually regenerated by the solar wind, it would take an enormous extended discharge to deflate the entire supply of stored energy.

We have seen cases like this where planets and comets aligned with the new moon passing in front of the Earth while they move into the August return current sheet. Such an incident occurred in 1999 with a very small comet Lee as noted and again in 2003 there was a multi planet alignment when we passed through the August return current sheet, which spawned about 60 tropical storms worldwide out of an otherwise clear blue sky.

Traditional astronomers were adamant that the small comet Lee would have little or no effect on our planet. On the day of these alignments five major hurricanes formed in the Atlantic Ocean at one time and the National Weather Service had no clue that this was even a factor. Hurricane Floyd became a category 5 hurricane very quickly and had following in his footsteps a second hurricane that clearly proved that warm water could not possibly be the fundamental source of energy for hurricanes. This is because the second hurricane followed a few short hours in the same path is hurricane Floyd, as noted a category 5 hurricane, which should have taken all of the heat energy out of the ocean if this were truly the source of energy which fueled hurricanes. But the second hurricane had no trouble forming in fact it became almost as large as Floyd itself. The details of this series of electrical alignments is described in the first book of this series.

In this example the moon enters a very important part in the overall effect of weather on Earth. As the moon moves around in its orbit of the planet Earth, at the new moon phase it passes directly in front of us … between earth and the sun. At this point it is blocking that the electron beam coming directly from the sun and secondly it is far beyond our protective magnetic shield so it is free in outer space to literally be a comet in its own right (recently the moon was discovered to have a comet-like "tail" of sodium). As the moon passes through new phase in its orbit and passes out of the way the electron beam coming from the sun, the electron beam and the solar wind reconnects with Earth … the solar wind comes pounding in to compress our local magnetic field (shield) which is only about 30,000 miles out in outer space on the sunward side. When this happens it is like a trigger mechanism that compresses our magnetic field, which compresses our ionosphere and its electric field … and drives this current in an impulse fashion down to the surface of the Earth. So the new moon in a sense is a "trigger mechanism", which enhances the already existing electrical discharge that is passing around the Earth at all times. Add to this the electrical currents from the comet (which might be 100,000,000 miles long even in a small comet) and another planet or two and then add to all of this the excess currents found in the August return current sheet and you have a major energy source to provide weather on Earth. Seeing these facts in advance has allowed me to predict the hurricane formations to the day and in many cases as much as a year in advance. As noted, absolutely none of this is understood or recognized by the standard scientific community or meteorological community, and none of this is included in their meteorological computer models (note that you do not need a supercomputer to make these predictions).

The next diagram shows clouds forming in the vertical electric field. In physics labs we used to make cloud chambers to perform modern physics experiments. It is interesting that to create the cloud formation in the chamber one needed a vertical electric field. This concept was either missed or never known about by space scientists, astronomers were meteorologists who never took advanced physics.

One of the fundamental building blocks of meteorology has never been the examined. That is, what would the weather of Earth be like if there were only solar energy entering the Earth. The answer is that earth's weather would be extremely bland, there would be no jet

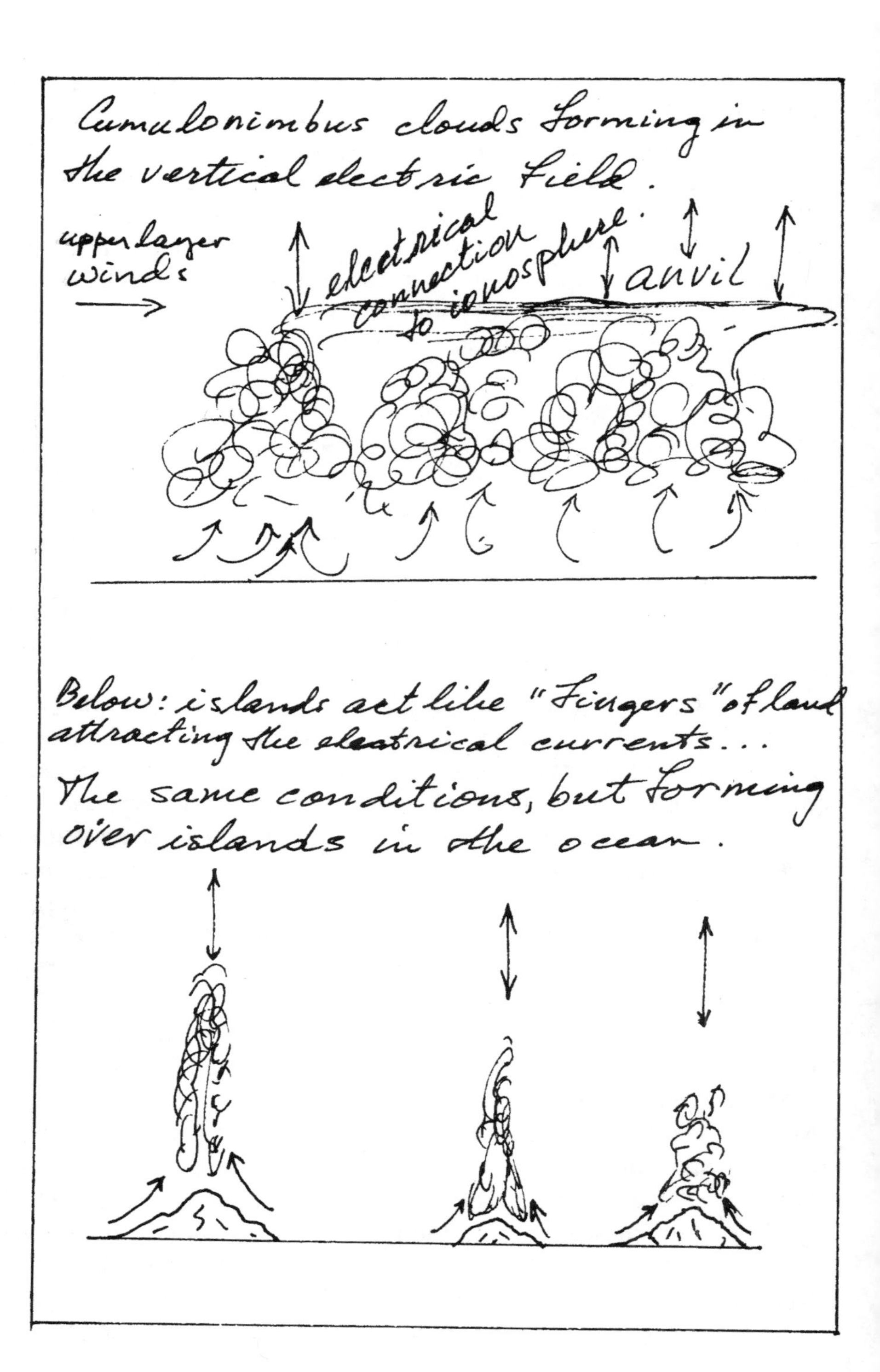
Cumulonimbus clouds forming in the vertical electric field.
upper layer winds
electrical connection to ionosphere.
anvil
Below: islands act like "fingers" of land attracting the electrical currents...
The same conditions, but forming over islands in the ocean.

streams, there would be no cumulonimbus clouds, there would be no hurricanes, there would be no tornadoes, there would be no higher low cells to create storms and the temperature profile of Earth would be exactly even around the globe at the same latitudes. This is what has always amazed me about standard meteorology. These fundamental very simple concepts seem to have escaped the thousands upon thousands of people who have studied this complicated area and never asked these simple questions. Apparently all of them read their textbooks, passed the tests and got their degrees to become professionals without ever asking these most fundamental questions.

The second part of the diagram shows clouds systems forming above islands out in the ocean. It is well known that clouds systems (primarily cumulonimbus clouds) form over islands and this in fact was how the Polynesians populated the islands of the Pacific very quickly ... because they knew to look for the large cloud covers that hovered over the tropical islands. Once again this building is caused by the fact that the island is like a finger pointing up to the sky which attracts the vertical electric field and also is an electrical ground, that is a better conductor than the ocean surface relative to the currents trying to make its way down from the vertical electric field ultimately received from the ionosphere.

This is also what happens as cloud systems move across the vast extent of the continent of Africa before they pass off the west coast of Africa to the Atlantic Ocean, which becomes very deep as soon as you move off the west coast of Africa. This is where the major hurricanes form. As already noted Central America does not have such a long expanse of land in the East-West direction in the latitude region where hurricanes form and therefore the Pacific Ocean has far less hurricane activity in the eastern part of the Ocean than the Atlantic Ocean. The energy is still going to find its way to the surface of the Earth, and it does so by way of joule heating of the Pacific Ocean. This is what we call El Niño.

El Niño it is a secondary effect, not a cause of anything. There are other simultaneous weather events occurring around the world at the same time, but they are not affected or influenced by El Niño. As such, El Niño is a secondary effect and is driven by the same source of energy as the other weather phenomenon such as the changing jet stream or a split jet stream.

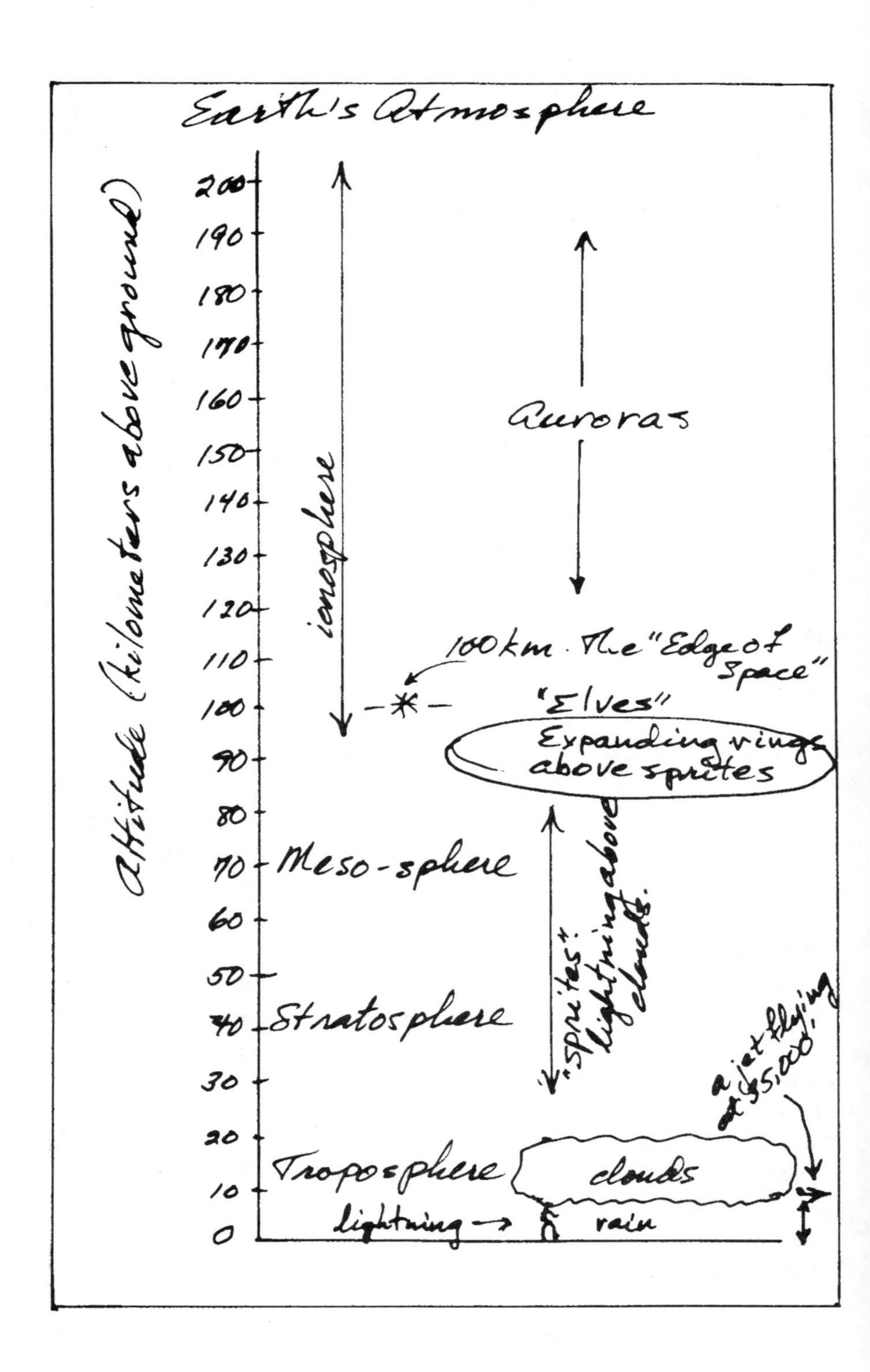
Earth's Atmosphere
Altitude (kilometers above ground)
200
190
180
170
160
150
140
130
120
110
100
90
80
70
60
50
40
30
20
10
0
ionosphere
Auroras
100 km. The "Edge of Space"
"Elves"
Expanding rings above sprites
Meso-sphere
"sprites": lightning above clouds.
Stratosphere
a jet flying at 35,000'
Troposphere
clouds
lightning →
rain

The above illustration shows Earth's atmosphere up to an altitude of approximately 200 kilometers (the vertical scale is in kilometers).

The region of our atmosphere that has traditionally been called the so-called weather region is known as the troposphere. This is a visible region where we see clouds, lightning, rain and storms. Above lies the stratosphere and mesosphere up to an altitude of 100 km (or 62 miles above the Earth's surface), which has been defined by international standard as the "edge of space". Only recently in these separate areas have been discovered electrical phenomenon known as "sprites and elves". Above that 100 kilometer mark is the ionosphere in which we see auroral displays. Astronomers, space scientists and meteorologists have never truly understood where the source of electrons existed that provided these light displays in a very uppermost atmosphere.

Lightning has always been believed to be caused by clouds themselves in the standard theoretical explanation that you will see in any graduate level or college meteorology course. It states that updrafts and friction within cloud systems creates the lightning, and this is said to include the lightning that extends outwards and downwards towards the Earth. The same is true when sprites and elves were first discovered ... the explanation was that somehow clouds were creating this energy and extending upwards just as it was believed that lightning extended downwards out of clouds and that the clouds in fact were creating this energy within the storm system. In other words there was some sort of mechanical energy involved in the creation of static electricity that emanated from the cloud to form lightning.

Sprites are flashes of vertical lightning that extended far above the cloud tops and up towards the ionosphere but elves are the most interesting of this entire phenomenon. They are expanding rings of light, which expand out from a central region above the cloud system and continue to expand out until they dissipate in a giant ring. One last phenomenon is observed from outer space and sometimes from the Earth itself. These are called nocto-luminescent lights and are simply a glow in the upper atmosphere ... once again obviously caused by electrical conditions that excite the molecules and atoms at the far fringes of outer space in our atmosphere. The point is that standard meteorology has always believed that sunlight comes into our planet, heats up the atmosphere and this is the sole source of energy that provides us with what we call weather. And as noted, any electrical conditions are said to be a byproduct of this rather than the other way around.

Standard meteorology has always considered the jet streams to be formed as a byproduct of solar heating also, however, the jet streams are far above the troposphere in the standard weather that is visible to the person standing on Earth. There is a theoretical contradiction here once again involving the second law of thermodynamics. One cannot take unorganized energy in the form of heat energy at the surface of Earth and somehow have it migrate far up into the atmosphere to create organized energy flows such as the jet streams. Clearly something else is going on here.

The jet streams in fact are once again electrical. The ionospheric jet streams with positively charged ions move in an easterly direction in the northerly and southerly latitudes in a snakelike manner ... many times going to as far north as the North Pole or as far south as the Antarctica and on rare occasion can almost approach the equator on their return paths. Normally they snake between these two regions bringing warm air from the south or cold air from the North to various regions of the globe. In a near perfect line around the equator of the Earth, and moving in the westerly or opposite direction as the mid-latitude jet streams ... and hovering almost perfectly over the equatorial region in a linear path, is the westerly moving electron rich equatorial jet stream. This is the source of energy for tropical storms. When one combines the North and South easterly moving mid latitude jet streams with the westerly moving electron equatorial jet stream, these combine to become part of our overall electric current equation and in fact are part of our magnetic field. They are one of lmany layers of coupling our local Earth's magnetic field (that we would measure with a compass on the surface of the Earth as a result of what we call the permanent magnetic field).

At this point it would be appropriate to take a slight diversion into the topic of magnetic fields. Attempting to draw a magnetic field diagram is far too complicated for the present text so instead I will describe in words the layering of Earth's magnetic field. The first layer begins deep in center of the earth's core with the original comet seed of Earth which is known to have a magnetic field, possibly the remnants of the celestial core of an old ancient star that exploded or possibly a planet remnant from a celestial collision that occurred long before the beginning of the solar system. From sounding experiments, this is known to be an extremely dense object (and not perfectly round) that forms a central core of our Earth, the original comet seed of our planet Earth. Around this exists a molten but solid core mixed with silicates ... the primary component of Earth's interior. The pressures in this region are so vast that although these temperatures at normal atmospheric pressure would allow this material to be molten, in the center of the Earth they act as a solid ... a liquid without movement. It is believed by some scientists that electrical currents move within this region to contribute to our magnetic field. Closer to the surface of the Earth are the crust and mantle, which are the most recent solid structures on Earth. These were the molten flowing materials that shaped our planet surface and then solidified. We see locked into this solid material the permanent magnetic fields, which had to lie in a plasma magnetic field for millions and millions of years as it cooled down through the Currie temperatures of iron and nickel to lock in the magnetic field that we measure today.

This is the magnetic field that you detect when you walk around the Earth with a compass. There are detailed maps of the surface magnetic field and it may vary considerably based on local magnetic fields locked in the local surface structures of the crust and mantle. The north and south magnetic poles are not at the physical north and south poles of our planet but in fact seem to be migrating back to those northerly and southerly points on an annual basis. This is due to the fact that Earth had a pole shift (a physical pole shift of the north and south celestial poles) in the not-too-distant past. This was possibly as much as 30 to 40° as the old north pole now lies somewhere in Ontario just north of the state of Michigan ... and Russian Siberia at the time was far more tropical prior to the pole shift. This pole shift was caused as a large celestial object passed near Earth and wrenched the core and mantle as described in previous works in this book series.

The localized magnetic fields that were locked in the Earth's mantle and crust were wrenched along with this pole shift and a future chapter will discuss this in more detail as they migrate back to the northerly position that they would someday call home. Above this in the atmosphere are the jet streams just described which couple the permanent magnetic field in the Earth's crust, mantle and core to the plasma field which exists outside of us in outer space ... this provides our protective shield from many forms of dangerous radiation that approach from the sun. Just beyond the ionosphere are the Van Allen belts, regions of the space with relativistic (moving at the speed of light) particles that once again are coupled to our overall magnetic field. Just beyond this is the smooth flow of the solar wind that rides around our planet looking very much like an elongated comet tale, short on the nose or sunward side and long and extended on the non-sun side ... or in the anti-solar direction. This in fact is a comet tail and we are a comet in the true sense of the word. Earth is discharging the solar capacitor, as are all the other planets in the solar system. As already noted, because we are in a circular orbit, our local discharge is very much reduced from that of an object in an elliptical orbit. A larger planet such as Jupiter of course commands a much larger discharge of the solar capacitor and the processes involved around Jupiter are far more energetic than anything we see near Earth.

When I was working with the Russians in 1990 they had already realized the interchange of energy between Jupiter and Earth and in fact had measured these quantities (as will be noted in the final chapter of this book).

The next diagram is possibly one of the more intricate and important diagrams of the book. It describes local environmental batteries around Earth and should be viewed in conjunction with similar diagrams in chapter 15. However I wanted a place this diagram early in the book because it is so essential to the visual understanding of all of these ongoing phenomenon on planet Earth.

The letters near the north pole in the diagram Ve6 represents the electric field that accelerates electrons in the form of a ringed band around the north polar region. Notice that there is a comet like extension that appears as a comet tale like attachment to a low pressure cell showing influx of water as the jet stream winds around in the northern hemisphere in the diagram. You see the eastwardly moving positively charged ion belts of the northern and southern latitudes as well as the central westerly moving equatorial ionospheric belt that powers tropical cyclones by way of the vertical electric field from the ionosphere.

Also noted is a cross-zone voltage discovered by Lou Frank, an eminent physicist who also discovered that our atmosphere has an influx of water and these were measured conclusively by satellite imagery in the last decade.

One can imagine that all of this electrical activity is going constantly around Earth yet meteorological models do not include

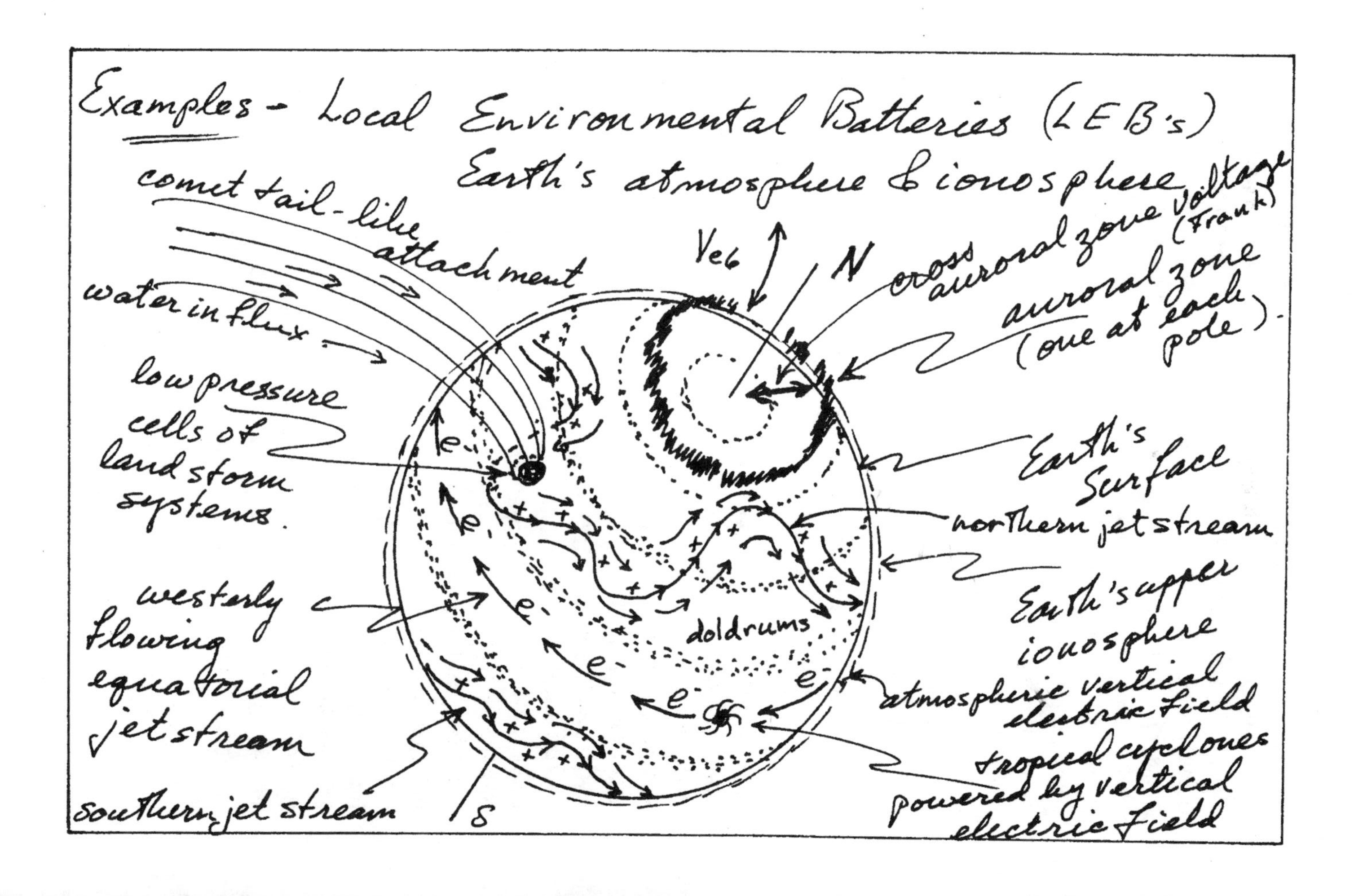
Examples - Local Environmental Batteries (LEB's)
Earth's atmosphere & ionosphere
comet tail-like attachment
water influx
low pressure cells of land storm systems.
westerly flowing equatorial jet stream
southern jet stream
S
Ve6
N
cross auroral zone voltage (Frank)
auroral zone (one at each pole).
Earth's Surface
northern jet stream
Earth's upper ionosphere
atmospheric vertical electric field
tropical cyclones powered by vertical electric field
doldrums
e⁻
+

even the slightest trace of any of this. Remember that most meteorological models use regression analysis to predict the future. In other words they look at situations that are similar to the ones occurring now or that have occurred in the past … then they combine these with short-range forecasts such as wind direction, temperature change and moisture content to provide you with a weather prediction scenario. This is why their predictions many times seem to be accurate but they are certainly missing essential ingredients that would allow them to predict farther into the future. The one thing that is most obvious is that when incredible storms occur, they are rarely if ever predicted by any standard meteorological models. That's because they did not include in any form all of the activity on this diagram caused by the electrical nature of the solar system in our planetary environment.

The next drawing shows the northward and southerly migration of the westward moving equatorial jet stream. By August it has reached its northernmost extension moving westerly over the Caribbean islands of Puerto Rico and the Dominican Republic. By February in the middle of winter it has moved south, moving along the north coast of Australia and into the island continent of Madagascar. Noted on the diagram is the location of the rare Brazilian hurricane of March 2004. Note that it is far below the winter position of the equatorial jet stream. One of the fundamental flaws of the warm water theory of hurricane developments is that it does not explain hurricanes that form or move into cold water. According to that theory, hurricanes should not exist outside of the range of about 15° north latitude to 15° south latitude, yet hurricanes are commonly seen is far as 50 and 60° away from the equator.

We have in past years seen more and more out of season hurricanes and also hurricanes that are nowhere near the warm water of the tropical waters. The National weather service typically has ignored these as if they did not exist. One hurricane made it all the way to England where the storm still had sufficient winds to tear airplanes off the runways and toss them about like matchsticks.

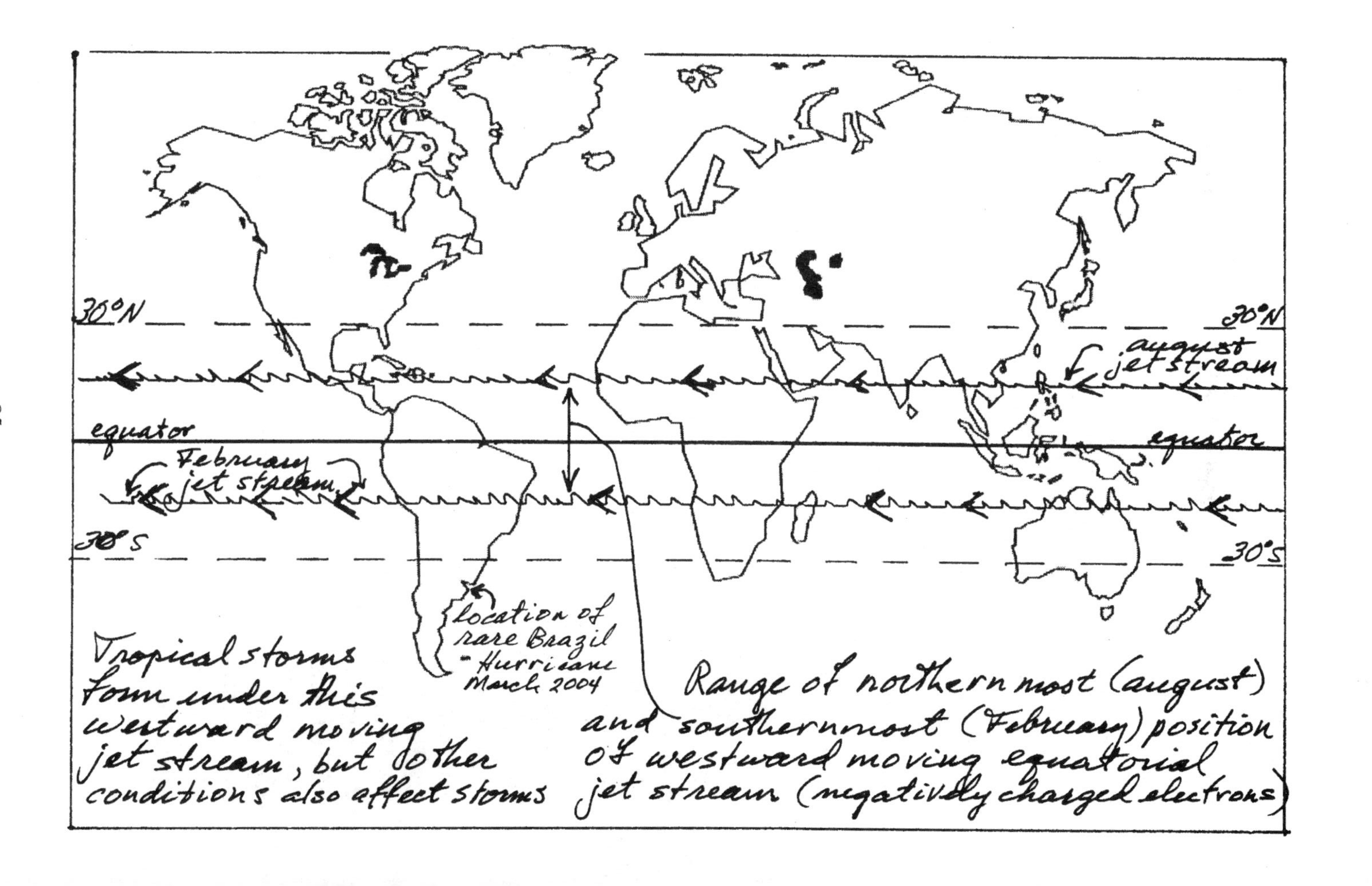

30°N
30°N
august jet stream
equator
equator
February jet stream
30°S
30°S
location of rare Brazil Hurricane March 2004
Tropical storms form under this westward moving jet stream, but other conditions also affect storms
Range of northern most (august) and southernmost (February) position of westward moving equatorial jet stream (negatively charged electrons)

A good example of a non-tropical cold-water hurricane is in the March 2, 1999 photograph from a satellite of a full-blown hurricane moving northward off the coast of Oregon and Washington states in the western United States.

I recall these hurricanes vividly as I personally called the sheriffs on the west coast of these states as we were seeing vast power outages and related high winds sleet and rain that were pounding the coastline. I asked the sheriffs if they knew that there was a hurricane off the shore a mere 90 miles from their coast. They were shocked and amazed and didn't believe what I was telling them. The National Weather Service made no accounting of the hurricane and said nothing. The people onshore had no clue that of full-blown hurricane was raging up the coastline west of the State of Washington. The other photo shows the same hurricane as it dissipates on March 22, 1999 along with another full-blown hurricane just west of Alaska in the Bering straight between Alaska and Russia. Where was the warm water that formed these hurricanes?

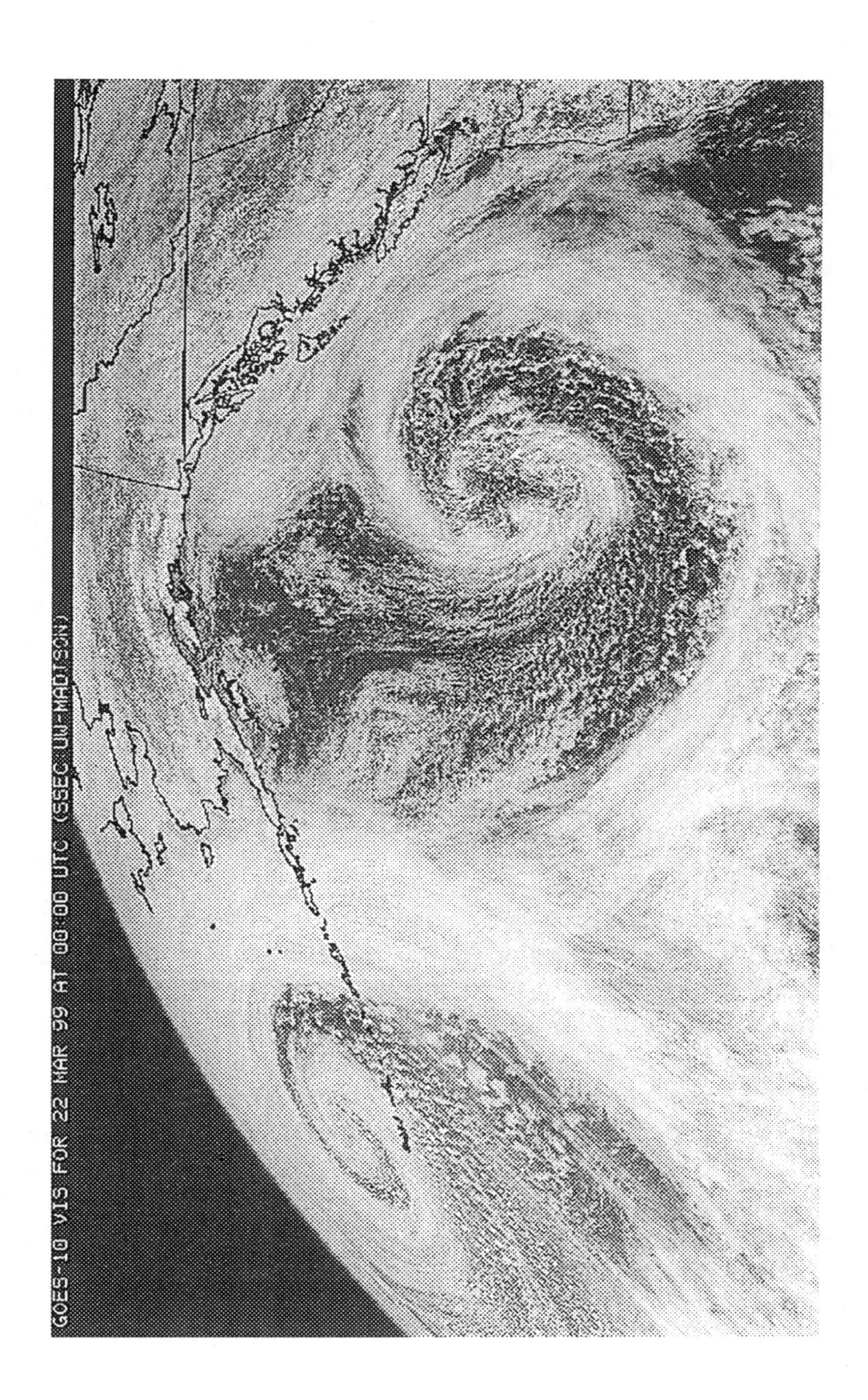
GOES-10 VIS FOR 22 MAR 99 AT 00:00 UTC (SSEC UW-MADISON)

Recall that the Hubble space telescope has taken photos (chapter 13) of hurricanes on the planet Mars ... Mars has no warm water oceans ... in fact it has not oceans at all. Clearly there is another mechanism that creates these monster storms.

There would be severe implications for the standard scientific community if they were forced to admit publicly to the existence of solar system electric fields. One would be the severe embarrassment of admitting that they knew nothing about the most important factor that affects our weather and planet Earth, that comets are not dirty snowballs, that the solar system did not form all at one time and all the other implications of recognizing this small little detail of electrical fields in the solar system.

However there is another major problem with that this admission as I have discovered. This comes from the energy industries which would then have to admit that there is unlimited electrical energy sitting right above us which was known about in the early 1900s and actually tapped into by a man called Tesla. They would have to admit that we have been burning fossil fuels (incorrectly named) and nuclear fuel throughout the past century and selling this to the public at great expense when all the energy you can ever imagine is sitting right above you and coming down around you every day in the form of violent storms. They would have to admit that they lied to the public all these years ... not to mention that the tremendous amount of damage that has been caused by these violent storms could have been averted with the benefit of supplying us with an unlimited amount of free energy.

There is one final point that must be made here to counter the criticisms of astronomers who do not understand the principles of electrical charging of objects in outer space. That is ... the larger the object, the lower the charge to mass ratio of the object. This is an odd and subtle set of observations that must be understood to avoid the glaringly incorrect criticisms of astronomers who do did not understand plasma physics. The sun has the greatest charge of any object in the solar system yet its charge to mass ratio is the lowest, meaning that in the movement of celestial objects it will move the least of any object due to the charge on the body itself. It is also critical to understand that the charge on the object is in a sense around the object and not firmly attached to it as if you had a handle on an object so to speak. So it is the electron cloud around these objects that is doing the electrical work and not the object that supports this cloud as in the sun or comet nucleus. Astronomers have made many wild and incorrect statements that are unfounded, claiming that if there were electrical forces in the solar system then things would go flying around at the speed of light. This is totally incorrect and once again shows their total ignorance or ability to understand simple concepts of plasma physics, which the public is now reading and learning first-hand.

In general, as one goes to smaller and smaller objects, the charge to mass ratios become larger and larger. Due to calculations that I have made, it is clear that objects the size of baseballs and larger will be relatively unaffected by the charges that they possess as they discharge the solar capacitor. Objects smaller than baseball size and all the away down to dust grains however begin to show marked effects due to the space charging of these objects. Dust grains move very rapidly in the comet tail but certainly not as rapid as the electrons that provide the primary surge of current in the discharge of the solar capacitor (or other LEB) in the solar system.

Galactic nuclei undergoing fusion also produce fusion capacitors so everything moving within this non-uniform electric field also is affected just as comets discharge the solar capacitor. This means our sun is "comet" relative to the plasma field of the galactic nucleus and its stellar fusion capacitor. As a result of a complete lack of understanding of these concepts, standard astrophysics and astronomy has had to paint a very bizarre picture of the universe ... many times presenting very bizarre theories including the belief that quasars are somehow at the edge of the universe. As it turns out there is a physical principle that I discovered with my earliest work in the 1970s called the Induced Electric Dipole Red Shift (or IEDRS).

This is an electrical effect that occurs when photons of light emerge from the non-uniform electric fields surrounding stars or other objects involved in the fusion process. This is explained the earlier texts, but in brief its shows that the red shift we see from quasars has nothing to do with their motion ... but in fact is a result of the internal electrical properties of the quasar as it charges in the local galactic electric filed by the same process used by comets. Quasars are generally associated with larger galaxies and these quasars lie within the non-uniform plasma capacitors of the galaxy. Thus the quasar is charging to a high negative potential relative to the potential of the galactic nucleus. Once again all electrical affects are local to the celestial bodies involved. The induced electric dipole force also works on small metallic objects in space and this is the cause of meteor streams that we see associated with comets. Standard astronomy says that these are boiled off and released from the central comet core in the dirty snowball comet model. But is it not interesting that all of these objects in the meteor streams contain metals. Not everything in outer space contains metals so why would one expect that everything in a meteor stream when related to comets is comprised of a certain amount of metal?

The simple answer is that the meteor stream is gathered by the electrical comets by the induced electric dipole force. This is the cause of meteor streams associated with comets as discussed in earlier books in the series. It should be obvious by now that any object coming into our solar system, whether larger small, will break into the outer edge of the nebular capacitor of the sun and become a comet. At the far reaches of the solar system the comet comas will be very large and diffuse.

So even very large objects will become shielded and shrouded, and as such will not be visible to typical telescopes at Earth or even above earth's atmosphere. One would have to look for a very diffuse cloud of water at the edge of the solar system … and deep within this cloud hidden from normal view would be the celestial object and its entourage of moons and other extra-solar system objects that orbit it.

That is why in 2008 as this book goes to press, NASA has planned to put a telescope into space that will look for these clouds. Apparently they have been listening to my radio shows and reading my books as this has no place in standard astronomical theory if you supposedly think that all the planets formed at one time and no new planets have formed since and nothing could come into the solar system from beyond … if you truly believed all of this why would you build and send aloft such a telescope?

VIII. VIEWS OF THE ELECTRICAL SOLAR SYSTEM (1979)

It might be helpful for some to understand what the condition of science was like in 1979 is I entered Cornell University is a somewhat naïve instructor. The rosy always-perfect world of science that I had imagined and was taught as a college and graduate student had not prepared me for what I was about to see.

Also, in retrospect, looking back even into the 1950s from our perspective now, it should have been clear that there were serious problems with the so-called standard accepted theories that formed the basis of astronomy even at that early date ... but the knight in shining armor or white hat status had already begun and nothing was going to change that. Once a theory was in place in the 'respected journals, nothing could remove it from its hallowed status ... you could only add to and worship it ... not attempt to alter or question it.

No more was the dirty snowball comet model, which in 1955 was known as the ice ball comet model, no more was this out of the box in "accepted status" when comet Arend Roland 1957 passed through the solar system with its intense sunward spike. This should have immediately triggered a serious investigation and a reversal of that newly accepted concept. But in this earliest day of the space program, already scientists were entering the state of denial that carried them for the next 50 years. They would rather hide behind in this case a very ridiculous concept and pass it along than to really examine the problem in earnest.

As it turns out the argument that was used to deny comet Arend Roland of its status as being the first sunward spike comet observed in modern times, it was pushed into the background and said to be only an optical illusion. As I re-examined the orbit of Arend Roland at long last in the year 2003 for a presentation I was developing of a comet viewing project and some radio shows, I discovered that in fact during much of its orbit when it was producing the sunward spike (for a period of almost seven days) it in fact gave us a very good broadside view of the comet ... enough anyway that the "optical illusion of a thin Type II tail" excuse should have never been accepted in the first place. So of the thousands of professional astronomers that have taught that in a singsong manner in universities from textbooks over the past 50 years, not a single one had sat down two really examine the orbit of Arend Roland.

In 1979 this was just another red flag in a series of red flags that told me something was critically askew with astronomical theory. So in this chapter I wanted to give you a view of what it was like in 1979 as data came in daily from the space probes and I sat in meetings watching scientists throwing out ad hoc theories (what I call hip pocket theorizing) only to realize decades later that once this was done, nothing could redirect the space program in the arena of theoretical space science from that time forward.

At this time "Chapman Physics" was involved. Chapman had made convincing arguments that space had to be electrically neutral and there could be no electrical activity in outer space. He and Hans Alfven (Nobel Prize winner for his efforts in plasma physics) were at odds and in the USA Chapman won. In addition to this, scientists had just gotten finished burying Velikovsky and any hints that there could be electricity in outer space were dutifully dismissed along with the person that made such claims.

But as I sat daily watching data that came into the University and the scientists watching this in meetings, an example of the Pioneer spacecraft's data showed that as it passed a small moon there was a tremendous tug not accountable by gravity alone. This data was swept under the rug as nobody wanted to deal with it. As the Voyager spacecraft passed Saturn after Jupiter, the Marconi oscillators on board began to fluctuate. The Marconi oscillator is the most stable oscillator known to man so it was not the oscillator itself that was changing frequency, there was something at Jupiter and then Saturn which was causing the oscillator to go into the red ... in other words the frequency was reduced in wavelength and then increased back to normal after passage this was due to some interaction with these so-called planets.

After this had happened at Jupiter and as I realize that this was caused by a non-uniform electric field at Jupiter (and not anything to do with gravity as scientists at Cornell were trying to imagine), I made the prediction that the Marconi oscillator at Saturn would be would have its frequency reduced even further than it had at Jupiter. This was because I had already recognized that Saturn had to be a more energetic young planet than Jupiter in terms of the fusion capacitor that surrounded it, the cause of the non-uniform electric field. The data bore this out. Saturn in fact had created a larger shift in the Marconi oscillator sending a signal back to earth than it hand at Jupiter although Saturn is known to be a much smaller and less massive planet than Jupiter … so clearly general relativity had nothing to do with it as some astronomers were starting to claim some form of space bending … and besides one would need a gigantic object far larger than Jupiter (let alone Saturn which is smaller) to cause any such reduction in the frequency of electromagnetic signals emanating from its environment. In 1979 there was no SOHO satellite and no one had never made any serious attempts to photograph the surface of the sun. The sun was believed to be a bright orange ball at 6000° with a very constant smooth surface. No one ever imagined that solar flares, CMEs (Coronal Mass Ejections where the entire surface of the sun ejects into space due to massive explosions) and other activity that we now know about today from the SOHO and other satellites.

Today, after all of this activity has been thoroughly measured and explored and after it contradicts completely the expectation of traditional theory, the traditional concepts somehow still hold on where they are in fact blatantly incorrect.

Below is a picture of me in 1986 showing the laboratory demonstration of a comet to a group of students. In the photo I am definitely a younger person as this is almost 20 years ago. But the

principle still holds true, as one can demonstrate in any laboratory for a group of young people how a comet works and how it attracts and holds the smoke and gas as in outer space just as the model does in the laboratory.

In 1979 there was absolutely no understanding of how tornadoes or hurricanes formed, there was no real knowledge of the solar wind, there was no computer modeling except for extremely rudimentary modeling, there were no supercomputers with parallel processing or computers available that to do the type of processing necessary to model complex weather systems or outer-space plasma systems ... and last but not least, the spacecraft that were going out to study outers-pace were incorrectly designed for the task that they were meant to perform. They had no electric field sensing devices and many times early in my career I had to learn how to take data from incorrectly designed spacecraft and interpreted them so that it would provide fuel for my theoretical work.

A good example was when they had an electron detector and an x-ray detector on the same spacecraft. Electron output would go down as the x-ray counts would go up. Both the increase in x-rays and electron count dropping at the detector indicated that the spacecraft was charging to a negative potential due to the increase in electron flow as the space craft discharged the local environmental battery. This is just a simple example of how I had to take data and change it because the spacecraft were simply incorrectly designed. The traditionally trained scientists however would read the values of data at face value and state that the electron counts were going down when in fact I knew that they were going up. The scientific literature at this point is so convoluted that most of it would simply make good fuel for a rainy day.

They always had to interpret the data based on some other convoluted concept but did not the include electric fields because they were not allowed to use electric fields ... even for the scientists that had a hint that possibly there was something going on out there like that. So the world of space science in 1979 was very different than what one might imagine now. I have to chuckle at new young astronomers who have no clue what it was like then and think that everything was as nice and rosy and perfect as it is today. The true history of astronomy is not taught to young astronomers.

IX. THE SUN-EARTH CONNECTION

At this point enough information has been given to start putting pieces together to model the sun earth connection, these are the real-life processes that connect the activity on the sun with weather on the ground at earth. With the new understanding that the solar fusion engine is high in its atmosphere, a difficult problem is created. There does not appear to be enough hydrogen fuel in the atmosphere of the sun to burn for 4 1/2 billion years, as scientists believe might happen in the core fusion model of the sun. This means that the sun would have to be replenished with hydrogen on an ongoing basis. In other words our sun is more indelibly linked to its environment than what we previously thought. With so many variables at work, it is amazing that the sun shows any sign of stability at all.

In the past decade we have seen the so-called solar cycle, which has been constant for hundreds of years, disrupted and no one seems to know why. In the 1990s I spoke of the great comet Hale-Bopp, which was discharging the solar capacitor over a period of six to seven years on a daily basis, as the true cause of the severe weather and solar conditions. This was the cause of the increase in solar activity throughout that period, but in and around the 1999 to 2000 timeframe Hale-Bopp was well on its way out of the solar system and no longer could be considered to be a serious factor.

One of my main criticisms of NASA has been what I call the build one - launch one satellite program. Using this method every satellite was built differently and on an individual basis and was extremely expensive. We needed fleets of satellites ... not onesie-twosies. These were designed to perform essentially the same tasks but at different locations and as a result we only collected data from one small point in outer space. This was certainly not enough to get a good composite view of what was going on in the solar system let alone around our poor little planet Earth. I am always amazed at the long lists of satellites that have been launched over the years ... all of them different. Scientists have begun to realize this in recent years and are sending two or three of the same type to the same vicinity of space, yet we still need many dozens if not hundreds of spacecraft moving around the planet and the solar system all at one time the gain a composite view that we so sorely need. Additionally I had suggested early in my studies of electrodynamics in space that we need space craft observing each other as a satellite cannot measure its environment since it in fact is altering that environment by its presence, so how can it possibly give an accurate view of space?

With so many factors affecting the Sun and its energy output, how could we ever possibly hope to understand or model it? At this point it appears that the solar energy depends on the continual influx of hydrogen from outside of the solar system, it depends on the oscillating 11 year cycle which apparently is locked to the planetary activity of Jupiter and its orbit and possibly to a rhythmic pulsation of the nebular ion cloud which exists beyond the planet Pluto and is held back by solar wind pressure. We have been lulled into a false sense of security that the solar system is somehow stable over long periods of time. This is simply not true. We have been blessed with thousands of years of warming weather, but the reality is this may not last very much longer.

If a comet comes by the sun and unleashes an incredible solar flare that comes our way, it could be the end of the power gridor the start of a series volcanism on earth … that is, the trigger that pulls the volcanoes into action such as the 25 volcanoes in the Olympic chain in northwestern United States or the many volcanoes in central America for example. The misnomer of climate, that allusion that somehow our earth has a long-term stability in temperature and heat content, has lulled many people into the false sense that we can continue on a path of buying SUVs and shopping in the mall … and life will go on far into the distant future in the exact same manner. As this book goes to press it is still uncertain what causes the solar cycle to oscillate and all the controlling factors that affect our sun and its long-term stability.

Could our solar system be moving through outer space as the Russians believed and is being affected by this “vacuum domain” space between stars that we are moving through constantly and of which we know almost absolutely nothing. If our sun did depend on a constant influx of new solar hydrogen to burn and we were about to head into our area devoid of such hydrogen, the sun all of a sudden could begin to cool uncontrollably. Or if the opposite happened when we moved into a region of hydrogen rich interstellar materiel with an associated increase in hydrogen input to the sun and it began to accelerate in its energy output.

These things may be happening but with standard science locked in this layer of incorrect astronomical theories, we will never have the satellites or the much-needed data to find out the answers to these ever-critical questions. On of the many unanswered questions of modern astrophysics involves the question of how protons accelerate out of the sun to form the solar wind. The answer is that the solar Corona which is a sheath of high-energy electrons that surrounds the sun (do to the fact that the inner core of the sun is actually positively charged as a nucleus of a super atom) the protons are emitted from the solar atmospheric surface due to local fusion explosions and the Corona acts as an accelerating screen much as a diode uses a metal screen in a laboratory to accelerate charged particles.

The following is a list of bullet items that all contribute to the Sun Earth Connection and to understand the total picture one would have to combine these factors with the additional knowledge of the current activity of each factor and its relative effect on Earth. As you will see this is a complex problem but as with many systems in nature, predictions or assessments can be made because many times one or two factors dominate the situation. When in the past I made predictions of hurricane activity, I was careful to do so in cases where there was a clear dominance of contributing factors that gave good odds of the predicted outcome, and I always predicted with the caveat that there are many contributing factors and weather prediction is a difficult "art" … just when you think you have seen it all you are crossed by a new set of data and facts that need new interpretations and introduction of new factors. So with this in mind the following is a list of factors that affect or influence the planet earth …

- intensity in the solar wind which includes velocity, pressure in density
- current levels of solar flaring and whether these flares are coming near us, directed at us or are moving off in another direction (by which they are not directly affect us but do continue to pump up the energy level of the solar capacitor which ultimately drives all the weather systems in the solar system)
- activity of comets in the solar system

- whether these comets are large or small or are on elliptical orbits
- whether these comets come close to the sun or pass through or align with other electrical discharges already in existence in the solar system such that the new comet may enhance the already existing discharges of the solar capacitor
- rhythmic variations within the solar atmosphere which affect its fusion and ultimately the solar energy output
- localized disturbances in the solar surface (for example sun spots) which enhance energy production and expulsion of solar flares from these vicinities
- the pressure exerted on the large-scale solar magnetic field by the inner planetary medium through which we pass continually
- rhythms in the nebular ion cloud that is held back by solar wind pressure far beyond orbit of Pluto
- the level of electrical current in the return current sheets which pass from the nebular ion cloud back to the sun to balance the electrical current equation in the solar system
- planetary alignments which are electrical, that is when planetary electrical discharges of the solar capacitor align, this not only enhances the electrical current passing by the planets but increases the current discharge back to the sun which increases solar flaring and other solar surface activity
- the movement of our moon in its orbit especially when it passes new moon phase or full moon phase as these are electrically aligned with the earth; the most pronounced effects occur when the new moon passes, where a few days after the new moon the moon moves out from directly between the sun and earth allows the solar wind to come pounding into earth's expanded magnetic field which then compresses … it is this impulse that drives earth's severe weather and many times triggers such events as hurricanes, volcanoes and earthquakes
- as the solar wind moves by earth, due to the magnetic field that lies about 30,000 miles to the sun or inside, the protons in the solar wind blow one way around earth whereas the electrons move the other way … this separation of charge creates a transverse battery around the sides of the earth causing current to flow across this region of outer space with earth in the center. This influences our upper ionosphere and the amount

of electrical current that has to drain on the Earth's surface in this cosmic electric circuit

- since the Earth acts as a comet it has an electron beam coming in the sunward side from the sun which creates the Auroras and upper atmospheric disturbances ... coming in the back side of the planet are protons and ions which contributed a small portion of the overall electrical current passing by earth as part of its overall electrical discharge of the solar capacitor
- in earth's upper atmosphere, jet streams of ions move easterly at the mid latitudes while an electron stream at the equator will move westerly to couple to the exterior magnetic field and these in turn drive the lower surface weather systems bringing cold air from the polar regions or warm air from the equatorial regions ... the interface of vortex motions between the jet streams is called the doldrums area
- regions in earth's upper atmospheric couple to comet-like tail structures extending out into outer space drawing in water and electrical energy which power and fuel low-energy low-pressure cells of high-energy on the surface of the earth
- within the earth's atmosphere the hydrological cycle brings moisture up high into the atmosphere and drops it down as rain ... this process migrates from the equator to the poles bringing moisture from the equatorial regions to drop it on the north and south polar caps ... building these up at a constant rate
- there are many more minor processes

Remember that none of the above factors are included anywhere in the computer modeling within standard meteorology. Within the research community scientists are grappling at this time, asking just the basic questions regarding what causes these phenomena and are trying to implement theories that are still trying to sidestep the concept of electrical fields in outer space. As this book goes to press, there has been a tremendous surge of topics in the scientific meetings that occur around the globe between scientists of NASA, the European Space Agency and related scientists to quickly include electric fields as if they somehow had known about these all along. In many cases they are copying ideas that I have been talking about for years on my radio shows, lectures, videos, books and my earliest published papers ... they attempt to redefine terms you are reading about and exactly the same topics. The situation in 1979 was that I had all the information theoretically on one hand, and on the other hand I had the data pouring in from spacecraft, which apparently only I could see what it was truly saying. So it did not take me long to put all of this together to come up with all the conclusions. Additionally I was not strapped with the axioms of astronomy nor did I have allegiance to what I knew were outdated in incorrect astronomical theories. So whether I was talking about the rings at Saturn and its sweeper moons or the excess current to protons from the solar wind, once I began putting the entire picture together there was suffucient material for many decades of future research and refinement.

Possibly one and most interesting conclusions regarding the sun earth connection and electrical nature of the solar system was that there was a grand design for traveling and moving about in this series of electrical currents, what I later came to call "electric highways to the stars" or "electric rivers to the stars". There was also a simple explanation in the suns workings itself and a method to take fusion and put it in a bottle ... the ultimate battery ... it turns out that earth itself experiences fusion on occasion and people have witnessed this at close range and it has even been reproduced in the laboratory. This is called Ball Lightning and it usually is initiated by extremely intense electrical discharges. These are the same conditions that exist within the sun when there are electrical discharges in the atmosphere separating the water molecules into hydrogen and oxygen, the hydrogen can be separated into its component parts of protons and electrons thusly creating a super atom condition ... the same conditions that we call fusion on the sun is a separation of charge and a stable state. The trick is to learn how to tap into the nucleus of this super atom and into the electron shell that surrounds it to tap into this battery. This is the trick that nature has given us and it is one of the primary components of the fusion engines in the electromagnetic propulsion system as designated in the ***Atlantis to Tesla*** book, the second book of this series. There is another propulsion system that is passive; it allows one also to ride the electrical currents, that is, one can derive propulsion through outer space and derive the driving energy as you move much as a sailboat moves through outer space, although this is not a solar sail concept. It is a very subtle mechanism for deriving energy and pushing against the localized magnetic field ... this design has not released to the general public or any other possible groups that might use this … as with all my work, I do not allow it to be used for military purposes.

There is a theoretical dilemma in standard astronomy in that the pioneer in Voyager spacecraft that are moving to the edge of the solar system at this time are not exactly where they are supposed to be. There appears to be a slight attractive force greater than that which can be accounted for by gravity alone. The force is not extremely large but it is consistent with all the spacecraft. If there were some quirk with one of the spacecraft or some condition in that part of the solar system, one might think that there was no such anomaly as only one of the spacecraft would be affected. However all three spacecraft are experiencing the same condition and there is an effort within NASA and the international space science community to try to understand the situation.

What is clear is that one needs once again the electrical interaction within the solar system, which is caused by the induced electric dipole force acting on the metal spacecraft. This force was first seen at Saturn when the pioneer spacecraft passed by a small moon and experienced an incredibly large "gravitational" tug. The only problem was that it was not gravitational and it additionally sensed large magnetic field. The field was far too large for the small moon that could not even be seen from earth based telescopes (less than 200 kilometers in diameter … a very small moon). This is what convinced me in this satellite data that in fact this small moon was electrically charged in that the force experienced by the pioneer spacecraft was the induced electric dipole force. The equations that govern this and the forces that would act on the spacecraft are printed in the Saturn Sweeper moons predicted paper published in 1980 in the scientific journals (reprinted in the appendices of the first book of this series). Once again standard science offers no explanation even as this book goes to press.

Since Mars lost its atmosphere due to a large passing comet only a few thousand years ago and since we see it regaining its atmosphere … almost doubling its atmosphere in the past 10 years … it seems clear that planets may lose and then regain their atmosphere over long periods of time. Possibly earth has lost and regained its atmosphere or changed its atmosphere on many occasions. With this information in hand scientists can begin looking for the traces of such events. But with Mars there is a possibility that we can impact or enhance the replenishment of its atmosphere by inducing the discharge of the solar capacitor thusly drawing in atmosphere at an increased rate.

This could be done by dragging a long tether out into space behind the planet and inducing the electrical discharge of the solar capacitor. Could we replace this atmosphere in a short period of time? It would be interesting to experiment with something like this with possibly one of the large outer moons of the solar system to see it in fact we could induce this type of change.

I wish to close this chapter with one last thought and that is regarding a side venture that the Russians and myself pursued in the 1990's when we were interacting regarding my work as related to their measurements of solar system conditions. We began to notice that there was an empirical correlation between man's activities and electrical alignments of the planets, moons and other objects in the solar system including comets. What we discovered was actually verified experimentally by the Russians that the unborn fetus was in fact very influenced by the alignments of planets. We concluded that this had to be an electrical condition, which was somehow lost or masked after we were burdened with all our senses that took over after birth due to our consciousness and incredible amounts of input in our daily environmental existence. So it was at this time that we actually looked into the possibility that the positions of the planets, based on electrical alignments and conjunctions, were in fact responsible for some of the behaviors and activities and personalities of people. They continued this work and I notice today many times that there is a significant correlation between solar and solar system conditions that affect people individually or in groups … this provided a scientific basis for the ancient "science" of astrology (the precursor science to the modern measurement science area we call astronomy).

X. THE CLIMATE AND GLOBAL WARMING MYTHS

There are no greater myths being propagated today than that of climate change, global warming and the greenhouse effect. Earlier chapters have already discussed the reasons for basic misunderstandings of these concepts. This is such an important topic that I included a separate chapter to solidify the basic premises.

Historically, this all began at the planet Venus in one those embarrassing events that happened to NASA scientists on a very early probe sent to our nearest neighbor in interplanetary space. Once again the entire scenario was due to a knee-jerk reaction that happened many years earlier as they responded to predictions that Velikovsky had made. Velikovsky stated that since Venus was a new planet, it would be expected to be hot, ***extremely hot***.

Throughout the early space program, astronomers and space scientists consistently underestimated the temperatures of planets. This was even after making detailed measurements from Earth based instruments and even in some cases by sending sophisticated spacecraft to measure at close range. Originally, Venus was thought to be very much an earthlike planet with the cloud cover and possibly even dinosaurs roaming its surface. Jupiter and Saturn were predicted to be cold balls of liquid and frozen hydrogen. Instead, all were found to be hot steamy planets and immediately, the standard astronomical community required new explanations overnight. Oddly enough the same thing has now occurred with comets that have extremely hot rocky nuclei (not the frozen snowballs of traditional astronomy).

Since Carl Sagan had already led the banner to "prove Velikovsky wrong", he again took up the banner to find a reason why Venus should be a tremendously hot planet. What happened was something I had seen many times as I sat in scientific meetings with NASA scientists while data was coming in from space probes. One of the scientists would come out with an idea (I called this shooting from the hip ... or hip pocket theorizing) and this would then become the topic of a paper in a journal and eventually this would somehow become accepted fact, eventually propagated through the scientific journals until it became more accepted. As with all concepts that find their way into the so-called "respectable journals", it would be near impossible to go back and rout out their presence and the damage they do to the progress of science. Not only was Venus hot, and the data so incredibly unexpected, that it proved to be an immediate embarrassment ... but the greenhouse effect was heralded as the cause for the tremendously high temperature of Venus given its thick clouds of CO2 and other greenhouse gases ... it was a cleat cut case of the need for an immediate "solution" and a dire case of shooting from the hip and hip pocket theorizing.

Almost immediately it was pointed out that in an open environment such as a planet and its atmosphere, the greenhouse effect actually contradicted the second law of thermodynamics. The second law of thermodynamics states that in a naturally occurring system you cannot pump heat from a cooler region to a warmer region ... in fact, the natural flow is in the opposite direction. What the greenhouse effect was claiming was that sunlight would enter through the thick planetary haze of Venus, strike and warm the planetary surface, then be reflected back up to the cooler clouds, which would then drive the heat back down to the warmer planetary surface. Here lies the contradiction to the second law of thermodynamics.

But Carl Sagan and the astronomers on the NASA team were not listening and many of these scientists had any sound training in Physics. So from the very beginning theoretically incorrect concepts have been propagated throughout the textbooks, newspapers, news media and meteorological community. There are many other problems with the greenhouse effect as applied to planet Venus. For example, Venus rotates extremely slowly, essentially showing it same side to the Sun for very long periods of times. We know from Earth weather that the night side of Earth becomes cold very quickly such that within 12 hours we sometimes see as much as a 12 to 20° temperature drop due to the fact of the solar light is not getting to that side of the planet. Even with earth's dynamic wind systems and jet streams there is insufficient movement of air to bring the heat from the Sun lit side to the dark side.

Venus has a far more difficult scenario, in that there is absolutely no wind at the planetary surface, or in fact anywhere in its medium to lower atmosphere. Measurements show that the temperature profile of Venus is exactly the same on the night side as the daytime side. So the question remains, even if the greenhouse effect could drive heat into the Sun-lit side of Venus, how is this heat carried to the backside of Venus?

Scientists at NASA never answered these fundamental questions, and the journals that published their articles never forced them to answer these questions. This of course is one of my main criticisms of modern science ... there is a clubhouse atmosphere amongst NASA and Inner Circle scientists who play the game ... they get their articles published without any referee or peer review, and they also prevent other scientists and critics from commenting on their work, or in this case raising critical scientific issues. This information then flows through the news media to the public, making it appear as though the NASA scientists actually know what they're doing, while the criticisms never see the light of day.

There is another severe group of problems associated with high temperature of Venus. During the original defamation of Velikovsky by Sagan & Co., Sagan used data from the Arecebo radio Observatory to prove that Venus would be found to have a moon-like cratered surface. Sagan claimed that the craters were moon-like and therefore the surface of Venus was extremely ancient, comparing it to the surface of our very own moon. As we later found out the craters were volcanic and so recent and young that this was truly a case that the surface of Venus was renewing itself almost on a daily basis by vulcanism. Once again traditional science was wrong, they used incorrect information to "prove" Velikovsky wrong, yet to this day astronomers still recite in the sing-song manner that Velikovsky was soundly defeated. The problem however is far more complex now that we know there is vulcanism on Venus.

Now we are expected to believe that the cooler clouds are pumping so much energy into the surface of Venus that it is actually creating a planet to become molten, thus creating vulcanism in the interior of Venus. If there was this much heat being generated in those cloud tops then most of it would be emitted ***outwards and into outer space*** since once again the second law of thermodynamics states that the natural energy flow should be to the cooler area (not again to the hotter planetary surface which is much hotter than the cloud layers). The simple fact is that we do not see this in the data.

Let me use an everyday example if you are still not convinced of the problem here. How many of you would believe that on a hot summer day you could open your refrigerator and freezer doors to create more heat in the room? This is what NASA scientists are asking you to believe. Not only that, but if you left your refrigerator door open long enough, your room would catch on fire and a piece of lead sitting at your counter would eventually melt. Remember, they're trying to convince you that the heat is coming out of the refrigerator into your room to cause the room to become hotter.

There are many other problems with the situation of Venus including large quantities of elements such as Argon 36 which was only expected to be found in the early solar system because it is extremely volatile, passing out of the atmosphere in very short order.

The problem with the greenhouse effect on Venus is further complicated by the fact that Venus reflects 98% of the sunlight that reaches it off of its very bright white cloud tops. The amount of solar light energy reaching the planetary surface is less than a flashlight with weak dying batteries. The problem was so glaring that Sagan and his merry band of non-physics astronomers had to come back to the drawing board and they then created what they called "the exaggerated green-house effect" which placated the journals but still did not address all of the fundamental problems with the greenhouse effect as applied to the planet Venus.

Now let us return to earth, global warming and the alleged greenhouse effect on earth. The quantity of CO2 and other "greenhouse gases" on earth are minuscule compared to the atmosphere of Venus. So if the greenhouse effect does not work on Venus, then it certainly does not work on earth. The simple fact is, in a naturally occurring space environment there is no such thing as a greenhouse effect.

The thousands and thousands of scientists, meteorologists who repeat this to get grant money by doing just that … securing a paycheck and not advancing science. The question remains, why is there such universal agreement amounts scientists on this topic? The answer is simple … this all comes back to control of the funding publication research cycle which then feeds the news media with information that goes to the public.

The other half of the equation is that there are groups who do not want the public to know that there are effects outside of this planet over which we have no control. They have figured out long ago that the one thing that would cause the public to drop attention to their control scenario is the public's recognition of something outside of this planet that would affect us in an uncontrollable manner ... something over which the controllers have no control and which would be obvious to the public.

When I first recognized this simple set of principles, I really didn't believe it myself at first, until I saw this working on a daily basis. Anything that possibly even hinted at a scenario that could come at us from outside of our planetary realm was immediately snuffed by the news media. It later became even more obvious that the people who were in control (the secret societies) also had access to some of the oldest documents on the planet which are being kept from the public, or which have been edited for public consumption (such as the Bible and the Old Testament) ... consistently, the parts that have been edited out referred to the ancient catastrophes. These are not taught in history courses in high school or college or university, and the true story of man's past has been stricken from any teachings you would get in most churches. Velikovsky called this collective amnesia ... or the public's will to allow the memory of the severe events to pass out of human consciousness and to create a mythological realm to place these terrible events.

On earth the temperature is stated many times on the weather programs to be stable at night due to the greenhouse effect if there is high water content in the air or cloud cover ... or conversely that the temperature drops rapidly due to lack of "greenhouse cover". There again a complete misnomer has been propagated. This "effect" is actually caused by a concept called "heat content" in that moisture-laden air holds more heat energy than dry air. This has NOTHING to do with the so-called greenhouse effect. The following graph shows the concept.

The "heat content" of air at 80 degrees Fahrenheit at 100% relative humidity is much greater than the same air with 50% relative humidity .. in fact it contains about one and a half times more heat energy. That means that when the sun warms this air to 80 degrees during the day, the higher water content air simply has more heat energy ... and this takes longer to dissipate after the sun goes down. Another way of looking at this is that air at 80 degrees Fahrenheit with 100% relative humidity has the equivalent heat content as the same amount of air at nearly 100 degrees with only 50% humidity. On the graph on the next page you can follow the numbers given in this example. Now imagine the desert night with 0% relative humidity ... what is its heat content?

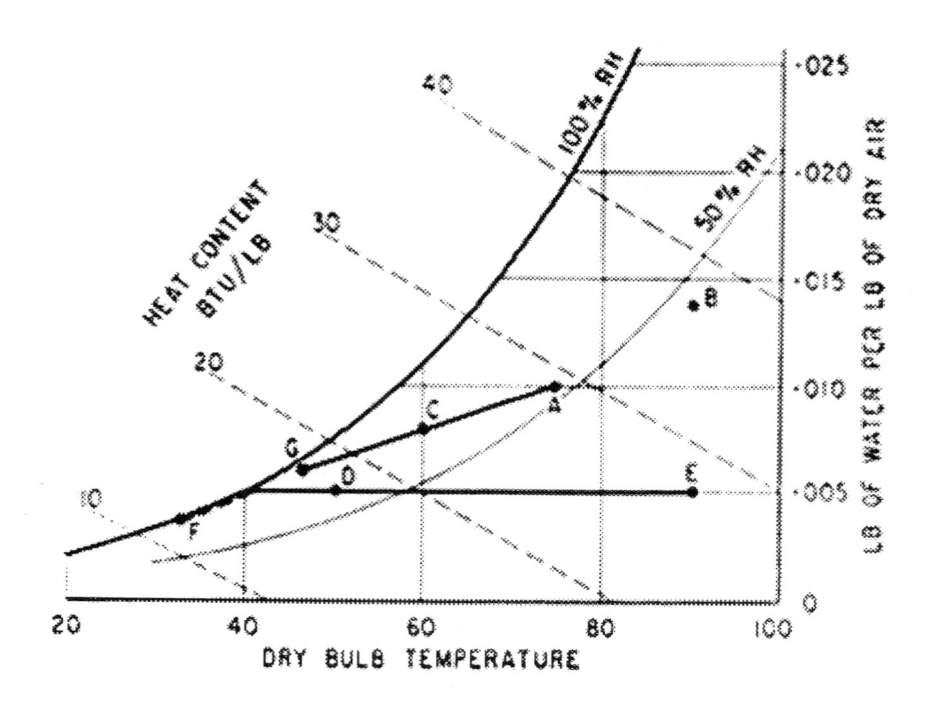

Graph of the Heat Content of Air

The topic of climate is very simple. There is a myth that has been propagated that somehow the earth ***of its own*** maintains a constant or slowly changing environment which includes temperature, atmospheric conditions, moisture content, CO2 content, etc. It is believed in standard meteorology, weather science and space science that all of the planets formed at one time and all had locked into their environments and immediate surroundings everything that they would contain for the rest of their existence as a planet in the solar system. None of these "standard" assumptions are even close to being true.

The following diagram shows two of the many hydrological cycles of earth. The top half of the drawing shows how low cells at the planetary surface connect to energetic comet tail like structures that attach to out ionosphere ... bringing in water, chemicals and electrical energy from our space environment. The second shows how this water quickly and efficiently is cycled to the poles to be deposited on the polar caps. The amount of water influx is seen on weather satellite date and is relatively small compared to earth's existing reservoirs.

The Hydrological Cycle of Earth.

Continual influx of water from Earth's comet-like attachments to local plasma environment... this also brings in other trace chemicals

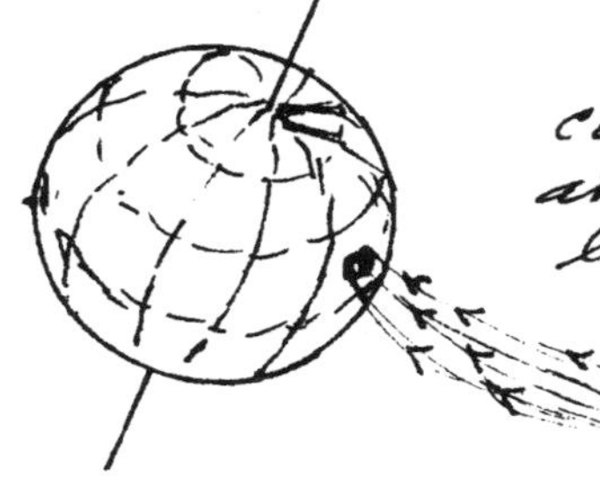

Equator to pole hydrological cycle moves water to the poles where it freezes on the ice caps

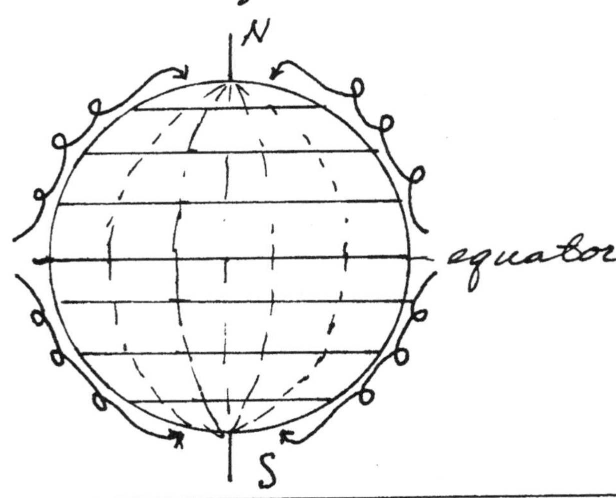

We depend on a minute-by-minute, hour-by-hour and day-by-day influx of solar energy. The so solar energy comes in two forms ... the first is solar light, only the visible portion of which actually makes it to earth's surface (with small amounts of ultraviolet and infrared light) ... the second is in the form of electrical energy which is totally unrecognized by the standard scientific and meteorological communities.

I have determined that the amount of electrical energy stored around the earth in capacitors and which is flowing by our planet earth every day in the solar wind is thousands if not millions of times greater than the solar light energy component of solar energy output. We are buffered from this energy as long as everything is flowing smoothly and the sun is not undergoing convulsions of some sort, or we are not involved in some sort of electrical alignment with other planets, comets, our own moon or other solar system conditions. It is during times of solar change, which can happen on a moment's notice, that the electrical input to earth changes drastically and without warning. It is invisible except possibly to some peoples' sixth sense or sophisticated instruments, which have never been put in place, as scientists simply didn't believe that such a thing could exist. So scientists have created all kinds of illusionary concepts such as El Niño, the warm water theory for hurricane formation, the believe that lightning forms in the center of clouds by friction, or the formation of tornadoes by front systems moving together. As it turns out, this entire weather phenomenon is driven by the electrical conditions of our planet, which is ultimately driven by the conditions of our electrical sun.

The believe that the so-called ozone hole is somehow created by man-made chemicals that are so intelligent that the only cooperate and create this hole at certain times of the year follows in the same vane as the greenhouse effect. It is favored by the Tier 1 group of scientists because it points to finger directly at Man as the cause ... this in turn provides the needed cover for the true cause which is the electrical conditions in our solar system. In reality, the ozone in fact is created by ultraviolet light from the sun. Ozone is a very short-lived molecule lasting only a few seconds after its formation. That characteristic electrical smell that you detect after a severe thunderstorm is ozone, in this case being created by the lightning of the storm and it only lasts a short time after the storm. In the upper atmosphere ozone is created as ultraviolet light from the sun creates the necessary energy to form the ozone molecule ... which as I said only lasts a few seconds before it decays back to regular oxygen molecules O2.

Here is another case where we have seen that a standard "accepted" concept has been heralded by the news media to the far corners of the world, but which is totally incorrect. In this case the refrigerants that were claimed to be the cause of the ozone hole were outlawed many years ago. The end result is that we still have the ozone hole. Another point is that when the so-called ozone hole was discovered, there was no previous data on the topic to tell us if there was an ozone hole previously or not. Scientists ignored that little point when they ran to Congress to get funding, and Congress didn't know enough to ask. I pointed this out, but in the whitewash of news media and press releases all criticisms were squelched.

The ozone hole exists because no ultraviolet light shines on that area during a certain time of year and has nothing to do with the type of refrigerant you have in your refrigerator. Rather than admitting the failure of another traditionally accepted theory, the scientists who heralded this idea and benefited from the funding now claim we need to wait another 10 years to be sure. By this time all of these scientists will be comfortably relaxing on their pensions.

The heating of the Pacific Ocean which is associated with weather conditions that was first discovered by fishermen in the tropics (which they called El Nino) once again has nothing to do with the casual movement of waves from one region of the Pacific Ocean to another. The simple proof of this came early in the first days when scientists were even discussing this phenomenon when the Pacific Ocean was seen to heat over a 6000 square-mile area by a temperature of 4°C in a matter of hours. This clearly was not enough time for the wave action to even begin to move warm water across this vast expanse of the Pacific. The other issue with the so called El Niño heating is that this is only surface heating and one has to look once again to electrical currents to find the source of this heat.

It did not take long to determine what was really gone on. Why was there no such heating in the Atlantic Ocean? The answer lay in an unusual configuration of land and the notion of electrical currents feeding energy to the surface of the planet. There is no large east to west landmass lying just east of the Pacific Ocean; rather we have only the thin landmass of Central America. To the east of the Atlantic

Ocean is the vast continent of Africa ... we are talking about the latitudes at which hurricanes and typhoons form.

The storms that build overland as they move westward across Africa have time to build strong tall clouds systems in the vertical electric field. As they roll off the western tip of Africa, the Ocean drops to a tremendous depth very quickly, thusly breaking the atmosphere to ground connection that previously existed through the cloud systems as they passed over Africa. At this point the path of least resistance for the electrical currents from the ionosphere is to the ionized air that sits at the surface of the ocean as the storm clouds and the leading electrical conditions of the storm meet the ocean air. The ions are drawn inward and sucked up a vertical circular column in the vertical electric field ... it is this vertical column that eventually becomes the eye of the hurricane. So the energy in the Atlantic Ocean during the hurricane season (which traditionally runs from June through November) goes into creating hurricanes and tropical storm systems.

The conditions leading into the Pacific Ocean are quite different. There is no vast landmass to the east to build up the big storm systems, which might then roll off to become tropical storms. Tropical storms still form and still move westward under the westward moving electron belt or what we call the jet stream above the equator. This energy still is coming down from the ionosphere, so in the Pacific in many cases it turns into "joule heating", literally electrical heating of the surface of the Pacific Ocean. The weather effects we call El Nino are then side effects of this same weather and energy dissipation process ... El Nino has been claimed to be the cause of everything from splitting the northern jet stream to the modification for hurricanes in the Atlantic Ocean. Clearly these are all *concurrent* phenomenon but of which El Nino and the heating of the Pacific Ocean are just one ... El Nino is not the cause of this heating. This becomes even more absurd when you consider that the weather at the equatorial region in the Pacific ***moves westward*** and has NOTHING to do with the weather in the Atlantic, which precedes the weather in the Pacific Ocean!!!!

As with the entire above-mentioned phenomenon, there is a simple scientific Law that can be applied to each to prove exactly what I'm saying is true. It is called ***the law of conservation of energy*** and simply states that if you have a phenomenon that requires energy, you must first calculate the amount of energy or measure it and then you must locate the source of energy that is creating the phenomenon that you are seeing. In the case of hurricanes and the warm water theory for hurricane formation, one can easily calculate the amount of heat loss (energy) from the ocean surface by a simple observation of the temperature change before and after a storm. This amount of energy is simply enough to account for the evaporation of water that we see in the clouds of the storm. There is not enough energy left over to create the hurricane force winds or maintain the low pressure cell at the center of the storm as the hurricane force winds rush into the eye continually at hundreds of miles per hour. If warm water were truly the source of energy for the storm and the cause of the low pressure cell, then it would be neutralized in a matter of minutes by the winds rushing from all directions.

This is one of those theories that in fact is similar to the dirty snowball comet model, which has a similar problem. As the comet coma forms around the comet nucleus, it blocks the sunlight that supposedly is needed to create the comet coma. The bigger the comet becomes the more sunlight is blocked … therefore this is a self-defeating mechanism. This becomes even more ridiculous when you see that for a comet to grow it in fact needs *more* sunlight … not less.

There is one additional group of earth based phenomenon that need to be explained in light of the electrical power that is descending on earth's surface at all times from the ionosphere via the many channels that we observe. Volcanoes and earthquakes are intricately related to our geological past and many of their secrets are locked in the depths of the earth. The long tortured history of earth is eminently displayed through the many active regions of vulcanism and earthquakes. On top and added to what we considered to be the normal geological factors that are incidental to volcanoes and earthquakes, once again are electrical conditions in the atmosphere that are ultimately driven by solar electrical conditions.

The earth is a composite of conductors and insulators mixed together. When electrical energy channels down and finds the path to earth, it quickly and naturally finds the path of least resistance … these paths mostly lie along earthquake fault lines and in the central channels of a volcano. The volcano has the advantage that it already is pointed up vertically towards the sky and it has a metal rich molten core ready to accept as much electricity as the atmosphere has to offer. There are regions of earth where the volcanoes literally can be seen at night due to the electrical activity that rises above them. In the chapter on hurricanes, tornadoes and storms there is a picture of a tornado coming out of the top of Mount Etna on a clear blue sky day with no torrential rain clouds in sight. In the chapter on weather of the planets there is a picture of a hurricane fully formed near the polar cap of Mars ... Mars has no warm oceans, in fact it has no oceans at all ... so how did this hurricane form if we are told that you need warm water to form a hurricane? The list of contradictions leads back to one main point, that all of these phenomenon are electrical in nature and the source of energy for all of these comes directly from the electrical nature of our solar system which is driven by our electrical sun and the solar capacitor.

In the case of earthquakes and volcanoes, both have tremendous amounts of pent up energy waiting to release. Thus we look for trigger mechanisms ... these are mechanisms which are small energy sources which can then release the large energy sources somewhat like a match starting a huge forest fire. This is why the solar storms, which have been misnamed "magnetic storms" (they are truly electrical storms from the sun), can trigger earthquakes and volcanoes. As the solar flare interacts with our upper atmosphere creating a change, this causes more energy to be released than in the normal steady state condition of earth. It is both the increase in energy and the impulse that can trigger earthquakes and volcanoes. Understanding this complex interaction takes a good deal of experience and study. Unfortunately in recent times there has been a rash of Internet sites that irresponsibly post earthquake in volcano data claiming that all of this is due to extra-solar system interactions. These people in general are not trained scientists and do not understand the damage that they are causing to people who are serious researchers. For this reason I posted the following short dissertation on my web site to clarify this issue.

---

a quick note ... why i do not post volcanic activity or earth quake activity on my home page as notice of ongoing events in the solar system as i do with solar data ... much of the solar data is visibly related to external solar conditions that we can see and i have the long term background to know what is significant and what is normal ... the internal earth conditions related to volcanoes and earth quakes are more obscure and this is where the inexperienced new internet posters fail of grasp the damage that they are doing ... there is an ever increasing number of internet sites posting and quoting volcanic and earth quake activity but NONE have done their homework ... remember that i was the person back in the 90's that first brought the relation of these events to the attention of the scientific community relating to solar activity ... and subsequently explained in detail the physical mechanism for the causes and effects ... i made it clear then and also to the new batch of people trying to make a name for themselves touting the apparent increase in volcanoes and earth quakes ... HOWEVER ... to properly put these data into perspective one has to subtract off the effects of the increase in the number of sensitive data gathering devices around the globe and also subtract off the "background noise and cyclic effects" in the data due to the long term patterns of earth changes that are NOT attributable to solar conditions but to historical activity of the earth (we are in a natural increase at this time in geological history for both volcanic and earth quake activity and this is not related to solar activity) ... NONE of these new internet sites have done this and it is a HUGE and very complex job involving data known and much unknown to us regarding the historical geology of the earth ... it seems easy to post the daily activity BUT doing the job correctly is vastly more difficult ... so instead of increasing the support for the case for extra-solar system activity they are actually diminishing the efforts of serious researchers who do understand the problems involved in quoting volcanic and earth quake data

---

Knowing when to apply and how to apply the principles of the Electrical Universe and Electrical Solar System are important and it would be incorrect to claim that everything is caused by electrical conditions. One still needs to find the cause and effect in all cases and avoid the blanket statements that everything can be explained by electrical concepts.

In the case of meteorology and climatology, many of the models already in place for computer simulation of our environments are adequate under normal conditions since the electrical conditions only come into play under certain conditions. Knowing how to interpret satellite data and apply it to our global weather system is a difficult job and hopefully this book has made advancements at clarifying the major issues to turn the corner from the old "accepted" theories and take the new direction that is so desperately needed today.

At this point let us imagine that there is still a die-hard greenhouse global warming person in the crowd (after all, the news papers have been pounding this into your head for decades so it must be true … right?). Take the following problem to any high school or college physics or chemistry student and have them do the math on the following. Calculate the joule heating of the atmosphere created by one gallon of gasoline as it is burned ***today*** in a car. ALL of this energy turns into heat and is pumped directly into the atmosphere RIGHT NOW. Then calculate the amount of CO2 created by this burning and estimate the alleged greenhouse heating that will supposedly occur in 10 years from now. You will find that the immediate input of heat energy from burning the fuel is thousands of times greater than any alleged greenhouse effect. So why do greenhouse theorists not calculate or fear this immediate warming??? SIMPLE … there is no grant $$$ to do so. And if they did said something like this (and include the enormous energy pumped into the atmosphere every day from nuclear power plants) the energy commissions would ban this "research" and run these scientists out of town on a rail. The earth sheds this extra energy every day. If this DIRECT HEATING were included at the true rate of daily energy consumption and included in the same equations used by global warming theorists, we would all have died long ago. ***The entire issue comes down to one of politics as already noted … the greenhouse global warming issue masks the real issue of pollution and allows the polluters to continue unabated!!!!!!!!!!!!!!***

XI. ACTION AT A DISTANCE

Action at a Distance is such an important topic that it requires its own chapter. There are so many different forms of action at a distance at work in the solar system that it would be impossible to place all of them in one short chapter in this book, in fact, this could be a book all to itself. The most bizarre part about this is that once again, none of these are included in standard meteorology or astronomy. It is the belief that earth moves along in the solar system, receives a certain amount of solar light input per day and that's the end of the story. Everything else they say the earth has done by itself. That includes the ice ages, climate change, mountain building, restructuring of the earth's surface, and even somehow covering ancient ocean beds with miles of the new surface (e.g. deep underground salt mines).

Once you turn the corner and begin to understand that many things from outside of earth affect us besides the simple collision every now and then by an asteroid, you will begin to understand how ridiculous standard astronomical truly is. The true story is that the greatest changes to earth have happened by objects that never even touched earth but simply came by. These kinds of events have happened many times. I estimate that at least 20 to 30 times in earth's history there have been severe close encounters with extremely large celestial objects to create the mountain ranges we see on earth today. When one looks closely at mountain ranges you can see the tortured past of the earth in the rocks that once were thousands of feet below the ocean floor that were raised up and smashed and crushed in a few minutes and now set at 14 or 15,000 feet at the top of a mountain. The forces that hurled the earth and created these mountains were enormous and beyond human comprehension.

That anything even lived through this is remarkable but we do see time and time again the survival during mass extinctions on earth and these are not explained by the mere collision of an asteroid. An asteroid can explain certain aspects of a mass extinction but not the pole shifts, not the magnetic field shifts and not the mountain building that occurs ***around the planet*** along fault lines that run from one pole to the other as in the American continents.

There is a common fallacy perpetrated whenever there is a solar flare ... that it missed us and therefore it had no effect in us. Nothing could be further from the truth. Every flare that leaves the sun is involved in building up to solar capacitor and raising the height and level of energy stored in the solar capacitor. This returns to the sun eventually by way of discharges to comets, the planetary electrical discharges or the return current sheets one of which I have already identified as being in the location where earth passes in the month of August.

Modern astronomy does not recognize the fact that distant large objects have come into our solar system and drastically altered earth and then left without so much as an apology. The ancients saw and are attempting to tell us about these and one would think that modern astronomers would be the first to openly want to know what the ancients had to say regarding astronomy and astronomical objects. But it is just the opposite … they cannot scream loud enough in attempts to tell you not to listen to these ancient "barbarians".

In addition to the close celestial encounters of planetary objects, there are many other forms of the action at a distance. In the late 1990s an earth orbiting satellite called Galaxy V was destroyed in an instant as an electrical current of electrons came from Jupiter and destroyed it. We've seen comets come by the sun to ignite the sun and cause tremendous flares to move out into space. The sun many times for unknown reasons has tremendous explosions of its surface and those in fact that hit earth directly on occasion cause tremendous damage to electrical power grids and provide the electrical impulses necessary to assist in the creation of severe storms. All of the electricity that comes down to the earth originates in the cosmic electric field and this is one of the more common forms of action at a distance that science does not recognize as being caused by the solar electric field.

Every time Venus passes between the sun and earth there is an increase in solar activity, which is characterized by an increase in sunspots. The ancients saw Mars lose its atmosphere to the passage of a large comet and earth encountered a large comet according to ancient history causing the great flood and a myriad of other catastrophic events including electrical discharges between the comet and planet Earth. The remnants of this disaster circle our globe yet geologists and astronomers deny that this ever happened in the face of the dramatic changes and evidence that is all over the planet Earth. Velikovsky noted that the naturalists that first came to what we now call the

United States all talked about the remnants of the great flood, yet by the year 1900 all traces of this were destroyed my man's conquest and building the old west. Scientists now refuse to read the information passed down to us and instead create their own reality.

The following series of plates exhibit many of the properties of a severe earth change caused by the ***hypothetical*** passage of a highly charged large (planet sized) comet nucleus and its tail during a hypothetical encounter of earth. This would not be a small comet like Halley's or even a medium-size comet like Hale-Bopp. This would be a very large comment like Venus sized with a Venus sized nucleus and immense tail that would stretch across the heavens when viewed from earth.

The charts in the next four pages indicate the level of volcanic and earthquake activity, ocean water level changes, the loss of sea shore lands to encroaching water levels as continental shelves are formed with the rising ocean levels, the level of worldwide glaciations, the loss and regeneration of atmosphere, the increase in oil reserve levels, the mean global temperature change, the formation of freshwater lakes, atmospheric pollution as a result of volcanic activity as well as the comet tail inserting chemicals into our atmosphere, the rapid depletion of land animals both large and small including birds, the depletion and recovery of sea life, the loss of human contact between adjacent civilizations on this planet, and last but not least the use of human technology as it recovers after being driven back to the cave age after such an event.

A fourth plate shows the physical and magnetic poll shifts whereby the surface mantle pole shift is caused by gravitational wave of as explained in the Surviving Planet X Passage pamphlet. The physical pole shift is separate from the magnetic poll shifts and one must understand the subtleties involved to coordinate the two and understand the full reality. There is been a good deal of misinformation propagated on Internet sites regarding magnetic pole flips and there is a misunderstanding that somehow an object passing with a magnetic field is the cause of the earth's physical or celestial pole shifts when in fact it is the large gravitational wave that in fact causes the poles to shift.

The charts in the next four pages are hypothetical of course and there could be a wide range of varying effects given the sizes and proximity of the passage of the passing comet.

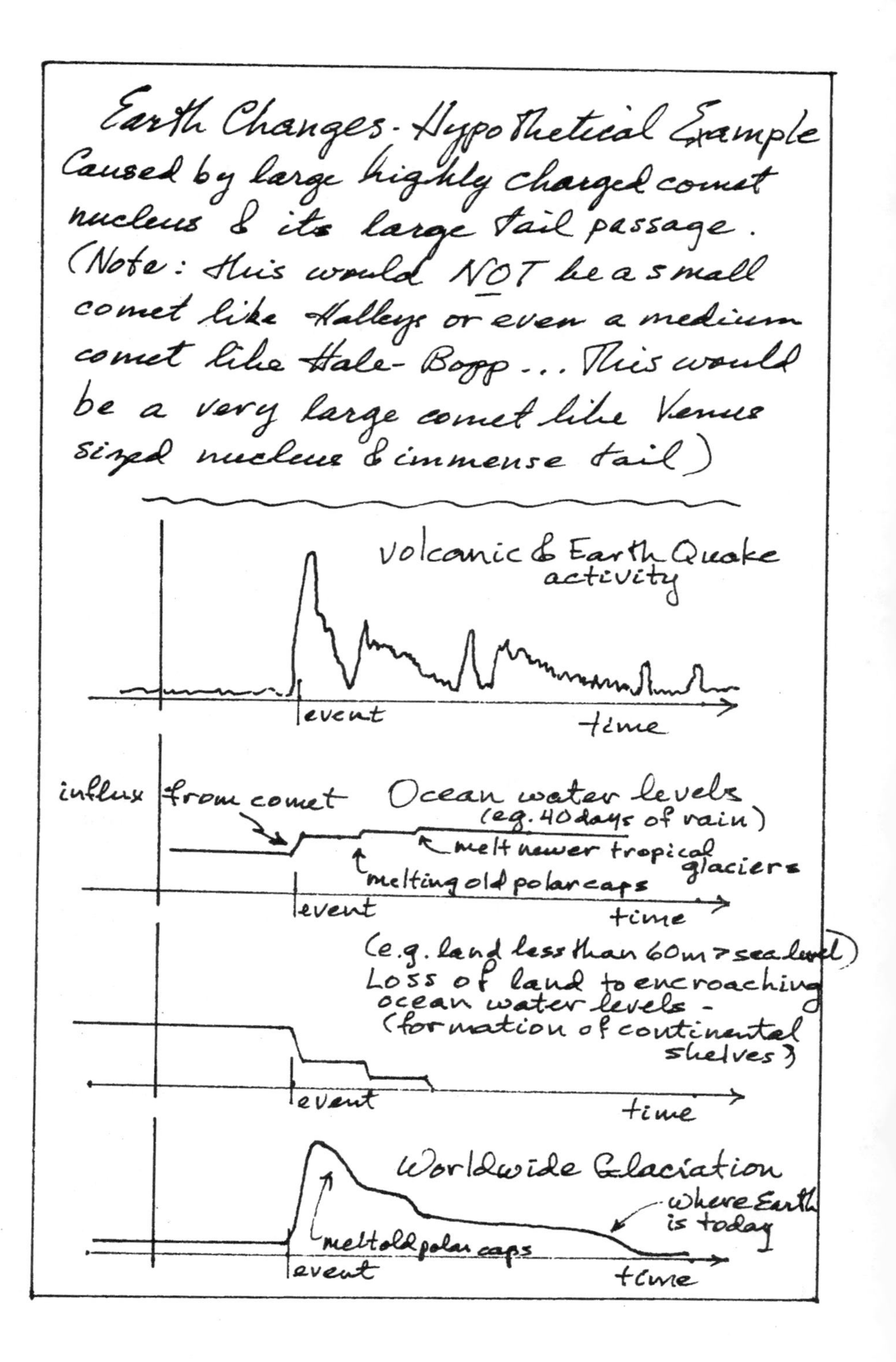
Earth Changes - Hypothetical Example
Caused by large highly charged comet nucleus & its large tail passage.
(Note: this would NOT be a small comet like Halleys or even a medium comet like Hale-Bopp... This would be a very large comet like Venus sized nucleus & immense tail)
volcanic & Earth Quake activity
event
time
influx from comet
Ocean water levels
(eg. 40 days of rain)
melt newer tropical glaciers
melting old polar caps
event
time
(e.g. land less than 60m > sea level)
Loss of land to encroaching ocean water levels -
(formation of continental shelves)
event
time
Worldwide Glaciation
where Earth is today
melt old polar caps
event
time

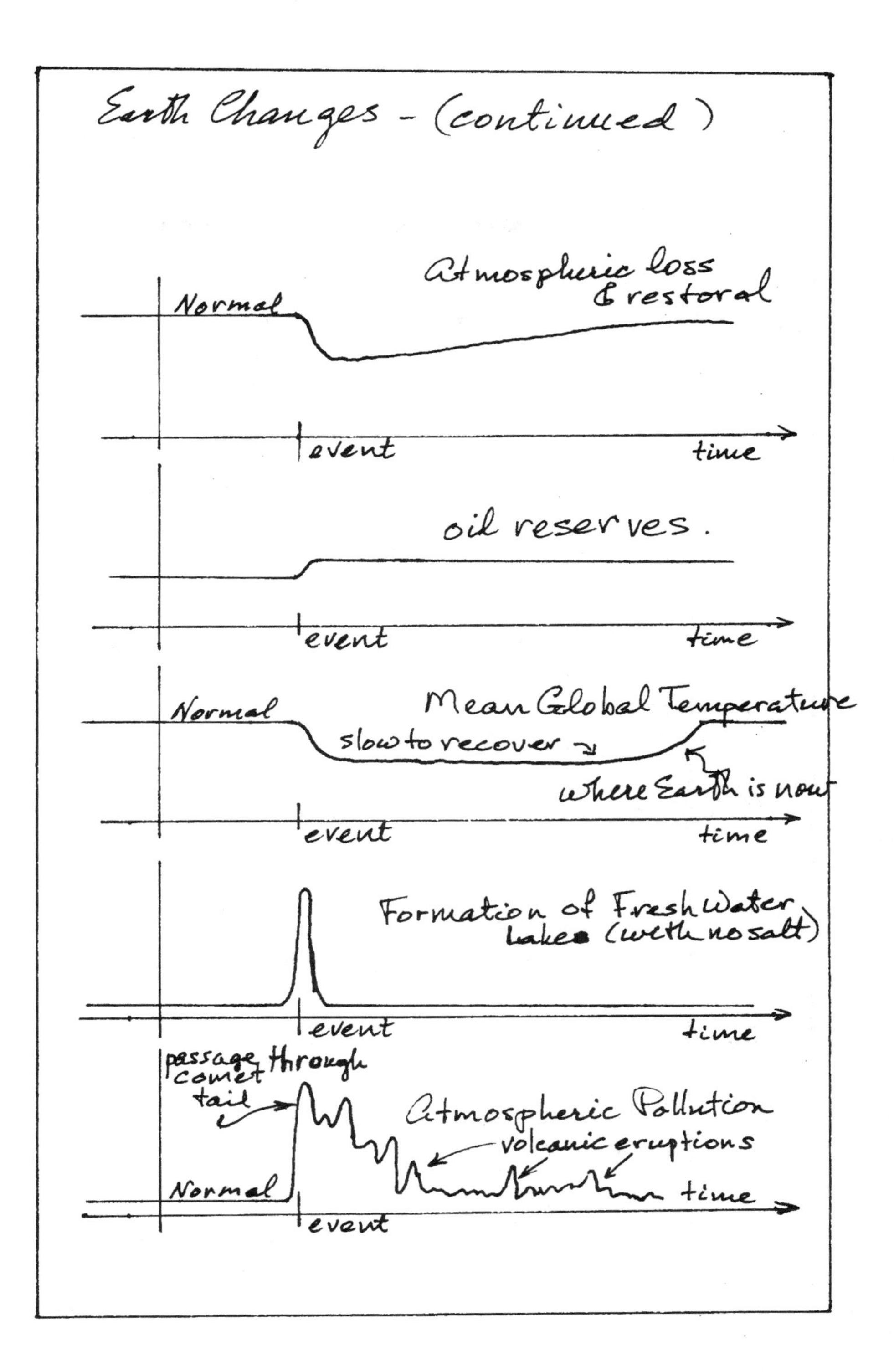
Earth Changes - (continued)
Atmospheric loss
& restoral
Normal
event
time
oil reserves.
event
time
Normal
Mean Global Temperature
slow to recover
where Earth is now
event
time
Formation of Fresh Water
Lakes (with no salt)
event
time
passage through
comet
tail
Atmospheric Pollution
volcanic eruptions
Normal
time
event

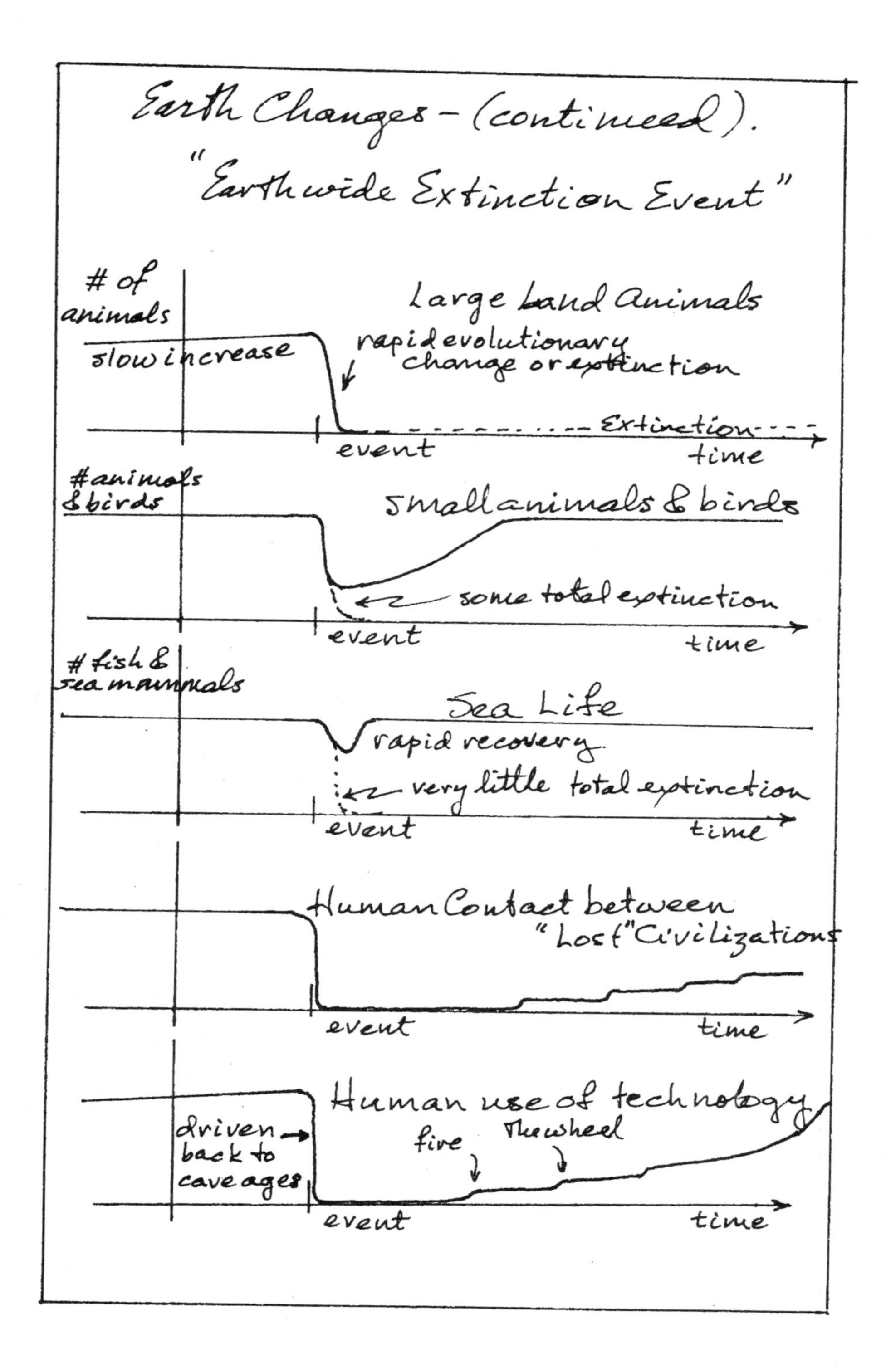
Earth Changes - (continued).
"Earthwide Extinction Event"
# of animals
Large Land Animals
slow increase
rapid evolutionary change or extinction
Extinction
event
time
#animals & birds
small animals & birds
some total extinction
event
time
fish & sea mammals
Sea Life
rapid recovery
very little total extinction
event
time
Human Contact between "Lost" Civilizations
event
time
Human use of technology
driven back to cave ages
fire
The wheel
event
time

Earth Changes (Continued)

Physical and Magnetic Pole Shifts

Surface mantle pole shift is caused by gravitational wave as explained in Surviving Planet X Passage

Physical Pole Shift

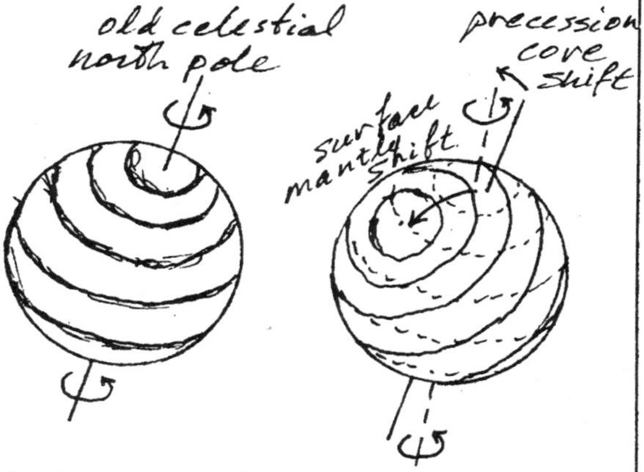

old celestial north pole

precession core shift

surface mantle shift

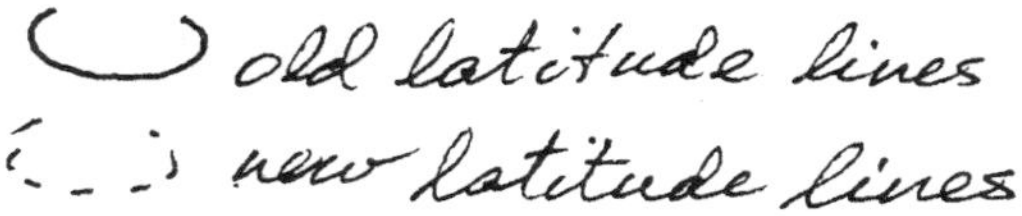

old latitude lines

new latitude lines

Crustal Magnetic Pole Shift & wanderings of N. Pole after shift

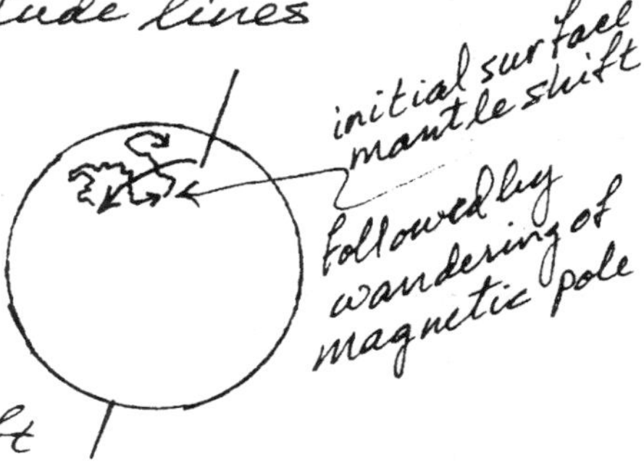

initial surface mantle shift followed by wandering of magnetic pole

Physical pole shift is NOT caused by "magnetic" pole flip...

Take the volcanic and earthquake activity for example the first graph of the first chart. Prior to the events one will assume that Earth has had a long period of tranquil nonviolent existence. As the comet passes the gravitational wave from the comet affects the surface mantle of the earth and the volcanoes would erupt around the world, spewing enormous amounts of pollution into the atmosphere. This generates one of the causes of cooling of the planet, a fact that figures heavily into extinction events. As the initial series of volcanic eruptions subside it almost gets back to normal before a cyclic pattern of volcanic eruptions occurs again … these volcanic epochs peak and subside for thousands of years … the eruptions continue in a cyclic pattern with some of them larger and some of them smaller … if earth is about 4000 years from the past event then this explains why we are still seeing remnants of this in both volcanism and earth quakes. Far into the future this continues until you eventually see stabilization of the volcanic eruption activity, down to near normal pre-event conditions.

The graph indicating ocean water levels, the second graph on the first chart shows an influx of water from the initial comet event is the earth moves for a great deal of time in the vast comet tail. Remember that this is not a little minuscule comet as would be comet Halley's, but a huge comet of cosmic proportions. The ocean levels rise from the influx of water from the initial comet passage then sometime later as the old polar caps that have shifted from the old northerly or southerly positions melt causing a second era of ocean level rising and this is accompanied by tremendous erosion of lands in the path of the melting glacier. In a short amount of time the glaciers that formed in the tropical locations during the comet passage melt rather quickly as earth struggles to get back to normal … so in fact there are three episodes of ocean water level rises that occurred after the comet event. Remember that there is both an influx of water from the comet and also a cooling due to volcanism … but moreover the passage of earth through the comet tail robs earth of its daily allotment of heat from the sun and the entire planet is thrown into an ice age.

The third graph on the first chart indicates the loss of land to encroaching ocean water levels. Earth has seen this numerous times. As we look at the continental shelves that exist around the shorelines of the landmasses that meet today's oceans, clearly at one point in history the water level was between 50 and a hundred meters lower than what it is today. Look at the old shorelines that lay a few hundred miles off the east coast of Florida that were carved away over long periods of time so that there were deep trenches immediately off these old shorelines, but when the new ocean levels rose after the last comet encounter, a good deal of this low lying coastal land was inundated and these areas now make up the banks and shallow continental shelves that exist just off shore around the land masses of the world (see the map of the inside cover of this book for an example).

The next graph shows worldwide glaciations. One sees almost immediately that glaciation worldwide increases dramatically due to the fact that there is a large influx of water and secondly because earth spends a good deal of time in the comet tail which actually by a blocks the solar radiation causing you can dramatic drop in heat content in the air and a drop in the worldwide temperature. The glaciation has an initial melt off and has a number of epics were glaciers are reduced on a worldwide scale in this hypothetical example ... the graph attempts to show where earth is today on the cusp of the final rise and is losing many of its glaciers. The idea being that Earth is not a planet that typically has large glaciers in temperate regions or even large polar caps.

The first graph on the second chart shows a slight atmospheric loss and then long-term restoral indicating that Earth possibly had a much larger atmosphere in the past than it has today. We know that the comet extracted the entire atmosphere from Mars as recounted by the ancients ... the question remains to be investigated regarding the past nature of earth's atmosphere.

It would be impossible to say if earth for sure had a loss in atmosphere or gained some during the last comet encounter because it appears that the comet nucleus, if assumed to be the size of the object that became the planet Venus, has a lower surface gravity than that of earth. This would be impossible to tell, but this is once again just hypothetical example to illustrate a point.

The second graph on the second chart shows an increase in oil reserves due to the fact that the comet tail has a rich reservoir of hydrocarbons. This is recounted over and over from ancient civilizations as they describe the black rains with a rain of fire and brimstone or in some cases the rain of burning naphtha. Oil is not a remnant of fossils and is misnamed a fossil fuel. No chemist has ever shown in laboratory how to take dirt and change it into oil. If this were the case it would be a thriving new business rather than growing corn to make oil we would simply take dirt and make oil … there is a lot more dirt on earth than corn.

The third graph on the second chart is possibly what I consider to be the most important graph possibly in this book. Prior to the events earth maintains a normal global mean temperature and heat content. After the "event" the mean global temperature drops as glaciers cover the globe and earth drops into a deep freeze because of the time it spent in the comet tail which essentially blocked solar light for a period of what we are told was about 40 days. The recovery was very slow in the beginning as noted on the graph. Eventually as the glaciers receded and the sun was able to contact a darker earth, the warming trend increased until now we are just returning to "normal". What people are calling global warming is simply that natural replenishment of earth's natural heat content and the return to normal temperature which we lost thousands of years ago during the ice age.

It has taken us thousands of years to recover from the last ice age and scientists scramble to find reasons for why the earth created an ice age all by itself. What is curious is that the ice age did not extend into Siberia which was tropical at that time. This would be odd to see tremendous glaciers extending all the way down the North American continent to the states of Nebraska and Kansas yet in what is now the Arctic and Siberia it was warm and tropical. The simply makes no sense and the only rational explanation is that there was a pole shift. The location of the old north pole was somewhere in the middle and of Ontario north of the State of Michigan. We are just recovering at this point from the global deep freeze of thousands of years ago and to many of us this is a welcome return to normal rather than something to be alarmed about. The flora and fauna are changing as this warming back to normal occurs and is not caused my man made greenhouse effects or man made global warming.

The next graph shows the formation of freshwater lakes (lakes with no salt). One of the great-unmentioned mysteries is of the fresh water reserves of the planet. The fact that we have ocean sized freshwater lakes with absolutely no salt at all is most curious unless you realize that these are the result of ice melting only recently … in the case of the Great Lakes of North America they formed with the melting of the old north polar cap … what we call the Laurentian ice field. Traditional scientist still does not have a rational explanation for why there is salt in these inland oceans. This graph shows a rapid increase in the number of freshwater lakes due to the fact that the old north pole and polar glacier lay over the land expanse which we now call North Central North American. When the Pole was shifted, it was a rapid loss of water or melting of this ice, which carved out the Upper Mississippi River Valley and left Hudson's Bay to the north and the freshwater lakes of Superior, Michigan, Ontario and Erie that flow to the ocean. It also left the millions of freshwater lakes that populate the northern midwest states of the United States and central Canada. It also left the aquifers that sit under the State of Nebraska and the marshes of Illinois that existed prior to the white man coming to this country (much of this was drained for farmland).

The final graph on chart two indicates atmospheric pollution as a result of two sources. The first was the comet tail through which earth passed for the estimated 40 days. The second source of pollution would be the volcanoes that erupted as a result of the comet passage. The chart shows a hypothetical example where there was a tremendous initial insurgence of pollution due to the dual causes of comet and volcanic eruptions. As this subsided, subsequent cycles of volcanic eruptions occurred with ongoing pollution of the earth. Eventually this tapered down to near normal but nowhere near the "normal" level prior to the event. If earth were 4 1/2 billion years old as is claimed by standard astronomy and geology with no devastating events in its recent history, the level of volcanism and earthquakes would be nowhere near the level we see today. Earth is definitely relaxing from a major event that occurred only a few thousand years ago. Yet scientists find every reason to try and explain away the data that is so obvious in showing us these details.

In the next page the graphs deal with extinction events of animals and sea creatures. The first graph indicates the evolution and numbers of large land animals. Prior to the event there is a slow and steady increase as the animals become successful and populate the earth. At the "event", the large land animals reduce in numbers drastically because they require the greatest resources … there is a serious extinction event. Some of them may alter characteristics and adapt and regenerate into new species or new variations of the old species at this time. From past extinction events we know that the large animals did not fare well.

The second graph shows that small land animals and birds would not experience so drastic an extinction event ... we see a percentage of the small animals going completely extinct after the encounter with the large comet. The survivors begin to recover on a slow steady pace because they require fewer resources than the large land animals.

The next graph down deals with sea life, that is, fish and sea mammals and other forms of sea creatures. Notice that their extinction event is not so harsh because they are buffered by the large ocean as it absorbs a great deal of the devastating effects that caused the land animals and birds to be driven to near extinction. Some of the sea creatures go extinct or are altered but the majority fare quite and return to normal quite quickly ... the shark for example has not changed in millions of years.

The next two graphs are characteristic of what actually happened on this planet many thousands of years ago. Human contact was lost between civilizations and the events ceased trade and travel amongst the civilizations of the world. This ended quickly and contact between adjacent civilizations was totally lost. Eventually, as the individual communities grew and prospered and recovered from the events, they began to move out to rediscover the "lost" adjacent civilizations. It was not until 1492 that the Eastern world met the remnants of the ancient Western world ... the native meso-american indians that Columbus discovered and were discovered by other explorers such as Cortez in Mexico. Even well into the 1900s we were still discovering so-called lost civilizations in the jungles of Central and South America as well its deepest darkest Africa and other remote areas of the world. To imagine that the civilizations somehow migrated from a central location as we are told in the history books is so absurd that it is beyond comprehension, yet it stands today as the accepted explanation for the origin of man.

In my astronomy classes at university level I used to spend an entire day with a lecture literally letting the students make this discovery by themselves. This lecture is described in a previous book of this series.

The final graph is of the human use of technology and its development. Prior to the event there is a slow gradual progression in the use of technology. During the event, man is literally driven back to the cave ages and is left to use his devices on a very rudimentary level to survive. It is interesting that we look back in history at the survivors of the last events and see that many aspects of language, mathematics, celestial understanding of astronomy, religion, systems of laws, speech and linguistics, and many other aspects of what we call the "caveman", simply could not have been from someone who crawled out of a pit and started hammering on a tree with a rock. The same thing would happen to us if these circumstances befell us; even as advanced as we think we are today. I use the example of fire in the development graph to show that there are surges in human technology use as the use of fire or use of the wheel are discovered. At the end of the long period of recovery comes a rapid increase in the use of technology by humans. Note that in the late 1800s technology advanced to give the essential manufacturing skills that prepared man for the 20th century ... within a mere 50 years we were on the cusp of the space age.

The fourth diagram deals with the physical and magnetic pole shifts that earth encountered during this celestial event. The surface mantle pole shift is caused by gravitational wave as explained in the ***Surviving Planet X Passage*** pamphlet. There is literally a physical pole shift of the mantle of earth and there is actually a core shift caused by precession of the core in the strong gravitational field of the planet sized comet nucleus passing by ... this is described in the top diagram. Along with this physical shift, is the movement of the north magnetic pole and then the subsequent wondering of this pole to try and regain its northerly position, something that is occurring on earth today.

To final diagrams in this chapter show the migration and wondering of our North Pole. In the 1800's it was far south of where it is today. There seems to be a steady constant northern migration of the pole as I said, to return to its northernmost position. Clearly, if you move the magnetic north pole migration backwards in time on the map, it would end up back where I've already described the old north pole in Ontario just northern north of the State of Michigan.

Another chart shows the daily wondering of the north pole on a daily basis about an oval 85 kilometers at its location above the Arctic Circle. This is due to the fact that the magnetic field is partially permanent and partially related to the plasma magnetic field, which is not locked into our permanent magnetic field but moves on a daily basis as the earth spins on its axis ... it is related to the plasma magnetic field as it is added to the permanent magnetic field.

80° N
2001
80° N
1994
1984
1948
70° N
1831
70° N
110° W
100° W
90° W

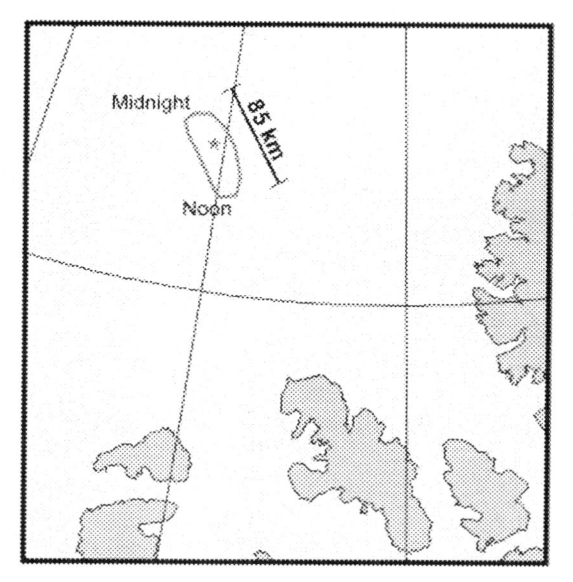

A satellite photo was recently released of an area in the State of Washington that extends over a number of states. It shows a tremendous wash area that occurred after a tremendous flood. Of course geologists strain to find reasons why the earth did this all by itself, but once again this is related to the melting of the old polar ice cap which extended to about that distance in the United States prior to the previous pole shift.

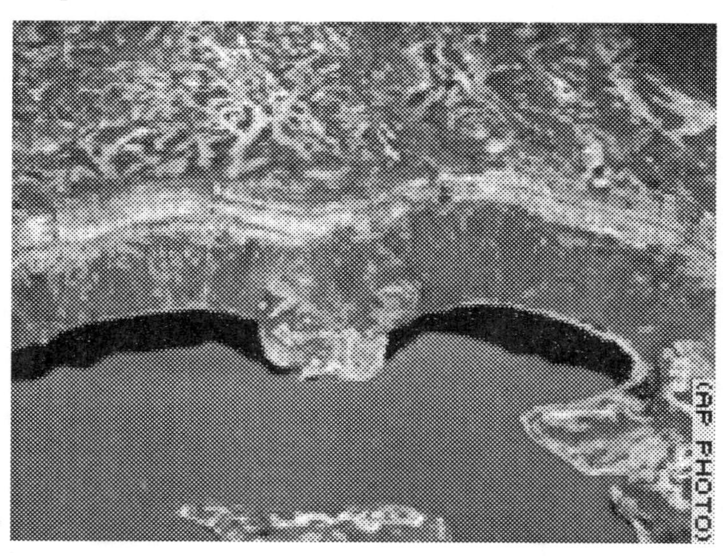

The last diagram is of an earthquake event on the border between Nevada in California.

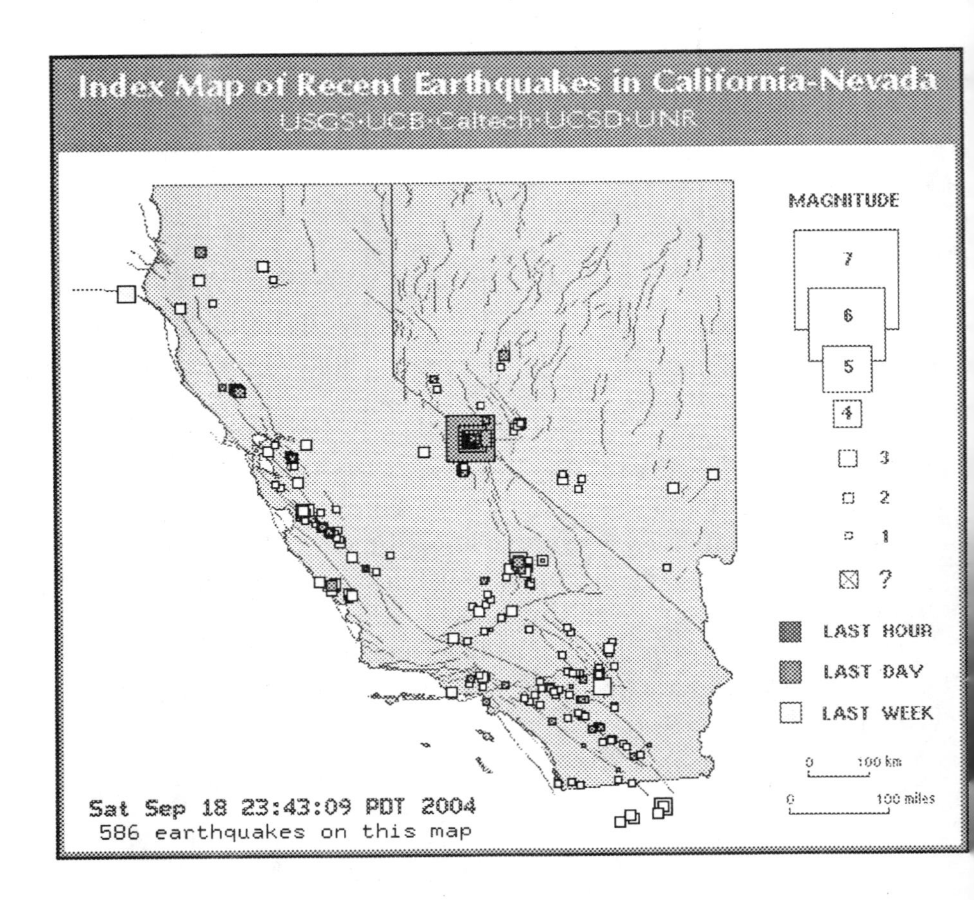

It shows a rapid series of earthquakes in the same spot and all of the other earthquakes along the California fault lines. There are two points to make regarding this diagram … the first is that if earth were indeed is old as people say it is and had not had any close encounters then the level of earthquake activity and volcanism would not be anywhere near the level it is today. The other point is that with the increase in solar activity that we're seeing today, it has already been described how solar flares can trigger earthquakes and volcanic activity. ***Not all volcanoes and earthquakes that erupt today are caused by solar flares!!*** Let me make that perfectly clear so there are no misquotes of this statement. However there is clear correlation between severe solar storms and increased volcanism and earthquake activity around the planet … once again action at a distance is the cause and we must look at conditions around the solar system that affect our earth from a distance.

Action at a distance is a reality. It is completely missing from standard geology, astronomy, astrophysics, space science, and meteorology. It is such a fundamental and important concept that none of these subjects can be properly taught without it. The true history of the world cannot be understood without it. And without the concept of action at a distance, we cannot possibly project into the future the road that we must take as a civilization and species to guarantee our future.

XII. HURRICANES, TORNADOES AND STORMS

The great red spot of Jupiter is a cyclonic storm which circles around the great planet endlessly since there's no natural grounding mechanism deep in the core of that planet. Both Saturn and Jupiter and also the outer gas planets Uranus and Neptune all exhibit these cyclonic storms in their atmospheres. The next chapter has a photo of a hurricane near the polar cap of Mars taken with the Hubble Space Telescope. None of these planets have warm water oceans over which to form such storms. The concept that somehow warm water introduces sufficient energy to create these huge monster storms on earth is already been dealt with in earlier chapters. In all cases, electrical currents coming from outside the planet power these storms.

The strength of the storm is directly related to the strength of the electrical currents in its connection outside of the planet. If one were able to visually see the actual connection, it would look like a spiraling comet tail emerging from the planetary atmosphere and extending out like a giant swirling comet tail into space trailing around behind the planet ... attached to the planet's upper atmosphere. As material is drawn up the central column of these cyclonic storms, they are continually powered by the electrical currents that rise in the vertical electric fields, with the material spiraling upwards in a vortex manner much the same as water spinning down the drain in a bathtub. Although Earth's surface storms are powered from electrical sources in the mid level atmosphere, ultimately they are powered by the solar electric field, which is the power source of all of the cyclonic weather activity of the solar system.

The first thing that is apparent from this model of the solar electric field as it affects weather on the planets, is that a classification system for the storms must include all of these factors. A simple classification system that only gives the wind speed at the center base of the eye of the storm is insufficient to give all the characteristics of the storm. There are many tropical storms on earth whose energy far exceeds a category one hurricane yet they are not even classified as the storm because the central wind speed does not reach a certain level. The damaging effects including the amount of water dropped from a storm can be far in excess of the normal hurricane from the wind source alone.

Therefore I have attempted to create a new system of classification of storms, which appears as a matrix. In column one of the matrix are all a characteristics dealing with wind speed. Only one of which is the wind speed at the center of the eye at the base of the hurricane. One value that would be in this column would be the total energy of the storm given the wind and momentum locked in this moving structure. From this value alone it would be obvious that warm water at the ocean surface would be completely insufficient to provide this level of energy to a storm.

In the second column would be the category of water. In this column would be the amount of water contained in this storm at a given time (these conditions might change with time), the amount of water that would be left if the storm weakens and thirdly the amount of water left to dump on land once the storm has reached landfall. I measure this amount in terms of "Lake Superior Volumes of Water" ... for example Hurricane Floyd 1999 as it dumped huge volumes of water and caused flooding from the Carolinas to Nova Scotia I estimated had approximately 2.0 Lake Superior Volumes of Water.

Another box in the second column dealing with water would be the amount of water that came from the moving air as it evaporated water while moving towards the eye and prior to moving up the column of the central eye. Another quantity in this column would be the amount of water coming into the planet from outside. Notice already how many factors are needed to truly classify a storm. In the third column would be the solar electrical energy input that is connecting to the storm from outside our planet and connecting to the ionosphere to power the storm. Another factor in this third column dealing with electrical energy would be the amount of available energy trapped in the ionosphere (already in storage in the earth to ionosphere capacitor) which would also be available to feed the storm.

In the next column would be a series of parameters dealing with the amount of vortex rotational energy in the storm, which would include the main eye, water spouts at the leading edge of the storm, and tornadoes as the hurricane made landfall. Along with this parameter would be included the total energy of these many vortex systems. Once again it would be this level of energy that when quantified would make it clear to everyone that the energy of these storms far exceeds the heat loss of the oceans as the storms pass over the ocean and therefore could not possibly be given credit for powering these storms.

Another column would deal with the overall extent of the storm relative to some given normalize standard. In the same column would be an energy density distribution and various altitudes through cross sections of the storm, as this varies greatly amongst the various large-scale storm systems. And finally the storm would be classified in terms of overall global energy distribution, or in other words, what is the storms overall percentage of energy distribution that is occurring on the planet at that time. There is a need to understand the overall energy content of the earth rather than dealing with just storms, which might be in the Atlantic, and possibly affecting the United States.

The topic of reclassification of storms would take a volume in itself as just alluded to here to show that this is one of the areas of research which I am personally pursuing at this time. But clearly, classification of storms simply based on maximum wind speed at the base of the eye of the hurricane is completely insufficient to describe the storm and its weather environment. One might also include factors such as upcoming solar flares that may increase the storm's energy if they hit within the lifetime of the storm. This would alter the storm's characteristics and would flow to the matrix altering the values of the storm. In this way storms might be compared in many different levels such as water content or the number of sub-storms in the outlying arms.

There is also need to classify low pressure cells that exist overland. I personally call these "himmicanes" as a sort of joke. But storms overland are no joke because that's where we happen to live. The following weather picture taken from a satellite shows hurricane Francis as it moves north across the Florida Peninsula. If one looks at the total amount of water content in the white clouds and the electrical energy and storm conditions in the satellite photo, compare this to the storm that exists through the Midwestern states ranging from Texas up into Canada in northern Minnesota. Clearly this storm system in the Midwest has far more energy and water in it than does hurricane Francis. Yet the meteorological community posts the Midwestern storm as just an average day on the farm. You also can see the vortex motion of the storm in the Midwest ... literally it is a hurricane overland, yet there is no classification system for such a storm.

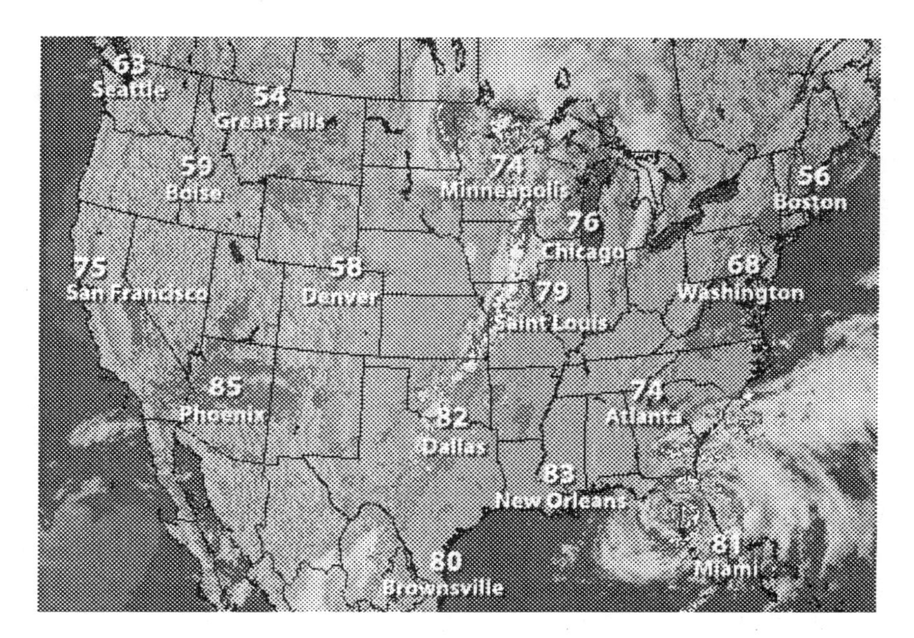

Understanding the paths of hurricanes is actually the topic of the future chapter dealing with predicting weather and storms. But what I learned is that storms react to the underwater topography of the ocean floor. In the front cover this book there is a map of the underwater topography of the Caribbean Sea and the Gulf of Mexico. The electrical currents of storm systems moving through this area begin to interact with these continental shelves as a hurricanes Passover these regions, causing them to turn and change directions and dissipate while they're out at sea. Once again this is completely unheard of in standard meteorology. There are certain hurricane paths that follow up along the central Atlantic Ocean, literally following the mid-Atlantic Ridge northwards as they plow into the frigid waters of the North Atlantic.

Another factor that one can see may be of importance in hurricane prediction is the fact that you have the electrical current moving up the central column of the hurricane. This is immersed in Earth's magnetic field and may in fact have something to do with the motion of hurricanes although I've not completely worked these details out in sufficient clarity in my own mind to print an actual result in this book. Once again this is in the background work of my ongoing research concerning storms and weather.

As the storm low cell moves through our lower atmosphere and interacts with the jet stream high above, and that in turn is being influenced by electrical connections that go far out into outer space, this becomes an extremely complex system to try to track let alone predict. Prediction of the paths of hurricanes is an extremely complex business and the models that are being used today, as you now might understand, by the National Weather Service and the National Hurricane Prediction Center did not include the factors necessary to even give them a beginning at predicting the paths of hurricanes. This is why I'm adamantly against allowing these people to publish paths of hurricanes. If a hurricane appears to be moving towards a populated area then the entire area should vacate irrespective of the economic loss that might occur over the next day or two ... rather than have the devastation and death as occurred with hurricane Charlie this past August 2004 in Florida.

The following two pictures were taken of the rare Brazilian hurricane of March 28, 2004. Brazilian officials were astounded and claimed that this could not have been possibly a hurricane yet the satellite photos are clear and the wind speeds were sufficient to classify as a low to medium power hurricane. The next photo shows a waterspout offshore as the storm system moves by a point of land and over the ocean of the Brazilian coastline. Meteorologists had no explanation for why a hurricane could form in such a location.

The following three photos show tornadoes over land. The first appears almost like a waterspout in the Brazilian hurricane yet it is a tornado overland. It is always been a ministry to meteorologists why tornadoes exhibit extreme amounts of lightning within the central column of the funnel cloud. The next figure picture shows a tornado rising out of the caldera of Mount Etna in Italy. This occurred on a clear blue-sky day with no storm clouds in sight. So much for the explanation that tornadoes are caused by updrafts from violent thunderstorm systems. The next tornado shows a small tornado extending down from the base of a very large tornado of the monster variety … the kind that cleared a mile wide path as of the Midwest back in the nineties. There was a period during the Hale-Bopp era when there were huge tornadoes that ran one mile wide along a 60-mile stretch devastating entire towns as it went. One of the storms came out of a clear blue sky and was a total surprise to meteorologists, however in hindsight I was able to identify the solar storms that created these blue-sky monster tornadoes. There was similarly a few years ago a killer tornado that came out of the clear blue sky and devastated down town Salt Lake City, Utah.

A tornado rises up out of caldera of Mount Etna Volcano in Italy out of a clear blue sky. This is the vertical electric field at work.

The next three plates and titled anatomy of a hurricane parts A, B and C. Diagram A shows the electrical current paths of ions being drawn along the ocean's surface towards the central vertical column. As they move over the ocean they draw warm moisture from the ocean surface and this feeds it into the vertical column where it eventually condenses and spills out forming the upper cloud layers of the hurricane. This is the cause of the cooling of the ocean surface and is a byproduct of the overall electrical current, ***not*** the source of energy, which drives the storm, as is stated in traditional meteorological theory.

Once again I use the example of a car going down the road. If someone did not know that there was a big engine consuming gasoline in the car and simply saw the car moving down the road with exhaust coming out the tail pipe, one might assume that the hot gasses coming out the tail pipe were the propulsive force that made the car move. This would be the logical conclusion since this is all you would be able to see. However by making a simple calculation of the energy required to move the car down the road relative to the amount of

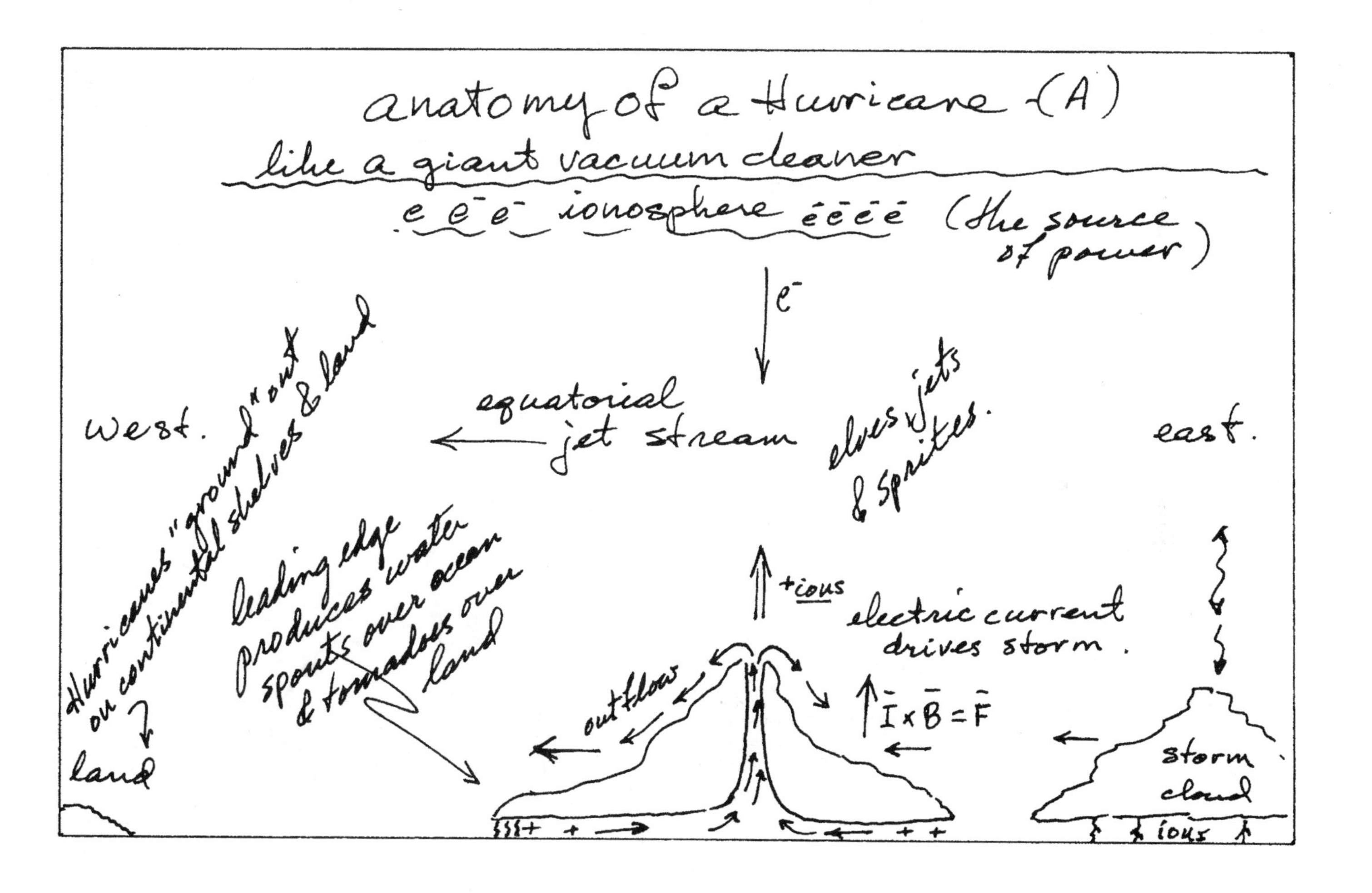

anatomy of a Hurricane (A)
like a giant vacuum cleaner
e e⁻ e⁻ ionosphere ē ē ē ē (the source of power)
e⁻
equatorial jet stream
west.
east.
elves jets & sprites.
Hurricanes "ground" out on continental shelves & land
leading edge produces water spouts over ocean & tornadoes over land
land
+ions
electric current drives storm.
outflow
Ī × B̄ = F̄
storm cloud
ions

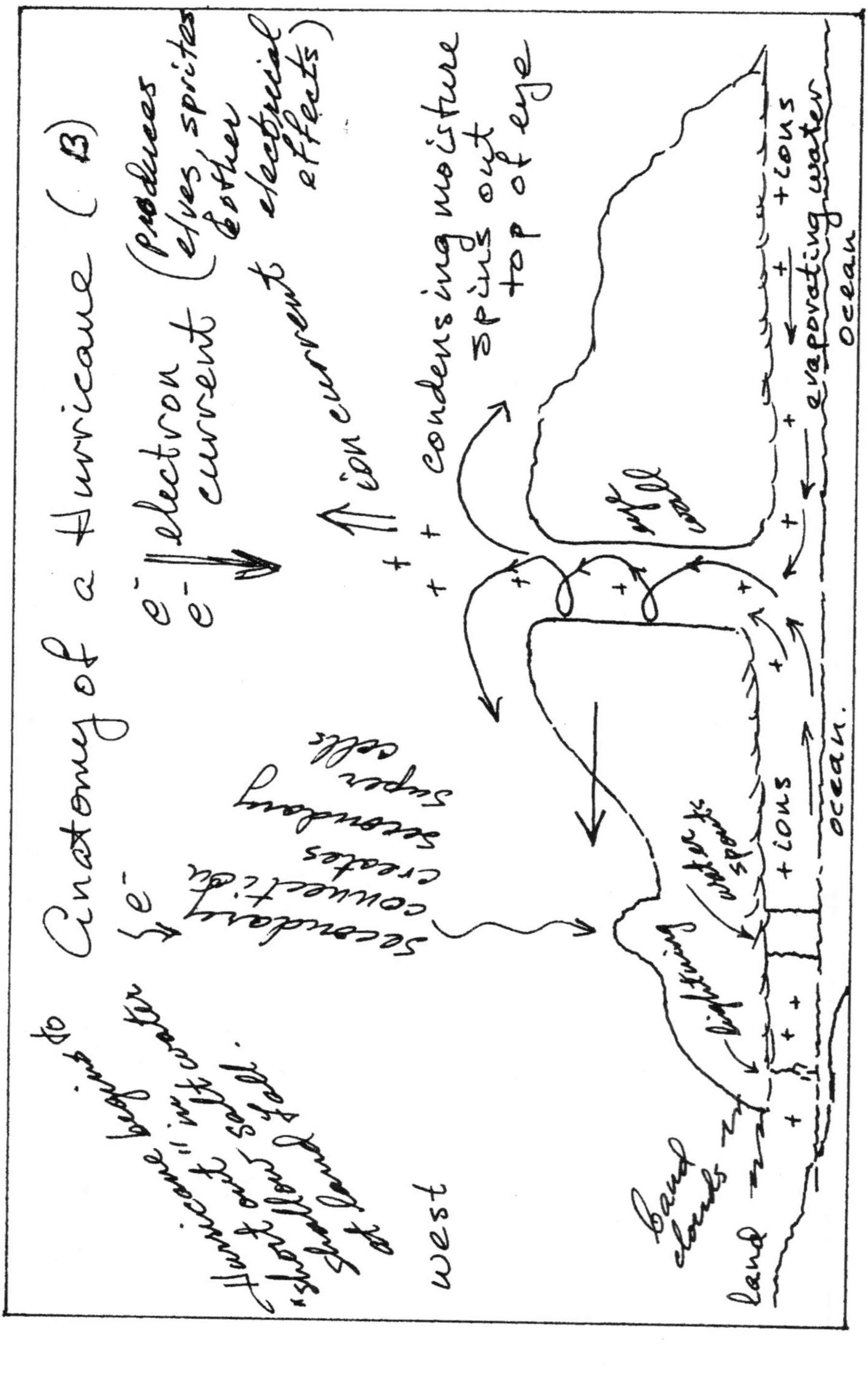

Anatomy of a Hurricane (B)

Hurricane begins to "short out" in shallow salt water at land fall.

e⁻

secondary connection creates secondary super cells

e⁻ e⁻ electron current (produces elves, sprites & other electrical effects)

ion current

+ + +

condensing moisture spins out top of eye

west

band clouds

land

lightning

water spouts

+ ions

eye wall

+ ions

evaporating water

ocean.

ocean

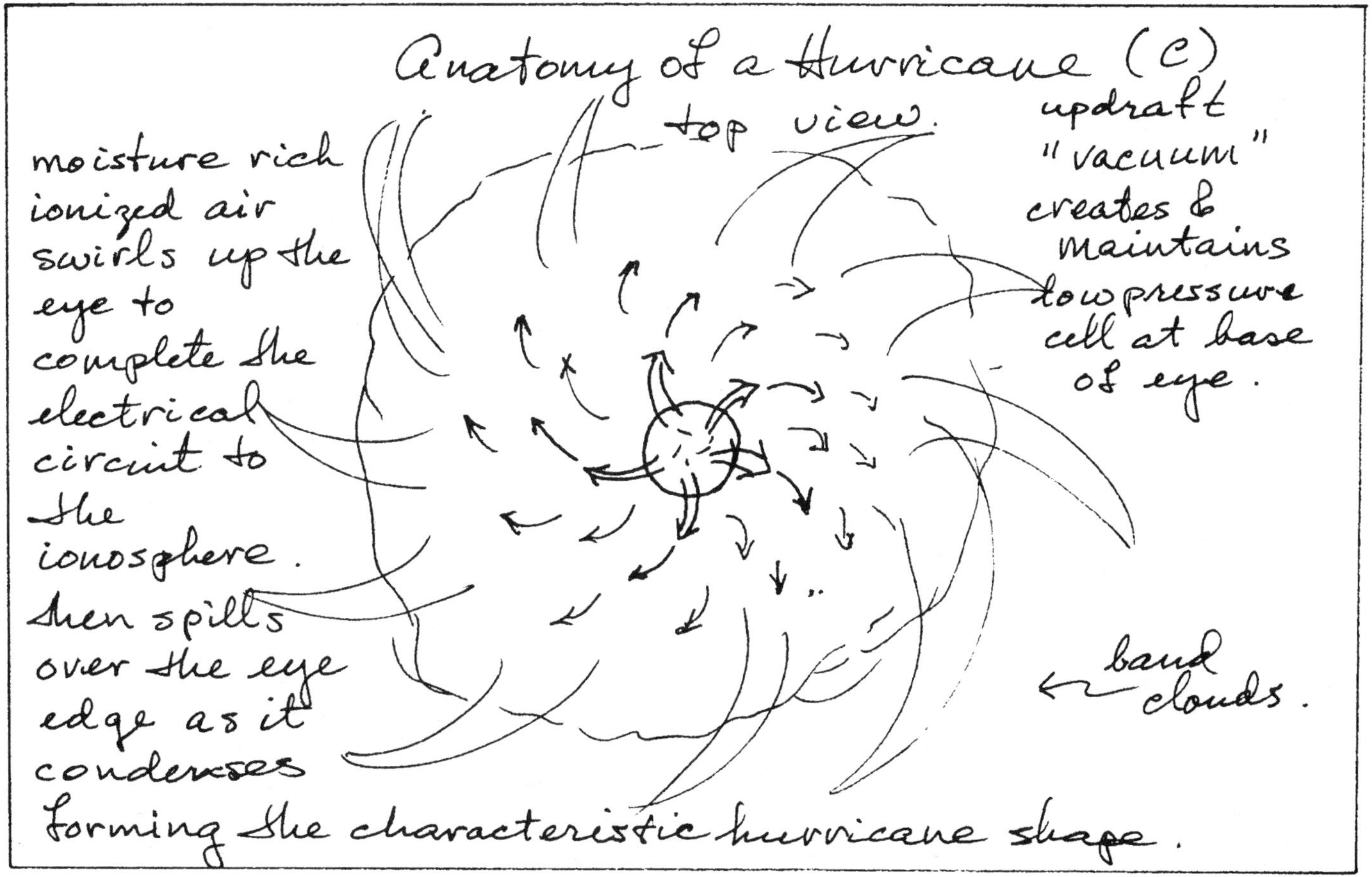

Anatomy of a Hurricane (C)

top view.

moisture rich
ionized air
swirls up the
eye to
complete the
electrical
circuit to
the
ionosphere.
then spills
over the eye
edge as it
condenses
forming the characteristic hurricane shape.

updraft
"vacuum"
creates &
maintains
low pressure
cell at base
of eye.

band
clouds.

energy coming out the gas the tail pipe of the car, one would soon discern that this was not the energy source creating the motion of the car. The same situation occurs with hurricanes. If you determine the amount of energy in the hurricane it in no way corresponds to the amount of energy lost from the cooling of the ocean as the hurricane passes over. This is a side effect not the cause of the storm. A simple energy calculation would prove to anybody that this is true.

In the Atlantic Ocean, the initial storm clouds build over the east to west expanse of Africa and as they spill out over the Atlantic Ocean, the electrical connection that had been made to ground previously is no longer there so the path of least resistance for the electrical current moving up to the ionosphere is now along the surface of the ocean connecting to the ionized air that sits above the surface of the ocean.

In diagram B a closer look is given to the hurricane showing the leading edge being the primary source of lightning, waterspout's and eventually tornadoes as it makes landfall. Also shown in this picture is the leading edge approaching the continental shelf prior to approaching land. The hurricane begins to short out in shallow saltwater just prior to landfall. This causes the water in the clouds to begin to dump. This is nature's very own method for diminishing the energy in the storms. This is the secret that I have learned ... we need to extend the grounding farther out from shore to eliminate the energy from the storms before they get close to land. This is the true simple and effective way to neutralize these massive storms.

Plate C shows the top view with the moisture rich ionized air swirling up the eye to complete the electrical circuit to the ionosphere. The water then spills out over the eye edge as it condenses forming the characteristic hurricane shape. If there were not an external energy source moving continually providing a vacuum from above, the hurricane would soon dissipate as the winds rushed in at a hundred plus miles per hour to the central low pressure cell at the base of the hurricane. This energy is provided by the vertical electric field that is ultimately driven by the solar electric field. There is simply not enough energy in the solar light energy or in the atmosphere or ocean warm water surface to provide the energy needed to power a hurricane.

XIII. WEATHER OF THE PLANETS

The whether the planets is such a vast topic that it could take 10 volumes in itself, so the trick here will be to summarize the essentials relative to the electrical nature of the solar system. When we talk about weather the planets, as with earth, one must include the total environment including the overall electrical discharge that they all incur as they pass through the solar capacitor. The majority of principles that apply to earth also are applied to the other planets with the exception that Mars has a very small magnetic field as does Venus, and the small planet Mercury has little if any magnetic field.

One might well classify the weather the planets into two categories, those with magnetic field's and those without. Interestingly enough this same categorization would find the planets with magnetic field's in the same grouping of planets that have moons ... and those planets that have no magnetic field in a grouping of planets that have no moons to speak of. Mars has two small moons but certainly nothing sufficient to create and sustain a magnetic field such as earth's moon or the extensive moon systems of Jupiter or Saturn and the other planets. It will be interesting when we get to put Pluto to see if in fact it also has a magnetic field since it has a relatively large close moon Charon.

Another major factor in electrical vision of our solar system is that the planets have very different ages and secondly that due to encounters with large passing celestial objects, the characteristics of these planets have changed over time. Mars for example had a vast atmosphere with oceans and was a blue planet only a few thousand years ago, so one might well consider what the weather at Mars was like prior to losing its oceans and atmosphere. This might be quite a bit more interesting than considering its weather right now with its almost nonexistent atmosphere and no moisture or oceans. We can even tell which direction the trade winds blew on Mars due to the erosion on for example the shore lines of Olympus Mons which sat in a large ocean. Now I will start with the discussion of the planets starting with the closest to the sun and working outwards.

So first let us examine the closest planet to the sun Mercury. Most space scientists would say that Mercury has no atmosphere and therefore no weather. This is not the case if you understand that

Mercury is close to the Sun and is discharging the solar capacitor. The first issue that truly needs study is the orbital anomaly, the so-called precession of Mercury's orbit that has been attributed to General Relativity. This entire issue has not been resolved or verified according to modern standards and the upcoming Mercury probe from NASA has no science defined to test this most important and fundamental concept.

Again this probe is incorrectly designed for the task as it has no electric field sensing probes and has no science instruments to measure the possibility that Mercury has a torus (as does IO of Jupiter) that would create sufficient tail drag (or possible electro-magnetic long term effects) to alter Mercury's orbit and account for the anomaly of its orbit. This is "weather" in the truest sense of the word as it affects the basic nature of the planet, its temperature and environment. Just as with comets or the other better-studied planets, the electrical size of the system is FAR greater than the physical size of the nucleus or planet that we see with the naked eye or telescope. There is also a known iron and heavy nuclei band of material circling the sun in the vicinity of Mercury which we can actually see with the naked eye from earth on certain nights of the year when this ring system around the sun is on edge from our vantage point ... it is called the Zodiacal Disk. This could be a source of heavy "tail drag" material that could affect Mercury's orbit. As with many of the incorrectly designed NASA probes, one can see the true effects in the data if you know what to look for ... that is ... if NASA scientists release the data without corrupting it first.

The other factor is that Mercury's orbit is inclined relative to the ecliptic (plane of the zodiacal disk and the plane of the solar system) and therefore only passes through this region twice per orbit. This would cause bursts of activity only at these select places so it would be a combination of data yet to be taken and calculations of the effect on the orbit that might combine to over turn the idea that Mercury's orbital "precession" is caused by General Relativity and a so called bending of the solar gravitational field OR is this truly an electrical side effect of tail drag and its interaction with the solar environment ... what we should call "space weather".

The first picture below shows Venus illuminating in x-rays. This is what earth would look like if our magnetic field broke down and allowed the solar wind to come pounding into the atmospheric surface.

This in fact does happen on a regular basis as I attempted to point out many times on radio shows. It seems that only recently other scientists have begun to pick up this story and examine it seriously as a public-health threat.

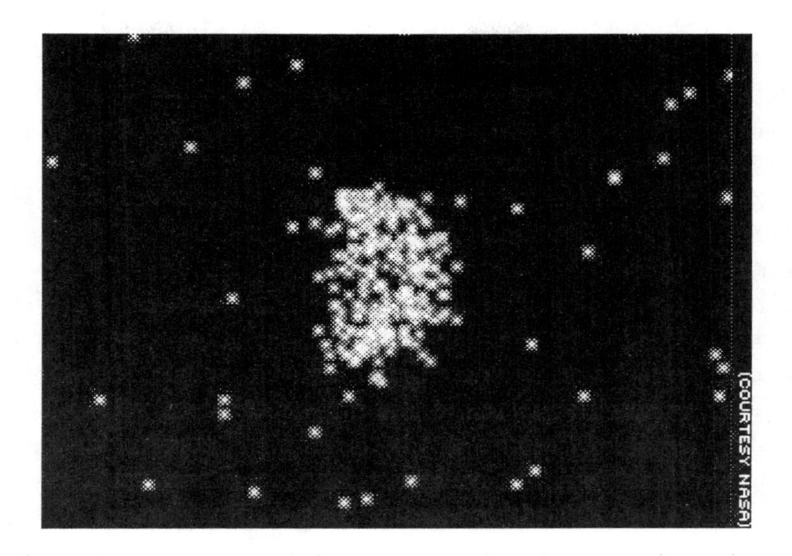

The weather on Venus is dominated by its hot interior which is belching forth heat from its recent birth is a young planet. The claims that its high temperature is due to the greenhouse effect have failed.

Moons are essential to driving the magnetic fields (as discussed in my earliest published papers) of the planets so we may someday move a small mini-planet object from the far reaches of the solar system and design the path to be captured by Venus or Mars to give them a moon that will produce large magnetic fields ... which is an essential ingredient for the protection of life on the planet just as with earth. This begs the question of earth as we look at all of the factors that earth has necessary for life ... is this all due to chance? ... or did some star fairing race come through this region of the galaxy long ago and create the right conditions that would support life?

The point is that currently Venus has no magnetic field. It is discharging the seller capacitor as are all the other planets, but the effects of this discharge impinge directly in the cloud tops that interface with outer space. As noted, this is the definition of a "comet". The comet activity of Venus has been reduced to a minimal value as its orbit became circular. Many scientists have looked at

Venus objectively and come to the conclusion that it is a young planet. It is impossible to reconcile its vast atmosphere and high-temperature and other conditions with a 4.5 billion-year-old planet. Its surface gravity is far less than that of earth yet its atmosphere is hundreds of times denser than that of earth. If one calculates using regression analysis, and estimates the loss of atmosphere of Venus relative to planet Earth which is larger, then 4.5 billion years ago Venus would have had an absolutely enormous atmosphere. It is closer to the sun and therefore according to traditional theory it should have been exposed to far more violent conditions which would've reduced its atmosphere, not increased it in the early days of the solar system. The vulcanism of Venus cannot be explained by any type of greenhouse effect but is only the results of the new planet recently formed from an energetic very large comet. The issue of how Venus got into its orbit inside of that of earth's has been resolved because of the understanding of the working of "tail drag" on the comets, especially the large comet as Venus would have been (as recounted in all the legends that come down to us from every nation that existed at that time on earth).

Even the scientists who had dared to say that Venus is a younger planet in general do not wonder across the line and say that it is very recent as in only a few thousand years ago. Only when the various branches of study come to grips with this issue of Venus being a young planet will the true history of earth be told. Until that point, there will be a never ending list of band-aide theories, stories that don't make sense ... and a denial that forces a base of false beliefs that somehow the earth did all of what we see by itself.

This is confounded by the fact that the controllers of the secret societies and families, which are in charge of the world governments around the world, do not want the public to know about this because they would lose control. So just as the greenhouse effect on global warming is a political issue that cannot be questioned if you work within "the system", the issue of Venus and the true nature of capture in the formation of the our solar systems and the true nature of comet's cannot be discussed by scientists who get paid by the system. That is why my books have been banned in bookstores, libraries and many other places that would allow public distribution on a wide scale.

The weather of Venus is dominated by its incredible internal heat source that causes vulcanism. The Magellan Orbiter data showed tens of thousands of active volcanoes on Venus and a changing surface on nearly a daily basis. Can you imagine earth with tens of thousands of active volcanoes of all sizes? The temperature of the atmosphere at ground level is hot enough to melt lead and sulfuric acid rains out of the sky from intense lightning storms. There is no wind at the surface with incredible heat belching forth from its surface. Yet only a minuscule 2% of solar light that reaches Venus actually penetrates the cloud tops of its enormous young atmosphere.

The circulation patterns in the cloud tops is dominated by the electrical currents in the discharge is the solar capacitor, with the electron beam arriving from the sunward side and the ion tail arriving from the anti-sunward side.

Spacecraft at Venus have detected incredible lightning activity which have been termed "Whistler's" by space scientists. This is due to the high frequency electromagnetic radiation that is generated above the cloud tops by the lightning below the cloud tops. When comparing energetic lightning bolts within the atmospheres of Jupiter and Saturn, Venus creates a significant amount of this type of radiation compared to those planets and far more than earth, once again signaling Venus has a far more energetic young planet than earth.

What would be far more interesting would be for scientists to speculate about the future weather of Venus. As the atmosphere cools and the internal conditions eliminate heat from its hot young interior, the gases and molecules in the atmosphere will form water and salts. In my early work I defined three stages of planetary development after the extremely hot formative stages as a comet. The first I called the nuclear stage with a short-range nuclear elements are decaying that were formed in the high-energy electrical discharge in a comet the size of one that would create a planet like Venus (not like the small comets we have seen in our solar system in modern times). This is exactly where Venus is today.

At some point the surface will begin to solidify to form a crust and mantle over the still molten interior. If it is lucky enough to adopt a large moon by capture it will then start to generate a large external plasma magnetic field that will exist as the planet cools through the Curie temperature, locking in a permanent magnetic field as we have on earth.

The second stage of planetary evolution I called the chemical stage. This is when a planet becomes cool enough for long-term stable chemical elements and molecules to form. Since lightning will still be a significant part of the weather system due to the discharge of the electrical solar capacitor, the evolution of large complex organic molecules will begin during this stage. That's why I call this the chemical stage. The planet is still extremely hot and cooling. Its atmosphere is stabilizing. A planet like Venus will have a serious problem becoming a life-bearing planet due to the fact that it does not rotate very rapidly relative to the sun, only showing one side to the sun for long periods of time.

The final stage is the biological stage during which the planet becomes cool enough to support rudimentary forms the biological life. It appears that the concept we call evolution requires brief periods of extreme stress, which are caused by the passage of a new large comet that possibly is also being adopted by the solar system, or possibly simply passing through on a very long orbital path. The entire concept of biological evolution being assisted in this process by possible intelligent life or a more powerful figure in the universe is one we simply do not have answers for today. It is one of those questions that exceeds our ability to collect data or answer these questions with any degree of certitude.

It is like the origin of the universe itself where scientists create theories and publish them in journals but which may have very little to do with reality itself. As with a person who wakes up in the middle of a strange forest we look around on earth and see life all around us in all stages of development. How this all came to be and what the future holds is beyond our capacity to understand at this point in the development of the human species. By definition we have no history for a true beginning but can only look at the clues and evidence left by nature. But somewhere in the cooling process of a planet, biological life is introduced as the environment stabilizes and allows development over very long periods of time.

As with a person standing in the forest with old trees, fallen down trees and young saplings we are standing in the middle of our solar system looking at planets and moons of all ages. Only when you realize this simple fact will the solar system truly begin to make sense. The story that is being purported today throughout the astronomical community that all planets formed at one time could not possibly be true anymore than the person standing in the middle of the forest could say that all of the trees were born on the same day.

In a brief moment, only a few thousand years ago, Mars lost its atmosphere to a passing large comet ... that comet became the planet Venus according to the ancients. Earth encountered that same comet on two occasions causing a pole shift and also altering earth's atmosphere. But Mars was the real loser in the celestial tug-of-war. The remnants of its ocean are very clear in the series of plates included in the book to show you the amount of erosion that exists visibly on Mars' surface. But the first picture below shows a hurricane near the polar region of Mars as taken by the Hubble Space Telescope. Isn't it amazing that Mars supports hurricanes yet it has no oceans? This proves conclusively that the warm water theory for hurricane formation can only be totally false. As they say in logic, one contradiction disproves a theorem.

The following plates give coverage of the entire surface of Mars ... examine them carefully for water and erosion. Also included is a picture of Olympus Mons the great volcano on Mars that is so large it is visible from earth with a small telescope.

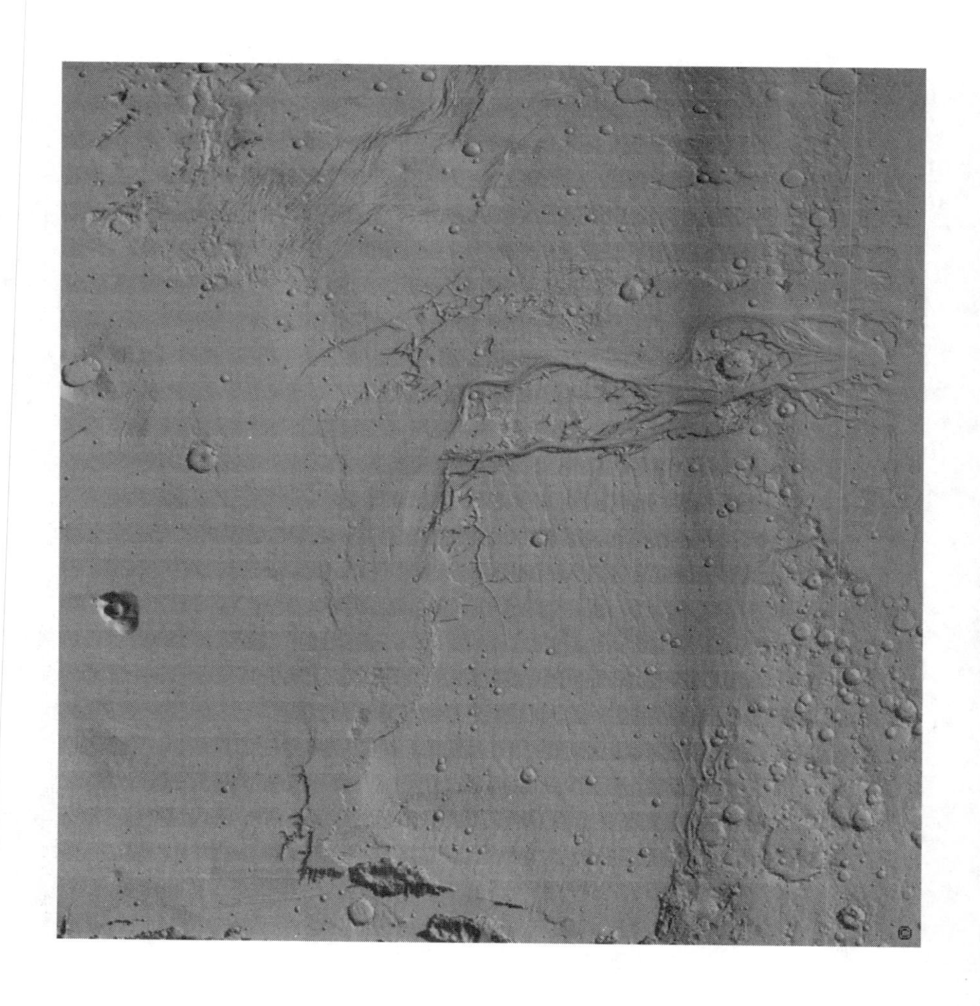

© Copyright 2002

© Copyright 2002

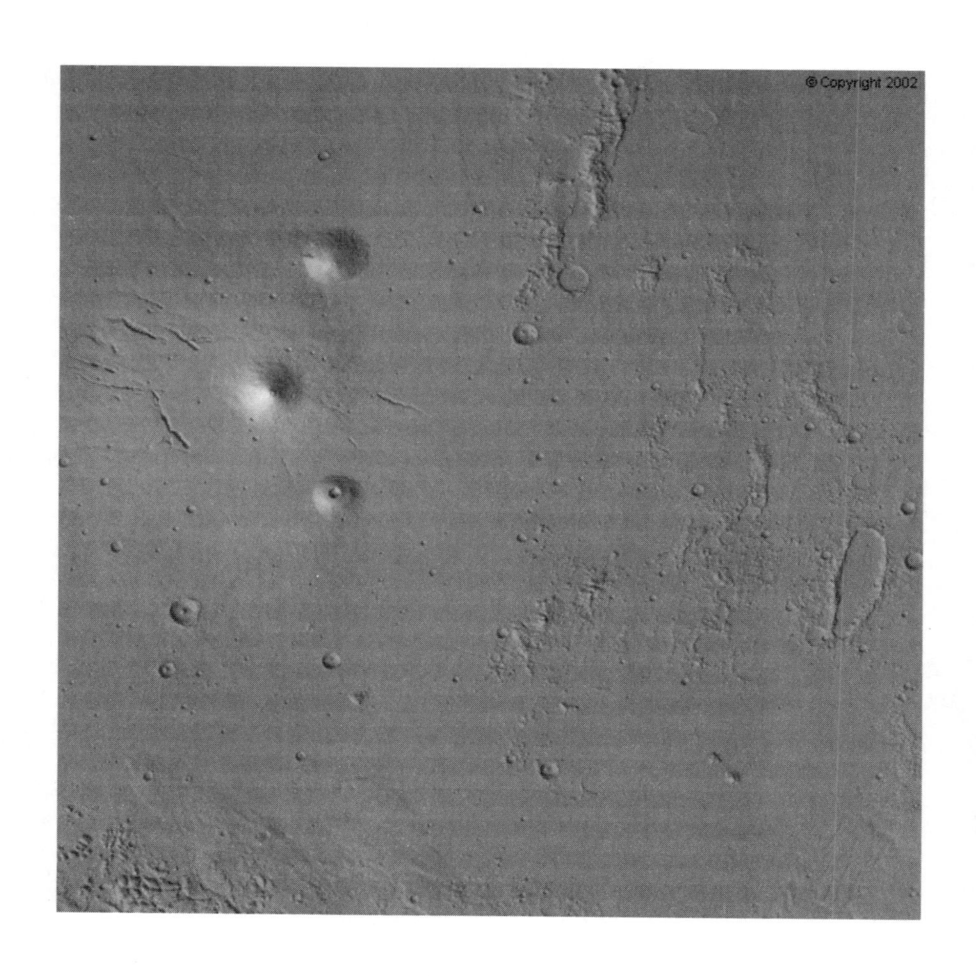
© Copyright 2002

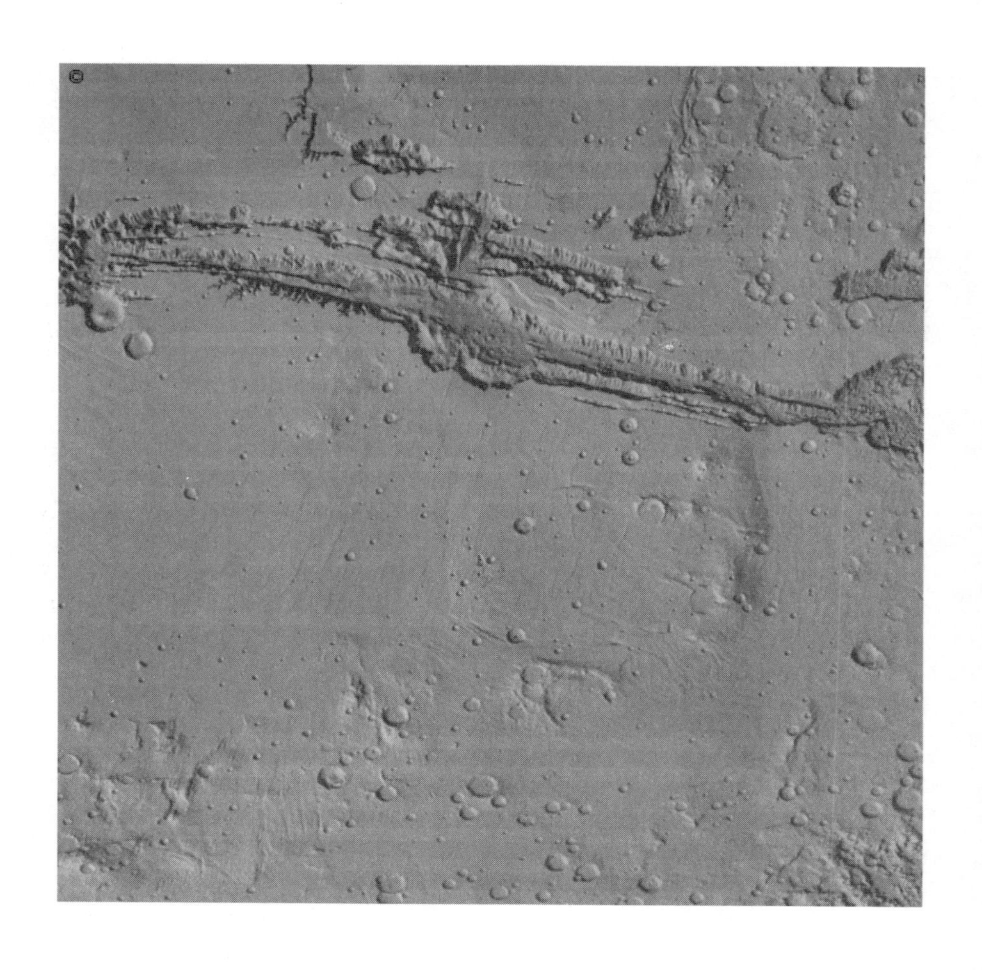

The most interesting feature about this massive volcano is the erosion at its base. If one looks at the Pacific Islands the erosion is exactly the same with the eroded cliffs facing the windward side. Early photographs of Mars orbiters showed pristine riverbeds meandering across the Martian surface. It always amazed me that NASA, in its quest for searching for the water on Mars, landed their Rovers in the middle of the equivalent of the highland deserts. Why would they not explore the basins of what were obviously recent riverbeds. But possibly the true purpose of these expeditions was to divert the public's attention from the incredible amount of surface features that screamed unquestionably the Mars had a tremendous amount of water and had to have lost these recently. Look at the amount of erosion in the photos.

Many of the craters near shorelines are eroded away or filled in with sentiment, obviously the results of water in that area that eroded away these features. Also note that the so-called low lands are almost devoid of craters unlike the highlands, which are heavily cratered. One can actually see the Martian coastlines where the rivers emptied into the shallow ocean basins and one can even see the river deltas. This tells us that recently Mars had a significant atmospheric water, rain, rivers and oceans. To have this ocean, as I pointed out many times in the past, Mars would need an extensive atmosphere to hold these oceans in place ... that is to provide atmospheric pressure required to hold the oceans in place so they would not evaporate away into outer space. This was such an obvious criticism of traditional theory that NASA scientists eventually had to come up with the ridiculous concept that a solar flare blew off the atmosphere of Mars a few millions of years ago (always long ago you know ... I often wonder where they come up with these numbers???), but they couldn't explain how this happened to Mars selectively without affecting Venus or earth which are far closer to the sun. As with all of the after the fact ad hoc theories, they simply don't make sense or have internal contradictions.

Recently it was discovered that Mars atmosphere has significant amounts of ammonia and methane. These volatile chemicals on earth if released would quickly move up and out of our atmosphere. Mars has enough of these molecules to be detectable from outer space. At first they tried to claim that this would be due to biological life and that they had actually discovered biological life on Mars due to this ammonia and methane. However it was soon pointed out that even on earth with all the natural sources of methane that we have, you would never be able to detect these chemicals from outer space. Clearly Mars does not have fern forests or decaying bogs or herds of cows to generate methane. Once again we return to the fact that Mars has had recent and significant volcanic activity. Traditional scientists have said all along that there could not be recent volcanic activity on Mars because they expected it to be an old cold hulk of a planet. Once again all the ad hoc theories create more contradictions than they do agreement with reality.

Olivine, a short-lived green glass material which results from recent volcanic activity, has been found all over Mars and very far from any volcanic regions. This tells us once again that there has been recent significant volcanic activity on Mars. All of this once again leads back to the fact that Mars had a close encounter with a large celestial object only recently and like earth is rebounding from that encounter.

We know there are significant dust storms that blow annually on Mars and these would erode very quickly any surface features, especially pristine riverbeds. If you notice ... many of these riverbeds are as fresh as the day the water left, certainly not hundreds of millions of years old. NASA scientists always want to place these events far into the distant past to prevent you from imagining that anything like this could happen today to planet Earth. By now you should be getting the picture of what is allowable within the confines of so-called standard science. Any reality that suggests that natural disaster beyond what the controllers can control is strictly forbidden.

What is far more interesting is to imagine Mars only a few thousand years ago with an earth light atmosphere and earth like oceans. The trade winds eroded the windward side of Olympus Mons and many other ancient geological features. Washes and rivers dumped into this ocean and it covered what we now call the lowlands. The oceans eroded away impact craters. Geologists looking at the data from the Mars Rovers said that the waters that were on Mars contained salts as in the oceans of earth. There is no mystery on Mars when you look at the pictures that show clearly the water presence in large volumes in the surface features of Mars ... the only issue is that all the water is missing.

There was a time in the late 1990s when something was clearly discovered on Mars that perked international attention. The Japanese quickly built a spacecraft and sent it to Mars only to have it go silent as it approached Mars. No one else has been able to successfully place a spacecraft around Mars ever since this time except for the United States. There are many that believed that there is an entire ongoing space program dealing with planet Mars that exists behind the scenes and about which we hear nothing. It is my belief that there are in fact ruins of ancient civilizations on Mars, the civilizations spoken of by the ancients prior to the last great catastrophe.

There is a great deal a secrecy regarding the planet Mars and as this book goes to press, one can only show through the action of people in the black ops groups that they do not want private individuals or other countries going near Mars.

The following plate shows a hypothetical graph of Mars losing its atmosphere and regaining it slowly over time. Satellites at Mars have proven that it has doubled its atmospheric content in the past 10 years alone (a satellite attempting to aero brake using Mars' atmosphere found it to extend far beyond the limit of the previous probe that measured the atmosphere just 10 years earlier). Also shown in the picture is a method to use a tether extended from Mars to enhance the

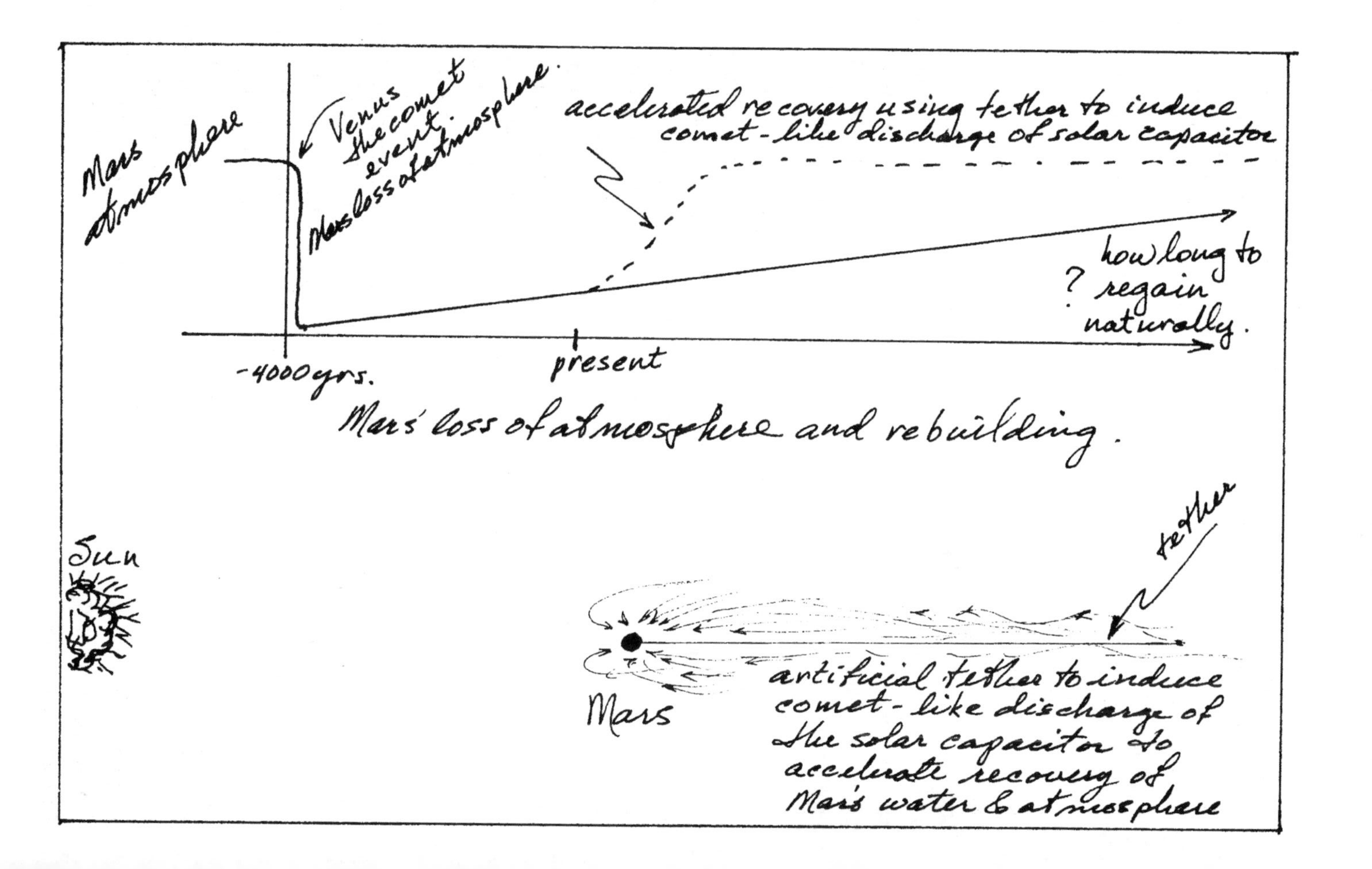

Mars atmosphere
Venus the comet event Mars loss of atmosphere.
accelerated recovery using tether to induce comet-like discharge of solar capacitor
how long to ? regain naturally.
-4000 yrs.
present
Mars' loss of atmosphere and rebuilding.
Sun
tether
Mars
artificial tether to induce comet-like discharge of the solar capacitor to accelerate recovery of Mars' water & atmosphere

discharge of the solar capacitor and possibly increase the rate of accumulation of its atmosphere. It is not known how long it would take to regain fully its atmosphere to the conditions prior to losing it to a large passing comet.

The asteroid belt is said by some to be the remnants of a planet that exploded as it was struck by a great collision in the ancient past of the solar system. It is interesting that some of the professional astronomers who make this claim also claim that there could be no such object such as a Planet X or extra-solar system object that could come into the solar system to affect earth. What an interesting contradiction in belief systems. Be that as it may, many of the asteroids present small atmospheric phenomenon around them. Mixed amongst them are small comets. This is also an area where objects captured by the great planet Jupiter would accumulate and stay without interruption because there is no planet in this region to disrupt their orbits.

There may be a bit of truth in both of these possible scenarios. Some scientists claim they can prove through computer analysis that all the asteroids, if you calculate their orbits back in time, would all end up at the same place millions of years ago (and were all part of an original planet). Regarding this argument there is simply not enough data on the asteroids positions and velocities to allow such a calculation. Secondly we do not have computer systems that can project and asteroid's path out even a few years let alone millions of years as claimed by some. I am not saying that this concept is incorrect, I'm only saying that given the information we have today and the computing power available today there is no way to prove such a statement. With all the speculation in the sciences, only those concepts which have experiments designated which would prove their correctness should be seriously considered. This leaves the burden on the proposer of such ideas to create realistic experiments that can prove the idea and which can be reproduced by other scientists readily. Without such available information these concepts are speculation only and should be listed as such.

The great planet Jupiter is really not a planet, it is a small unlit star. Like its next nearest neighbor Saturn … as we move out in the solar system … both have winds of protons emanating from their surface. These make a third group of planetary or celestial objects when we talk about weather. There are planets without magnetic fields, planets with magnetic fields and objects like Jupiter and Saturn which have magnetic fields and produce starlike conditions because of low levels of fusion in their atmosphere.

The Voyager spacecraft measured the proton winds as they passed these planets in the early 1980s. This is probably one of the greatest pieces of hidden data discovered by the space program that is being ignored. The closest moon Io of Jupiter is greatly misunderstood. Since it lies within the proton fusion capacitor of Jupiter, it is discharging this capacitor just as a comet would discharge the solar capacitor. There is a split electrical current that flows continually between Jupiter's polar regions and the moon Io has a large torus of sulfur dioxide and other materials. The standard explanation is that the sulfur dioxide is coming off the surface of Io and that the moon moving through the magnetic field of Jupiter causes the electrical discharge.

Once again standard science has a backwards. It is the electrical discharge it helps create Jupiter's very large magnetic field, not vice versa. And secondly the sulfur dioxide is moving towards and being drawn into Io ... it is not being blown off the surface of Io. It is very likely that Io is a young moon also and newly acquired by Jupiter. This would make sense given its high internal heat content. But scientists have used the hip pocket theorizing technique to come up with a Band-Aid that says that the heat would be caused by pumping of Io's interior as it moves in orbit around Jupiter. The volcanoes, however, are not in the correct location for this theory to be correct. Yet it stays in vogue because scientists do not have to confront the reality of a newly formed young moon around Jupiter.

One of the greatest contradictions in all of space science is floating around the planet Jupiter in the form of icy moons. If the dirty snowball comet model were correct, then the icy moons of Jupiter would be the largest comets you could ever imagine. They set out in the solar wind exactly as a comet should, and large comets have been seen far beyond the orbit of Saturn. So what's the problem? Why do we see no comet tail emanating from any of these icy moons? The simple answer is that the dirty snowball comet model is incorrect and the moons of Jupiter prove it every day as they orbit the giant planet in clear view of earth by any small telescope or binoculars.

By far the most interesting weather system in the solar system belongs to Jupiter. The great red spot is a cyclonic storm driven by electrical conditions that attach from outer space. We've already seen this type of behavior on earth based low cells that connect into outer space with the jet stream's moving around the outside of the low cells. The great red spot is a hurricane in the truest sense of the word and continues to revolve around Jupiter without end because there are no landmasses as there are with earth that is there are no land mass ocean interfaces as on earth to create the conditions that would short out this electrical storm. It is well known that the great red spot interacts electrically with Io and affects the auroral regions of Jupiter.

When comet Schoemaker Levy 9 approached Jupiter, 21 pieces of the comet nucleus came in from interplanetary space to the realm of Jupiter. Far away from Jupiter there were 21 pieces all exhibiting perfect water comet tails. But as they came into Jupiter's realm, magically the water tails turned into sulfur dioxide tails. There is no explanation for this in the dirty snowball comet model however the plasma discharge comet model explains this perfectly showing that the tail material comes from the environment and not vice versa. Additionally, as the 21 pieces approached Jupiter's atmosphere and before entering their Jupiter's atmosphere there were tremendous explosions, far greater than could be explained by 21 small insignificant pieces of ice. Standard dirty snowball theory predicted that there would be nothing to see when the comet impacts were viewed from Earth. The explosions that occurred were so incredibly large that the ultraviolet and x-ray signatures reflected off the moons of Jupiter and this was detectable at earth. This is the topic of a paper included in the upcoming chapter on my work with Russian scientists.

Jupiter too is a comet in that it is discharging the solar capacitor and many people have suggested that its orbit is somehow linked to the solar cycle of 11 years. Until we connect the dots with cause and effect physics, this will remain unknown or speculation. It has been measured directly by the Russians (see chapter 22) that earth and Jupiter have coupling of their magnetic fields and it was a enormous beam of electrons coming from the planet Jupiter that destroyed the Galaxy V pager satellite a number of years ago. Did we interact with Jupiter's sunward electron beam? It appears so ... but remember according to standard science ... there are no electric fields in outer space.

The greatest mistake of modern astronomical theory is not understanding the sunward electron beam of the comet nature of all the planets including and especially Jupiter. This provides the electrical currents that drives the enormous magnetic fields and also the charged particle streams which power their auroral zones. A picture of Saturn is included to show the two auroral zones … one at each pole

Saturn Aurora HST • STIS
PRC98-05 • ST ScI OPO • January 7, 1998 • J. Trauger (JPL) and NASA

The gas giants of Jupiter and Saturn support all the conditions of the sun in their own mini-solar systems while also discharging the solar capacitor. One sees the importance and universal nature of the comet phenomenon as applied to space weather around all the celestial objects and also around the small unlit stars.

One last mention is of the Rings and moons of Saturn that I predicted in the 1979 paper ***Saturn's Sweeper Moons Predicted*** reprinted in the appendices of the first book in this series. The rings show also all of the properties of comets and allowed me to successfully explain the historical observation of the ring edge fading on the inner ring edges but the sharp edges on the outer ring edges. The moons have been discovered sweeping the rings and they are interacting to cause the spokes that were observed by voyager space craft. This is a complex area of study but I was able to decipher the code from the earliest data that the moons are electrically charged and affecting the rings as predicted by the plasma discharge comet model. These small ring moons are acting just as comets do in the solar capacitor as they move in the fusion supported capacitor of Saturn.

Uranus and Neptune oddly enough with their cooler atmospheres show the distinctive signatures of the sunward electron beam as they discharge the solar capacitor. Both planets show ultraviolet signatures where the electron beams hit their nose side. These planets are probably growing on an ongoing basis as they collect material from beyond their orbits via their comet tails … just as Saturn's sweeper moons collect materials in their paths and far to the outer regions of their orbits.

Pluto as noted may have volcanism as noted by changing surface features that have been noted by the Hubble telescope. Such a small distant planet from the sun should be cold yet it apparently harbors a methane atmosphere and since it is too small to hold such and atmosphere it must have acquired it recently … another relatively new planet ???

Sedna is also a planet now passing 3 times the distance to Pluto and its orbit extends to 80 times the distance to Pluto. Is it still within the solar capacitor? And what of the so-called Kuiper objects … these are certainly small objects in formation as they discharge the solar capacitor in the vicinity of the orbit of Pluto.

I hope that in the future I will have time to devote an entire book to the weather of the planets.

XIV. COMETS – HARBINGERS OF DOOM

If astronomers were truly investigators of the skies one would think they would be the first to analyze the words of the ancients to gain insights into celestial happenings that were observed by these ardent watchers of the skies. Remember that the ancients had no TVs or light pollution or Nintendo games. Their entertainment came from observing nature and when something happened in the night sky, the entire world was watching. The ancients worshipped the objects in the sky and read their future by it. They were keenly tuned to it.

Is it not odd that modern astronomers are the first to deny that anything not acceptable by modern theoretical standards is not only discarded out of hand, but also so violently opposed by this professional group EN MASS!!! They are so pompous that they believe that these ancients were a bunch of poorly educated morons who could not keep records … and the records that were passed down to us need editing to conform to modern standards.

Every ancient culture has passed down to us the same story … that comets are associated with earth wide disasters. The stories always include a plumed serpent god of the sky that lifted the oceans on its backs (the tidal waves associated with the passage of a huge comet) and they created high winds and un earthly rains of black burning liquids (naphtha or oil) with rains of rock burning as they killed the majority of life on earth. We find caves with different kinds of animals that would normally be mortal enemies co-existing as they too hid from the devastation going on outside.

But according to modern astronomers, non of this happened and anyone that claims that the ancients were accurate in their descriptions are pushed out of any academic positions and banned as the "lunatic fringe". The public has never bought the astronomers' story and there is a great sentiment that is underlying and in fact indelibly burned in the subconscious of man that these events did happen.

The most sacred of all books of all cultures also talk about these events and the most striking texts out of these revered books are explicit that the rain of destruction came from the sky and destroyed almost all of mankind and every animal. People attend the churches and places of worship that harbor these books BUT NEVER TEACH THIS AS THE TRUE HISTORY OF MAN. It is moreover taught as some sort of fanciful myth rather than a true and most important element of man's history.

I look in the history books of high schools and colleges only to find any semblance of these most important elements of man's history to be totally missing. In its place is an impossible fable that all of man's races somehow were born in a "cradle of civilization" in the valley of the Tigris and Euphrates river and somehow these people wandered out and around the world in a few thousand years time to create the races we see today. This fable in no way accounts for the fact that many of the races that were discovered since only the 1500's are totally unaccountable by this fable and these lost civilizations have a long and rich history of their own ... in all cases they refer back to the time when the comet that eventually became the planet Venus raged through the solar system and devastated earth.

In brief, NONE OF THE HISTORY THAT IS CURRENTLY BEING TAUGHT IN SCHOOOLS OR UNIVERSITIES COULD POSSIBLY BE TRUE, yet daily professors collect paychecks and retire after long careers of writing text books, winning prizes, publishing papers while teaching total lies that even a well educated grade-schooler could determine were just that ... total lies.

But as with any lie, it begets another and another and another until the list and story is so convoluted that you could hardly make any sense of it at all. The king pin of this pyramid of "knowledge" as I found out as I was teaching at Cornell University in 1979 was the Space Science and Astronomy departments in association with the Astro-physics departments. The other departments fell into line and anyone who did not was ex-communicated from the royal ranks.

And so the lies continue to be propagated down the chain to the press and in every other field including archaeology, geology, evolutionary biology, earth and planet sciences of all genre and on and on. The meteorological community that is subservient to the National Weather Service, NOAA and ultimately NASA are all linked to the same system of lies.

There is a grand series protection mechanisms now built in to the surrounding structures that support and promote these groups. The first is Congress. The scientific agencies have been "Congress-Proofed" long ago by a subtle and seemingly positive program. As the military learned long ago, if you take a small percentage of the overall budget and make sure that this filters into every congressional constituency in the country, you now have Congress proofed their program. No senator or congressman in there right mind would vote against a program that would cut the funding that flows into their constituency. This would be political suicide as the overseers would quickly broadcast to the far reaches of the country that this senator was against his own constituency, which needs this money for jobs. What a beautiful plan. It works quite well.

The beautiful thing about agencies of the government is that no matter who is elected they remain year after year - election after election - decade after decade. So the most important element of all which is money and funding, are guaranteed for the people in the system. Since they referee their own work and those of their buddies, it preserves the status quo. Over the decades it has formed a scientific monopoly within government agencies who also control the experimental equipment that costs billions and billions of dollars per year. This allows the scientists a monopoly role in publication in the so-called respected journals, so we see the same scientists decade after decade saying the same thing with no competition. There once were independent scientists but they have gone the way of the dinosaur.

The final nail in the coffin of free thought in scientific endeavor is the news media. Once again, as with Congress, the news media is locked into a program of support of the existing government science monopoly. As an example, can you imagine a sports announcer coming on the air and saying that professional athletes are overpaid and the public pays too much for tickets for athletic events and that the owners of the teams should build their own stadiums with their own money and that this is one big fleesing of the public. That announcer would never announce another sporting event in his life. The same is true with science, we are talking about big business, big-money and big egos. You will simply never find a true science reporter ... one who goes out to discover the real news and report it like it is. I've seen a few science reporter's attempt this, and their careers ended quickly.

HOWEVER, in the background the CREEPING CRUD as I call it, marches on ... this is the never ending encroachment and changing of ideas as new data comes in from space probes. After a time the obvious becomes overwhelming such as the fact that comet nuclei are not white and snowy, but are pitch black and hot. Yet the news media still states that comets are dirty snowballs. In fact some articles say it so many times that one has to wonder ... are the science writers trying to convince themselves or me? The word within the inner scientific community is that they are 100% knowledgeable of the fact that all of my science work is correct. The only question is how can they first discredit me, and then steal it such that nobody notices. Recently there has been an absolute free for all borrowing of my material with people using very similar verbage and mixing it with the standard incorrect astronomical concepts. There is hardly a week that goes by without a major announcement that scientists have recently "discovered" an amazing fact that you could read it nearly word for word of my previous writings. But of course there is never any credit given.

One can ask the question that possibly these scientists are truly discovering this and they really never have heard of McCanney. In answer to this question, I have had many people tell me that they had either talked to NASA scientists and in one case the head of NASA itself and asked for a comment on McCanney's work. In all cases the response was that they cannot talk about it, but they are noticeably aggravated by the question. The other answer to this question is that these people are professionals supposedly and it is their job to know about everything going on in their field. One would have to be completely brain-dead to have not heard the radio shows, had these books passed to them or seen the references to my papers which in fact are published in the scientific journals which they read daily. With computer searches of all the online literature available today there is no excuse for scientists working with Saturn and its ring system for example to have never heard of or read my material on this topic. I also have the feedback from many of the radio shows that I do, some of which have an audience of over 40 million people that every NASA scientist is listening. It is almost comical to see the damage control come out in the next morning's newspaper as the scientists scramble to protect their story and turf.

The most telling side of all of this is that in 2008, NASA intends to send up a satellite with 100,000 times more sensitivity to look at large faint clouds of material in the outer solar system with possible brown dwarf stars at the center ... the following is a direct quote from the NASA announcement ... " to search for comets and brown dwarfs that could come into the solar system and destroy all life as we know it". If there is no such thing as an inbound extra solar system object that would damage earth, then why is NASA sending up the satellite to look for exactly that?

It is most interesting that NASA hires people who pretend they do not work for NASA to make claims that there could be no such thing as a planet-X object. NASA provided pictures for one of the greatest disinformation campaigns to try and desensitize the public to the entire topic of planet-X and supported behind the scenes activities of a person who claimed to have intimate knowledge of such an object "from aliens" ... the behind the scenes plan eventually surfaced was that eventually there was to be a large mass suicide to make this topic as incredibly crazy as you could possibly imagine and spread it over the front page of every newspaper in the world.

This disinformation campaign failed largely due to my continuing efforts in the years, months and the weeks leading up to May 15, 2003 to expose this charade of this government sponsored misinformation program. They even had professional astronomers who were hired to represent NASA, but as noted these astronomers pretended as if they did not work for NASA. The benefit to NASA, it never had to say a single word about this entire topic over the 10-year period that this insanity was perpetrated. Isn't it strange that our national space agency never said a single word during this entire time leading up to May 15, 2003? Clearly this was a misinformation campaign designed as early as 1995 to instill in the public the concept that "anything coming into our solar system that might damage earth was ridiculous".

This campaign was orchestrated from above in the chain of command or the controllers for a very good reason. As already noted, they know that the one thing that would cause everyone in the world to stop and turn their attention from the daily control of the controllers would be an object coming in from outer space that could affect earth and over which it would be obvious to everyone that the controllers have no control ... in other words they wear no clothes. So it is eminently forbidden for any NASA scientists or government supported scientist to raise any speculation or statement that there could be possibly an imminent danger to earth. If any statement of such danger ever does make it to the press, it is carefully crafted to be out in a far distant future so far that everybody will forget about it. In fact many of the announcements are made with no substance at all only to be retracted a week or two later. But the frontline headlines in the retraction have its effect on the public. It is the old cry wolf story used over and over but in the modern context.It is clear from the actions of the Tier 1 scientists who set above NASA and now even the actions of NASA itself that the one thing that dominates the actions of the controllers is exactly what we are talking about here ... the possibility of an inbound object that could affect planet Earth.

The plate on the following page was drawn to illustrate the plasma discharge electrical snakelike connection between a passing comets and Earth. It shows auroras in the upper atmosphere and two coupling electrical connections to the planet Earth that would scar and burn the planetary surface. To someone standing on the surface of the Earth looking up, these would look as flailing electrical cyclonic pillars of fire extending up into the smoky sky. This is exactly what the ancients tell us they saw including Moses as they approached the Red Sea. The ancients also talked about seeing this display as a large comet passed Mars and it appeared as though a serpent's mouth was wrapping around the planetary globe as it sucked the atmosphere and oceans from the once blue planet.

The ancients also talk about the comet lashing out to every object it met and one can only imagine that every asteroid and minor planet became an object of this electrical connection as the comet passed yearly through the inner solar system. The ancients also talk about two large comets and sometimes more that interacted as they fought a celestial war in the sky. The ancients were not lying or exaggerating and as it is said many times ... the truth is stranger than fiction. The public now has what they have never had before regarding this information handed down from every corner of the globe ... they have a correct scientific theory that explains in great detail everything the ancients saw ... it also shows why the standard astronomical concepts that were used to "prove these ancients wrong" were in fact themselves totally incorrect.

The plate on the next page is an image that one can extend to reality as this would be a comet that visually would stretch from horizon to horizon and lashing out with wildly flailing tail streamers. Venus in its comet stage wandering through the solar system was said to have had as many as 7 giant tails at once. This was confirmed with the medium sized comet (new planet) Hale Bopp which had as many as 17 tails at one time (see photo in the first book of this series). The BIG comets are in fact "harbingers of doom" and they will affect earth in the future ... the only question is WHEN?

Comet to Earth Electrical Discharge

The descriptions of the ancients are confirmed by modern theory.

snake like sunward "spike" of the comet

Auroral discharges... from a distance it would appear as though a snake's mouth encircled the globe.

snake-like electrical discharge from the highly charged comet nucleus to a planet.

To a person on the planet, this would appear as huge tornadoes of Fire reaching up through the clouds and into the heavens.

XV. LEBs (LOCAL ELECTRICAL BATTERIES)

One of the most important concepts of my theoretical work is the identification and categorization of LEBs. This term was introduced in the ***ATLANTIS TO TESLA –THE KOLBRIN CONNECTION*** book although the concept goes back to the earliest days of my publishing as I identify the areas of electric fields as well as regions which are guarded or "shielded" from the effects of electric and resulting magnetic fields. This is evident in the paper on Saturn and the early 3- part comet paper (reprinted in the appendices of earlier books of this series).

These areas are constantly changing in size and strength and sometimes the direction of the fields change based on the myriad of factors in the plasma environment of outer space. One of the most easily understood regions of local electric battery lies to our sunlight side as our magnetic field encounters the solar wind. As the magnetic field that is carried in the solar wind plasma changes, it can change and even reverse our own external magnetic field. This can be measured at the surface of the earth in the extreme cases with a handheld compass. When the magnetic field reverses in outer space, you have to understand that it opposes but does not change the permanent magnetic field that is locked in earth's core and mantle. What does happen however, is that the solar wind is no longer blocked and comes pounding into our upper atmosphere.

Chapter 13 has as its first picture the planet Venus, which has no magnetic field and continually fluoresces in x-rays. This is what happens when our own magnetic field breaks down. The influx of x-rays is dangerous to inhabitants on earth, yet standard science in their fear of alarming the public refuses to talk about this simple fact. It is a quantity regularly monitored and talked about in Russia but never heard about in the Western press.

There is a region in a comet which sits behind the comet nucleus called the "neutral zone" (see the appendices of the Atlantis to Tesla boo). This is a region where neutral or un-charged molecules and atoms may exist without strong electrical currents or electric fields to influence their behavior. It is much like a region behind a rock in a stream of rushing water where fish hangout to get away from the currents. Many times plasmas act the same as currents in a river. On the upstream side of a rock in a stream of rushing water, a pressure builds up. The same is true of the electron beam coming from the sun side ... it creates a pressure, but in this case is an electrical pressure or buildup of electrical charge ... in this case negative charge. Due to the fact that electrons have thousands of times more mobility or ability to move in an electric field than anything else in outer space, they provide the bulk carrier in any electrical discharge. This is the cause of charging of everything from spacecraft to asteroids to the earth to comet nuclei. Such a simple observation has totally escaped the scientific community because it never thought enough to look for such electric fields as they were told in grad school that such fields were impossible.

The first two photos show pictures of an antique battery known as the Edison battery that was patented and around the year 1900. It had a single metallic plate coated with two electrodes coming out the ceramic top. A glass container held a solution very similar to that of seawater. This solution chosen by Edison was calcium chloride solution. The battery provided approximately .7 volts and these were hooked in series or parallel to increase the voltage and power needed for a particular operation. The solution did not freeze down to very low temperatures and was used in the early days of railroad for guide lights and other electrical functions. When the electrical charge provided by the solution was used up, the railroad linemen would simply replace the solution in the jar and it was ready to go again. Recharging batteries did not come until later. This patent was quite interesting as at the time a man named Tesla was working for Edison. As stated in my earlier works it is my belief that Tesla had access to ancient documents, which gave him the start to understand many of the inventions of his career.

The batteries are mentioned here because the ancients are now known to have used seawater batteries. These were large cement or rock structures in which seawater was allowed to flow in and remain until the electrical charge and energy were dissipated through large cables that ran inland ... then the water was let back into the ocean and fresh seawater entered the battery chambers to renew the charge. This may have been used as an exclusive source of power ... OR it may have been needed to generate power to initialize the Tesla type towers that extracted energy from the vertical electric field of earth.

The next photo is cerca 1900 of one of the Tesla's towers which were actually used to extract energy from the vertical electric field prior to being torn down by the energy mafia which still exists today and controls the world energy situation. One can see that this is no toy. The control electronics were housed in the small wooden building in the center and this created the initial alternating voltage using the grid power that was needed to initiate the "drilling through to the ionosphere". One can only imagine this sight in operation at night as the electrical current came down and was collected by the hundreds of point collectors on the tower.

The following two plates demonstrate how a Tesla tower works.

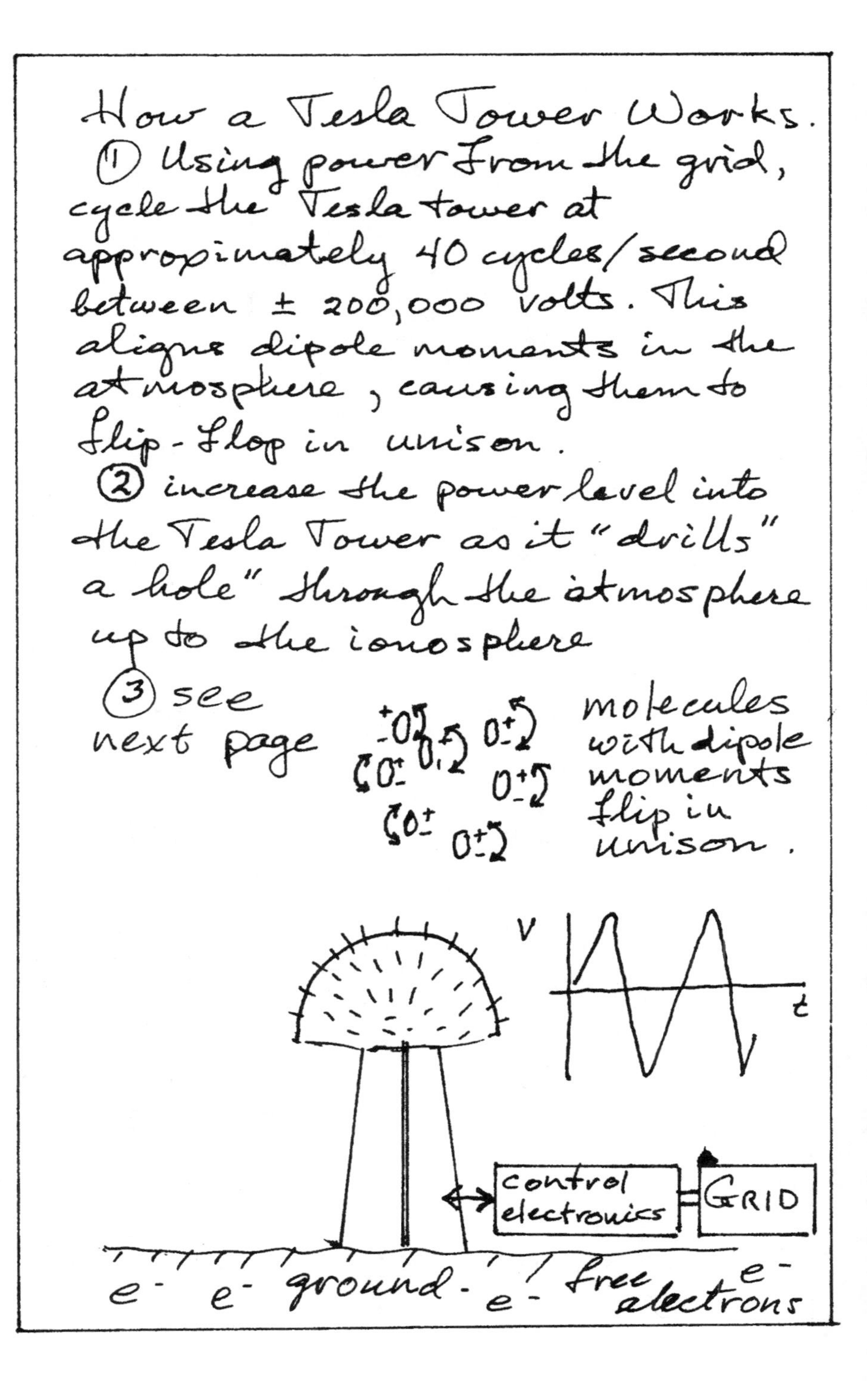

How a Tesla Tower Works.

(1) Using power from the grid, cycle the Tesla tower at appropimately 40 cycles/second between ± 200,000 volts. This aligns dipole moments in the atmosphere, causing them to flip-flop in unison.

(2) increase the power level into the Tesla Tower as it "drills" a hole" through the atmosphere up to the ionosphere

(3) see next page

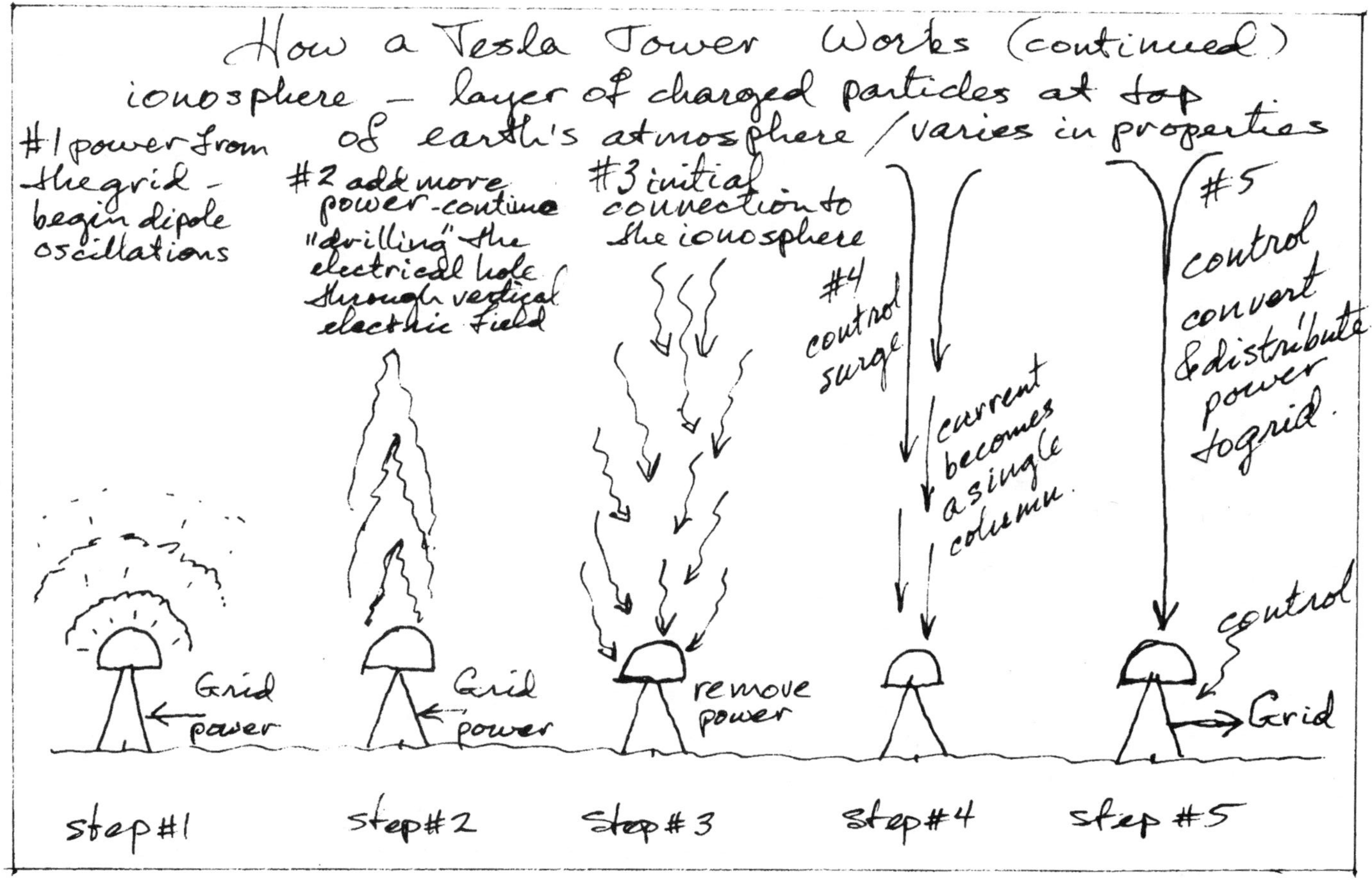

How a Tesla Tower Works (continued)

ionosphere – layer of charged particles at top of earth's atmosphere / varies in properties

#1 power from the grid – begin dipole oscillations

#2 add more power - continue "drilling" the electrical hole through vertical electric field

#3 initial connection to the ionosphere

#4 control surge

current becomes a single column.

#5 control convert & distribute power to grid.

Grid power

Grid power

remove power

control

Grid

step #1

step #2

step #3

step #4

step #5

Understand that these are extremely dangerous devices and should not be used or built by anyone without an extreme level of education and experience in dealing with high-voltage devices.

The damage done by the mishap experiment in Canada in August of 2003 which caused the Northeast power outage is a good example of how even trained scientists may not know what they are doing in the handling of such a dangerous devices. Since this is described in prior writings in Atlantis to Tesla book I will not reiterate the same material here. A future small book is planned along with detailed experimental evidence to show how a large tower can be used to supply free energy to a grid system in a commercial manner.

The local electric battery or LEB that drives the Tesla tower comes from the ionosphere to ground and although Tesla used his towers in the temperate mid latitudes, I have learned that there are better places to place these towers. Although much is known and I have gained a great deal of knowledge about these tremendously powerful devices, a good deal more study remains to be done as with any complex science project ... especially one that interacts with nature.

The final plates of this chapter shows the solar wind separating as it moves around the magnetic chief of earth. Eight local electric batteries are identified in this picture (see also Chapter 7 for additional diagrams). These are labeled Ve# where the # represents various electrical fields generated in the plasma environment around our earth-moon system. Spacecraft in fact have identified all of these in an around earth and around other planets. For exampleVe8 is the voltage generated between our moon and earth ... it is the same voltage that provides the energy source for the power of the incredible electric current that moves between Jupiter and its closest moon Io, and also causes the torus of that moon ... a cylindrical comet tail orbiting behind the moon as Io orbits Jupiter.

Our own moon has a tail of sodium and there are indications that there are other atomic and molecular species in the lunar tail also. This particular battery is very complicated as it depends on where the moon is relative to its magnetic field. The moon passes through our own comet tail that extends far to the non-sunlit side of earth.

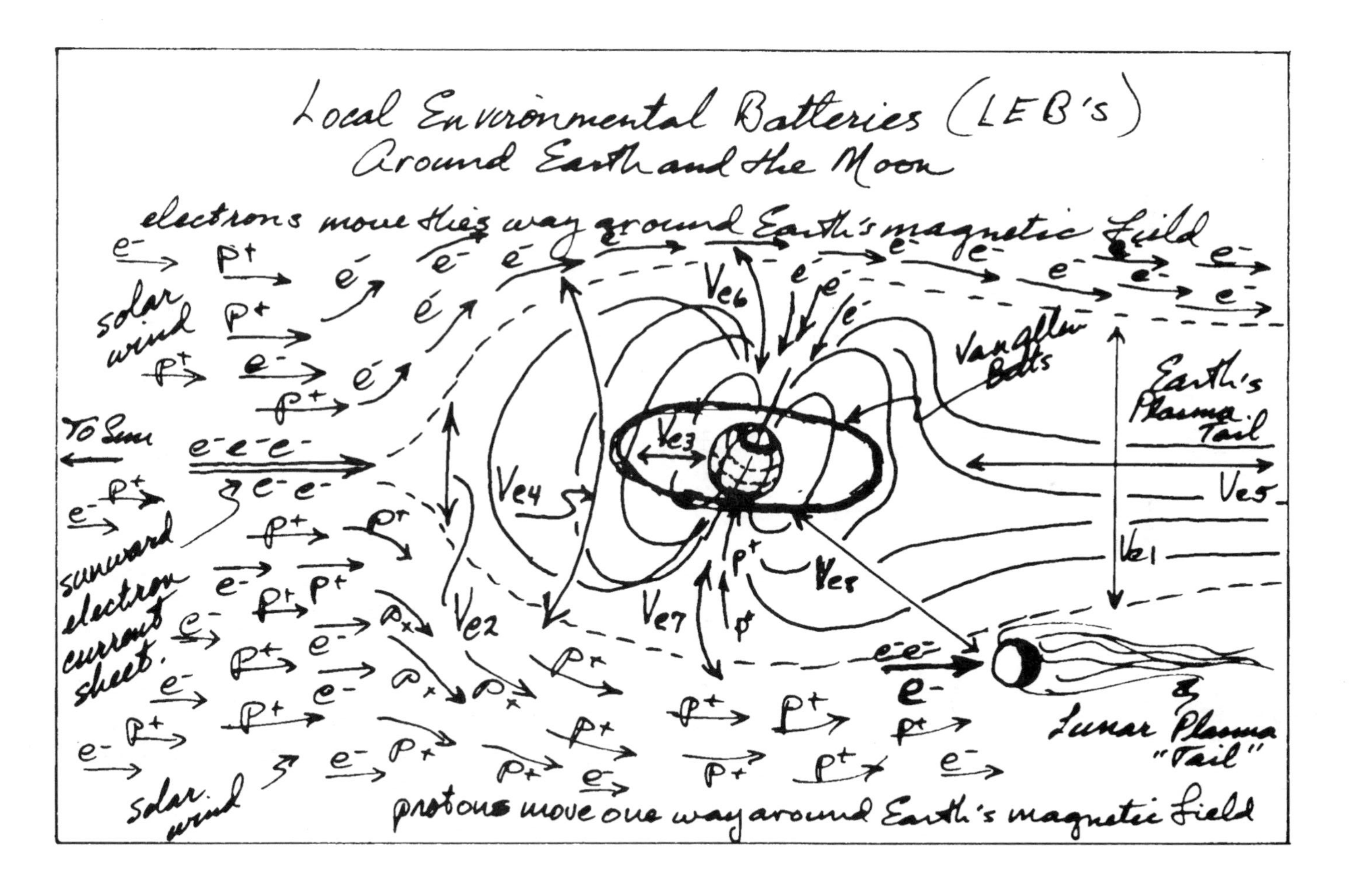
Local Environmental Batteries (LEB's)
Around Earth and the Moon
electrons move this way around Earth's magnetic field
solar wind
To Sun
sunward electron current sheet.
Van Allen Belts
Earth's Plasma Tail
Ve1
Ve2
Ve3
Ve4
Ve5
Ve6
Ve7
Ve8
Lunar Plasma "Tail"
solar wind
protons move one way around Earth's magnetic field

A number of days after full moon, the moon passes out of this magnetic tail, which is really a comet tail, and the moon develops its own electrical discharge of the solar capacitor as it is totally independent of earth's magnetic field at that point. As the moon moves between earth and the sun, it absorbs the solar wind and sun side electrons that arrive from the sun for a few days ... which causes the earth's protective magnetic field to relax and expand. As the moon moves out of the way after new moon, the sun side electron beam and the solar wind re-establish their connection to the Earth's magnetic field and come pounding in with a great impulse. This causes a compression of earth's magnetic field and is in fact one of the triggers that can generate large storms such as hurricanes and tornadoes and also generate a rapid increase in the size and effects of the other local electric batteries in and around our planet.

Ve1 is a cross potential of earth's plasma tale.

Ve2 is the electric field generated in as protons and electrons split into two different flows as they initially hit earth's magnetic field on to the sun side of earth.

Ve3 is the voltage generated between earth's upper ionosphere and the Van Allen belt. This is the region I identified early in my work as one of the main local earth electrical batteries and it was regarding this field that I told NASA scientists not to extend the tether out from the space shuttle in an experiment which attempted to generate electricity by dragging along a tether through Earth's magnetic field. They were totally oblivious to this LEB field and would not listen to what I told them. The end result was that even before the tether was even a few hundred yards out of the bay of the space shuttle (it was intended to be extended a few kilometers) an intense electrical discharge occurred that nearly blew one bay door off the space shuttle and took out all of its computer systems. One lowly backup computer remained which they used to limp back to Earth's surface. Not much was said about this within NASA and they never could figure out what happened. Needless to say, they never tried this experiment again.

Ve4 is an unusual electric field gradient that wraps around the plasma shield of earth over the north-south region and under the in an east-west direction relative to Earth's magnetic field.

Ve5 is a result of the solar electric field that extends radially outwards from the sun and through which Earth passes continually as we orbit the sun. Although this is seen as a local electric field near

Earth in the diagram, it literally extends to the far reaches of the solar system.

Ve6 is the electric field that follows magnetic field lines down to the polar regions of earth and is listed as Ve7 at the South Pole. These are opposite polarity with electrons coming in one side and protons coming in the other side to create the plasma in fact we call auroras. Once again the same fields exist on all the planets that have magnetic fields.

And once again the Ve8 is the electrical field that extends between the earth and our moon and is responsible for many of the magnetic effects of earth, including the explanation for the plasma magnetic field that had to exist as earth cooled its mantle and core through the Curie temperature to allow permanent magnetic fields to become locked into the solidifying iron and nickel. Without the moon, earth would have no permanent magnetic field except for that locked in the very innermost core, which was the original planetary seed as earth was a large comet during its years of formation many billions of years ago.

The entire topic of the local electric batteries could provide numerous university graduate level courses and so far I have identified approximately 17 such LEBs around earth. The number of LEBs continues to grow as do their complexity and ever-changing nature as well as the inter-relations and coupling between them and their relations to the geo-magnetic field. The Ve3 field is the one that could be used by spacecraft space stations to discharge this local capacitor down a long tube in the center of the space station whereby this would push against earth's magnetic field to move it out of and away from the vicinity of earth and into interplanetary space. This again would be the topic of almost an entire separate book.

XVI. BIBLICAL WEATHER

When Velikovsky wrote ***Worlds in Collision*** and his other three initial books and released them in the early 1950's, it seems odd in retrospect, in fact it seems down right strange .... the lack of response from the official seats of religion of the world. As with astronomers, one would think that religions would be the most interested in the findings that ancient texts from around the globe all said the same thing, and attributed the great flood to a major comet event that was associated with a newly formed planet ... Venus. After all comets were known to contain water and even though one might argue about theories such as the then termed "ice ball comet model" (the name this concept held in the 1950's) one might imagine that comets had something to do with this, and after all it was science that had to agree with religion and not visa versa (as was the mentality of the majority in the 1950's and especially with the papal and world religion leaders).

I recall as a child seeing Christian literature that showed earth being devastated by a comet looking thing coming from outer space and the warnings that if man did not pray that the earth would be destroyed ... and this time it would be by fire (as God had promised, according to teachings of the church, that He would never destroy the earth by flood again). The next time would be by fire.

We all feared the Armageddon of nuclear war with Russia in the 1950's, but every church goer had the message of fire and brimstone imprinted in his mind just the same as god had destroyed Sodom and Gomorra for their sinful ways. There is no doubt about this religious story from the Old Testament that this rain of destruction came from above.

The Old Testament is literally a genetic trail and a tale of destruction and the rebirth of man after a great conflagration, which included the flood at the time of Noah and the Exodus of the Israelites from bondage in Egypt concurrent with the 7 plagues. Is it not interesting that the Hopi Indians of North America similarly have the story of 7 stages of Earth Changes, yet there was certainly no connection between the ancients of North America and old Egypt (was there???) at least not according to standard knowledge?

What Velikovsky was teaching was that calendars had been reconstructed and the introduction of a new planet that had been a large comet was the cause. Velikovsky was not studying astronomy nor was he interested in creating a panic amongst astronomers. The truth was that in the 1950's astronomers did not have a coherent idea of what a comet was or how the solar system formed. In fact it was a knee jerk reaction that "solidified" the concepts we still hear repeated today ... the fact is that one would not get a Ph.D. today if they questioned the standard axioms. In this respect Astronomy is more like a religion than are most religions, as astronomers have accepted a host of ideas on faith and dismally little data yet pound heavy handedly on their ivory pulpits that comets are harmless little dirty snowballs and could never do what the ancients said as reiterated through the writings of Velikovsky.

What is interesting about the major religions is not what they said, but what they did *not* say. In 1995 when the Hale Bopp comet was inbound the Vatican put out a large sum of money and built a world class astronomical observatory in Arizona and staffed it with NASA astronomers. I knew some of the astronomers who worked there as they were from the University of Minnesota. They were 'comet specialists". The observatory was built to study the great comet Hale Bopp and we uncovered a memo directive from the Vatican to NASA ... the question they wanted answered was ..."is Hale-Bopp Wormwood?" Wormwood is the term in the old testament which literally translated as "poisoner of waters" and refers to the biblical planet that comes into the solar system to devastate earth on a regular basis. Possibly the organized religions had more interest in these issues than they ever admitted to the public.

The same comet (Hale Bopp) spawned an alleged suicide incident that later was shown to be a mass murder by government agents of a group that was organizing thousands of young people to go to a single location to meet the incoming "people" that they believed would be accompanying this great comet (actually a mid sized comet with a nucleus about the size of our moon). The "Heaven's Gate" suicide was not a suicide at all, but a elimination of a group that was leaving society as an inbound large object drew their attention from the controllers. This is an ever present theme throughout this book and it is central to understanding what is going on in the world today as world leaders abscond with vast resources and create vast cave cities into which they will retreat when the devastation of earth ensues ... leaving the unsuspecting public out to dry. The question that is always asked of me is WHEN???? Once again there is no definitive dates of any object coming into the solar system as this book goes to press and even if an exact location and orbit were known ... the orbits of the large comets change drastically due to the tail drag and therefore, as with the medium comet Hale Bopp, the orbit is simply not predictable.

In the Sermon on the Mount Christ was asked this same question and he was educated in these issues ... he stated clearly that "of this time no man knows the date or time" and gives a story that there will be people going about their daily business and it will in a sense come as a total surprise to inhabitants of earth. He also notes that there will be false prophets who will come to lead you astray and God knows we have seen our share of these imposters in the last few years.

The Sermon on the Mount is most interesting, impressive and final of all the sermons and was given to the largest number of people. Interestingly also this is what spawned the denouncement by the roman authorities as the people were walking off their jobs and following a man who was saying they should spend time worshipping their creator and not the roman empire. Today the story remains the same and the same group of insecure leaders are using the same age old techniques to control the public ... and they fear the same issues as in those historical times.

Christ was not the only prophet that talked about these issues and the old texts have been taken off the market ... and any semblance of these ancient stories of the comets that devastated earth have been removed. The greatest part that was removed was the part that gives man a true picture of his history. Any leader knows that if you want to neutralize a civilization you have to remove their history and connection to that history. This was used by the white man to destroy the native Americans ... this was a way of life that they are struggling to regain today.

Likewise the modern Bibles have had all remnants of the ancient devastations removed. This is where the ***Kolbrin***, the ancient texts taken from old Rome by Joseph to Scotland and which still exists today (as noted in my past writings), is a text which contains the ancient writings. There is no question that the ancient destruction and subsequent weather was a result of the comets (these were the HUGE comets talked of by the ancient and there were at times multiple comets in the sky at once). It is clear that the comets did not collide with earth but created the effects by "action at a distance" as described in previous chapters. There is evidence that the earth's atmosphere prior to this event was much thicker and contained more moisture and this supported the worldwide lush "Garden of Eden". None of this will be known until the ancient books are released from their secret storage locations in the basement of the Vatican. Is it not interesting that the organization that built the observatory in Arizona and paid NASA to search for Wormwood (and subsequently built two more world class observatories ... one in South America and the other in Antarctica) is harboring the information that would connect the masses to its true past?

The ***Kolbrin*** has extensive references to these ancient events, but there is only a room here to allow a few short quotes.

" It is known, and the story comes down from ancient times, that there was not one creation but two, the creation and a recreation. It is a fact known to the wise that the earth was utterly destroyed once then reborn on a second wheel of creation. At the time of the great distruction of earth, God caused a dragon from out of heaven to come and encompass her about. The dragon was frightful to behold, it lashed its tail, it breathed out fire and hot coals, and a great catastrophe was inflicted upon mankind. The body of the dragon was wreathed in a cold bright light and beneath on the belly, was a ruddy hued glow, while behind it trailed a flowing tail of smoke. It spewed out cinders and hot stones and its breath was foul and stenchful, poisoning the nostrils of men. Its passage caused great thundering and lightnings to rend the thick darkened sky, all heaven and earth being made hot. This seas were loosened from their cradles and rose up, pouring across the land. There was an awful, shrilling trumpeting which outpowered even the howling of the unleashed winds. Men, stricken with terror, went mad at the awful site in the heavens. They were loosened from their senses and dashed about, crazed, not knowing what they did. The breath was sucked from their bodies and they were burnt with a strange ash. Then this passed, leaving earth enwrapped within a dark and glowing mantle which was ruddily lit up inside. The bowels of the earth were torn open in a great writhing upheaval and the howling whirlwind rent the mountains apart. The wrath of the sky monster was loosened in the heavens. It lashed about in flaming furry, roaring like a thousand thunders; it poured down fiery distruction amid a welter of thick black blood. So awesome was the fearfully aspected thing that the memory mercifully departed from man, his thoughts were smothered under a cloud of forgetfulness. ... the first sky monster was joined by another which swallowed the tale of the one going before, but the two could not be seen at once. The sky monsters reigned and raged above the earth, doing battle to possessive it, but the many bladed sort of God cut them in pieces, and their falling bodies enlarged the land and the sea. In this manner the first earth was destroyed by calamity descending from out of the skies. The vaults of heaven had opened to bring forth monsters more fearsome than any that ever haunted the uneasy dreams of men. Men and their dwelling places were gone, only sky boulders and red earth remained where once they were, but amidst all the desolation a few survived, for man is not easily destroyed. They crept out from caves and came down from the mountainsides. Their eyes were wild and their limbs trembled, and their bodies shook and their bodies lacked control. ... The earth, only true alter of God, had offered up a sacrifice of life and sorrow to atone for the sins of mankind. Man had not sinned in deed but in the things he had failed to do. Man suffers not only for what he does but for what he fails to do. He is not chastised for making mistakes but for failing to recognize and rectify them."

The tale of destruction continues to talk about the great flood, the endless pouring of water in such quantity that the entire earth was flooded ... once again this coming in from the comet that was encircling the earth. Remember that the flood from above is distinct and separate from the tidal bulges of the oceans that were said to have been "carried on the backs of the comets" ... the ancients way of saying the comets caused the oceans to rise up and overflow the land. This was not the same as the flood waters that came from the sky and this is a very important point that you read in the ancient writings. This is why it is essential as Velikovsky did to return to the original texts as the modern "scholars" have edited and changed and removed many parts to the point that they are not recognizable. There was also more than one large comet, a topic which I have talked about extensively on radio shows and will be an ongoing topic of my work.

To the ancient scholars this catastrophe was part of their knowledge base yet they had no science to corroborate what was really happening any more than the Caribbean native Indians had a scientific knowledge of the god they called HURICAN (the base word for our modern derivation "hurricane").

The topic of biblical weather may become another book in due time as the subject is so vast that it would take a long time to treat each line of text with the emphasis that they deserve and to interpret the passages in terms of the plasma discharge comet model and the electrical understanding of the solar system.

The chapter on Action at a Distance shows a diagram of a comet approaching the earth but with the earth still exterior to the comet tail. As the earth would enter the comet tail all of the pollution in the comet tail would begin pouring into earth's upper atmosphere including the hydrocarbons (oils of burning naphtha) and would be ignited by the lightning and burning meteor streams (the sky boulders). Everything that the ancients talk about is perfectly understandable from a theoretical point of view of a large highly energetic comet raging near the earth as it discharges the solar capacitor. If you were of the incorrect opinion that comets were little harmless dirty snow balls and you had spent your life getting a PhD, writing text books and publishing papers for NASA, one can see the reason for the resistance at the public finding out that you have no clue what is really going on.

At this point I want everyone to read the works of Velikovsky with the new understanding that he was totally correct regarding his interpretation of ancient texts and that there is a sound theoretical explanation for all that he discusses. Remember he was studying calendars and not astronomy. His goal was the reconstruction of ancient calendars based on worldwide events that could produce a standard chronology of history around the globe for the ancient cultures. In doing so he discovered the recurring tale of the Venus event and this lead him to understand the destruction of the comet encounters with earth and also Mars. Then read the passages relating to the flood and the Sermon on the Mount in the New Testament or the other references listed in the last appendix of this book. These events did happen and were the result of a celestial events ... it has happened in the past and it will happen again in the future ... we just do not know when.

XVII. PREDICTING WEATHER AND STORMS

It has been many years since I first publicly predicted the storm system that spawned Hurricane Floyd and its four companion hurricanes of September of 1999. That prediction was made in May of that year and printed on the Millennium Group Home page. The investigation was prompted by what was actually a bogus government plant that a small comet called Comet Lee would be a harbinger of doom. It was then that I had a great deal of effort to keep the internet spin-masters from causing another misinformation campaign. Comet Lee's orbital path was to come up and behind earth but clearly posed no collision threat to earth. The government spin agents were doing their best to create a bogus story and suck me into buying it and broadcasting it. I did my own orbital analysis and the small Comet Lee posed no collision threat to earth, HOWEVER in their ignorance (which is so typical of the government disinformation crew) they got me looking at the other electrical conditions of the solar system.

The conditions of the electrical alignments of that particular prediction are described in detail in the first book of this series so I will not repeat them here. In short, Comet Lee was the "spark plug" so to speak that was needed to join all the other electrical alignments of planets and our moon and on the date I predicted in May of 1999 for the following fall ... September 6, 1999 ... Hurricane Floyd erupted in the Atlantic with four others along with a host of other storms around the globe. If you look on the internet today NASA still has their disinformation program displayed claiming that I stated that Comet Lee would collide with earth when in fact it was the government spin agents who tried desperately to make that statement in the face of my correct to the minute hurricane predictions.

I had worked with the Russians as described in a later chapter and I had honed my theoretical concepts to understand the true causes of weather to include the electrical alignments of the planets, moons, and comets and also included the identification of the electrical return current sheet of August. I learned when these would and would not be factors.

I also learned how to take into account the underwater topography and its influence on tropical storms. Included on the next page is a map of the Caribbean with the islands listed and the underwater topography offshore. One notices the incredible continental shelves surrounding Florida and stretching down into the Bahamas and north of the island of Cuba. A similar shelf extends out from the Yucatan in Mexico into the Gulf of Mexico and eastward into the Caribbean attaching the Yucatan and Cuba area with Florida. There are numerous other ridges and plateaus just barely under the surface of the water throughout Caribbean all the way down to Venezuela. When storms move across the Atlantic and approach the Eastern Antilles islands they begin to ground out and this alters their path and changes their storm profiles. I have seen storms come across the northern coast of Venezuela and lose almost half of the storm to the shoals and shallow regions north of Venezuela, and watched hurricanes come up through the channel between Mexico and Cuba and once again have part of the storm depleted as that part of the storm shorts out to the shallow ocean beds on that continental shelf. Similarly up the East Coast of Florida many times hurricanes turn and moved northwards as they catch the Continental shelf that lies a few hundred miles offshore to the east of Florida. Many times hurricanes will move up through the central Atlantic into colder Watters (where hurricanes should not even exist according to the warm water theory of hurricane formation) but they will follow the mid-Atlantic Ridge northwards time and time again.

Predicting storms has become more than a hobby in the background of my other work. Above my desk is a map of the entire world including the ocean floor. On the other desk is a globe of the world. I refer to these continually as I watch storm systems react to the electrical conditions of the plasma environment around earth and move over the ocean surface. There are times that I think I know and understand the underwater ocean topography better than I do the land topography. I've even studied the weather of the ancient world based on the old polar locations of the north and south pole prior to the last pole shift.

I also monitor the many satellites and solar ground stations that provide information on a daily basis of the conditions at the sun and conditions at the earth. It generally takes three to four days for

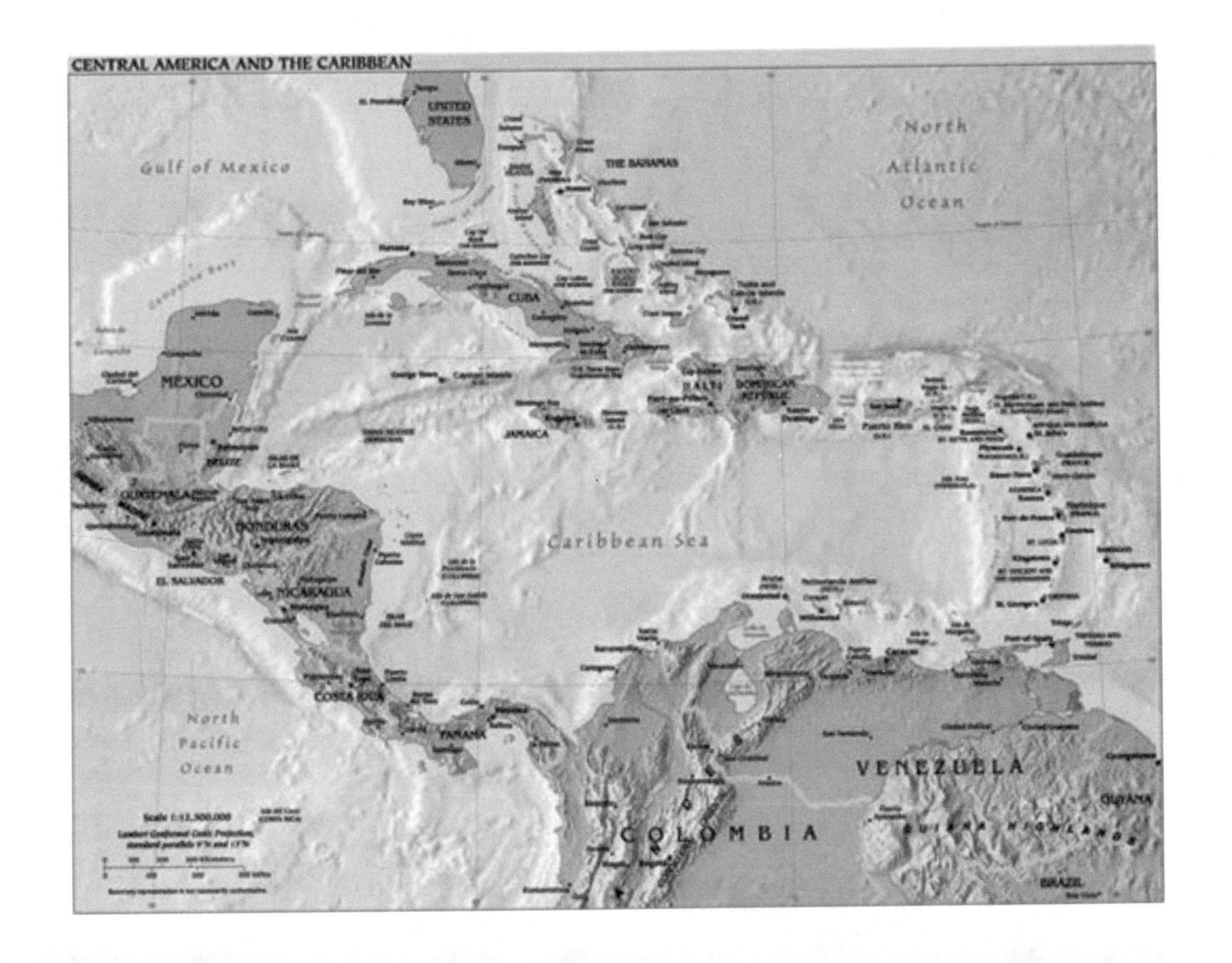

CENTRAL AMERICA AND THE CARIBBEAN
North Atlantic Ocean
Gulf of Mexico
Caribbean Sea
North Pacific Ocean
UNITED STATES
THE BAHAMAS
CUBA
JAMAICA
HAITI
DOMINICAN REPUBLIC
MEXICO
BELIZE
GUATEMALA
HONDURAS
EL SALVADOR
NICARAGUA
COSTA RICA
PANAMA
VENEZUELA
COLOMBIA
GUYANA
BRAZIL

solar weather conditions to reach earth but during times of peak flaring the energy can sometimes reach earth in a matter of eight minutes, coming to us at the speed of light as with cosmic ray flares (see the very last pages of the Atlantis to Tesla the book for details).

The following two charts are commonly used daily and come from the SOHO satellite that monitors solar conditions 24 hours a day (unless NASA turns it off when they don't want us to see what it sees). The following examples are taken from August 31, 2004 ... notice that there is a small flare arriving at earth between August 30 and 31st as indicated by the spike on the proton data and the electron and Kp index data which is a measure of magnetic storm disturbance arriving in the solar wind.

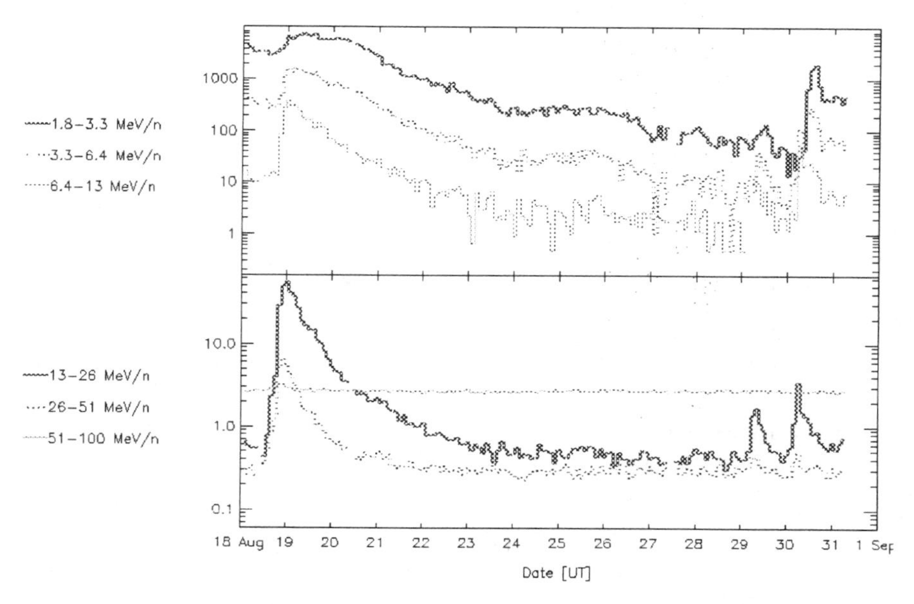

This is a small flare but other conditions caused the satellite itself react to this just as a comet would discharge the nonuniform plasma that surrounds the sun. Looking on the other chart one can see the electron counts dipping dramatically while the estimated Kp index on the bottom chart moves up into what we call the red region (darker and taller bars on the chart). This is a good example where the electron count is dropping at the detector on the spacecraft while the actual electron count in the spacecraft vicinity is going up. This apparent

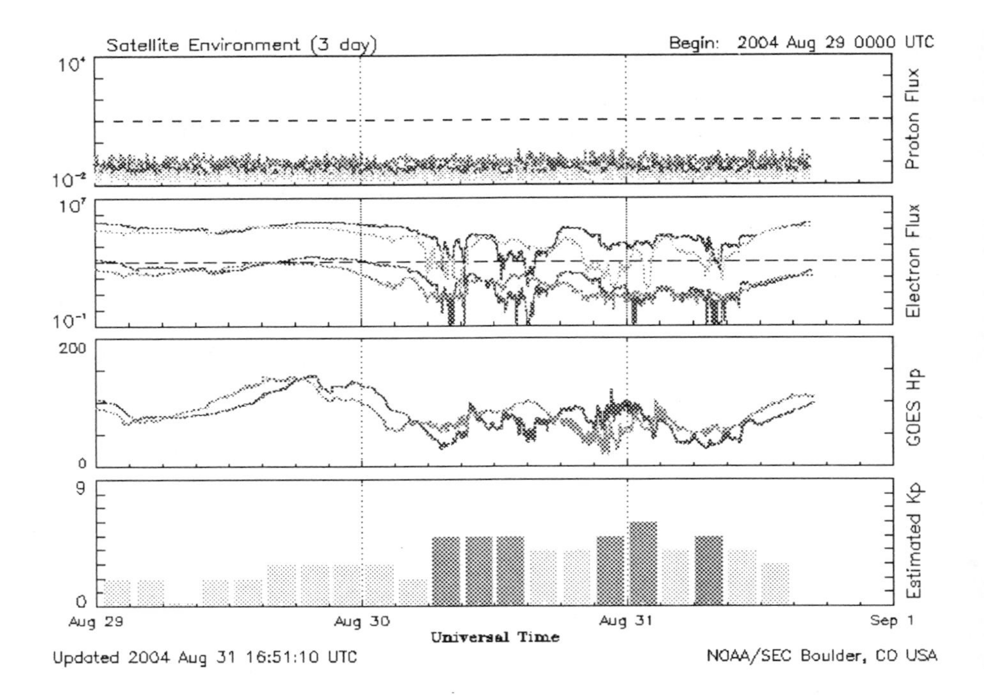

contradiction is due to the fact that the spacecraft charges in response to the flow of electrons. So traditionally trained scientists would read the electron counts literally and state that electron counts are going down when in reality the opposite is true. In the Kp index which is a measure of magnetic field disturbance is really responding to local conditions actually caused by the spacecraft itself and may have very little to do with the actual conditions in the solar wind. Once again, the spacecraft are incorrectly designed for the task that they are meant to do

Around the August 27, 2003 time frame I was on many radio shows as guest talking about what then was a very famous prediction once again made the previous spring. Note that I don't do hurricane predictions as a norm because weather prediction is difficult and there are so many factors, but in this case the number of factors pointing to storm conditions to erupt on that day were so overwhelming that I made another public statement much like the prediction of Comet Lee and hurricane Floyd back in 1999. I had charted out all the electrical alignments of that year and the August 27 alignment was by far the most striking. There was a new moon passing, earth and Mars were at closest approach and perfectly aligned with the sun and these alignments all sat within the August return current sheet, which is a major factor in hurricane development.

The particular understanding that the new moon would trigger the hurricane conditions is already talked about in previous chapters. It moves in front of the earth blocking the electron beam that normally attaches to earth's polar regions, and the moon blocks this along with the solar wind (the moon in the sense becomes a comet in front of the earth blocking the solar conditions). This allows earth's protective magnetic plasma sheath to expand. As the moon moves out of the way, the electron beam re-attaches with earth ... and the solar wind comes pounding in to compress earth's magnetic field. There is a cross compression of the magnetic field also which compresses the local electric batteries, forcing the expanded conditions of Earth's ionosphere to move closer to earth. These are the conditions that drive the storms. So it was clear that on August 27 the moon passing out of new moon phase would trigger the conditions on earth for severe storm development, and prior to that there would be none.

I could see all of this happening and also knew that we were in a condition of extreme energy within the solar system so the effect would be even more exaggerated than normal. So I made the prediction, placed it on my web site and broadcast it on the standard radio shows where I am a regular guest.

I recall the laughter and thunder from the standard scientific community as they watched the earth on August 26 with virtually nothing happening in the way of storms around the earth, not a single storm to be had. Somewhere around midnight all hell broke loose and over 60 topical storms formed around equatorial band of Earth in a matter of hours including four hurricanes in the Atlantic Ocean alone. The silence from the standard scientific community was deafening. A good deal of information regarding this time frame can be found on my web sight and archived radio shows.

In retrospect, I have gone back to many previous storms, including the famous "Perfect Storm" which was actually a series of three storms which joined together to make an incredibly large hurricane in the north Atlantic (something that is not supposed to happen according to the warm water theory hurricane formation). According to the standard meteorological theory regarding hurricanes they are supposed to dissipate when they hit cold water since there would be nothing to feed them energy. So how could we have a perfect storm off the coast of Nova Scotia in early November in the freezing waters of the north Atlantic? Oddly enough, all three of the storms that combined to make that incredibly large storm formed over land, something else that should not happen. One of the storms came through the northern states of the United States and blanketed the north with 3 feet of snow one day and another 3 feet the next day before it moved out into the Atlantic Ocean as one of the three storms. An October hurricane over land is what it was a true "himmicane". The second storm came through the Southern Appalachian region of the United States and moved northwards up the Eastern Seaboard states of the United States, once again forming over land before passing into the Atlantic as the second full-blown hurricane. The third hurricane came up the coastline and should have never continued to become the third hurricane in the frigid north Atlantic ... but it did.

In a previous chapter are pictures of a hurricane that moved up the West Coast of Washington state in March of 1999 while at the same time another hurricane raged off the Aleutian islands in the Bering straight between Alaska in Russia. Another picture shows a hurricane on Mars near its polar cap and there are no oceans at all on Mars to feed that hurricane. Clearly hurricanes have nothing to do with warm water, but are driven by the electrical conditions that come down from the ionosphere which are ultimately driven by the solar electric field.

NASA has a program called the Sun Earth Connection, which has just begun asking the questions that I already had answers to long ago. The quest to understand weather prediction is more than just bragging rights over a theory nor a single prediction. It is essential for the well being of hundreds of millions of people who live in the topical regions of the world and whose lives are completely destroyed every time one of these monster storms passes through.

The same is true of tornadoes which form in exactly the same manner as hurricanes when electrical currents passing up vertical columns connect to earth and create the suction and vortex motion ... like a hurricane, a tornado is a cosmically driven vacuum cleaner ... but with the winds possibly in excess of 500 mph. Hurricanes spawn tornadoes and many times the tornadoes cause the most severe damage leveling in entire housing districts as they go. With the culmination of this book my newer research efforts will be to implement what I've learned to help the poor people of the world.

XVIII. WILL MAN SURVIVE?

The rules of nature are quite simple, and in the case of survival as an intelligent species (one that is capable of altering and controlling its environment) the rule of ultimate survival is clear and very simple.

As a species ... collectively ... if you do not use the time and resources allotted to you to gain access to outer space and gain the knowledge to survive ... you will be doomed to extinction.

This clearly leads to some secondary basic rules of nature regarding the use of time and resources.

Petty wars and the use of resources to fight these wars can have only one possible result ... and nature in its own time and manner will repay those species ... collectively ... who fail to control their leaders who promote these wars.

If there is a smaller group that attempts to use the resources of the many to save their own few and selective hides ... these especially will be doomed to die a most lonesome and hideous demise.

The successful species that eventually will populate the stars will not allow those "unsuccessful" species to enter their hard-earned space and bring their petty wars and selfish ways into the cosmos. This is called the "rule of survival of the successful" ... and is universally understood and commissioned to be executed upon those who fail at the first three rules.

These rules are stated to be inherent and self-evident. As a species we have failed. There are no less that 54 wars ongoing at the time of this writing. World leaders are out of control. As an observer of the Sun and comets, and a person with inside contacts to very high levels of the intelligence agencies, I will say that the writing has been on the wall for some time and there is little doubt that the leaders in these intelligence communities have been warned. Let the reader decide ... based on the inherent rules of survival ... will man survive?

XIX. LIVING WITH A STAR – CAN MAN SURVIVE IN OUTER SPACE

It has been speculated that man is alone in the universe and standard astronomers have pooh pooh-ed the idea of "extra-terrestrials" and in fact have tried to make it into a crazy issue. The sidelining of this issue is once again most bizarre coming from the professional class that is commissioned to study the stars and the universe ... the professional astronomers. The topic of "crazy alien" and the people who believe in them is another craftily designed disinformation program that has its roots in pre-world war Germany. The German rocket scientists that came to this country talked about how the "alien issue" would be manipulated to control public agendas.

This is but another example of how man has distorted what he really needs to be doing ... and that is reaching into the heavens with the proper attitude and for the correct reasons. Our space program is not one of going into space, but one of how to make money in corporations out of the appearance of going into space. Remember that we have only had about 300 astronauts in outer space since the entire "space program" since NASA began. This is hardly what one could call impressive.

Today there is a major program within NASA called ***Living With A Star*** which has thousands of scientists working on hundreds of funded programs ... the main thrust is to try to figure out how to get through the Van Allen radiation belts that circle our planet. This begs the question ... If this were not such a problem in 1969 when NASA sent a man to the moon in the Apollo Program, then why is it such a problem now? The size and scope of the Living With A Star project actually exceeds the World War II Manhattan Project.

The following photo is of a galaxy rich region of the near universe. With billions of stars in the countless galaxies and considering that we have had just a few short decades where we knew that any of this even existed, is it not a bit presumptuous for astronomers to even hint at knowing where all of this came from let alone the exact time it may have formed ????

The need to have a standard answer that everyone agrees on is absurd at this point in the game. For a small group to set themselves up as the all-knowing authorities is beyond pompous. And to shield themselves from the rest of scientists who do not agree with the so-called "Big Bang", for example, is just another example of how quickly power groups move to seize power and control within the government supported scientific monopoly.

The point of all of this is that this begs the question ... is man ready for outer space? ... or better yet ... is outer space ready for man? ... with his petty personality insecurities? Is outer space ready for a race that has trashed its own house and then intends to take the systems that spawned and nurtured that greed into three-dimensional space to do the same thing there for eternity?

Has man shown that he can elect officials who have the common interest in mind and who can resolve issues without pulling out weapons? Have the leaders shown that they can give up their own worldly possessions to dedicate their efforts to making a better world, or have they used their positions to harbor power and rake in more profits for their friends and business associates?

If you were a race of beings watching from afar the activities of the inhabitants of earth would you allow them off into your nice quiet universe? I fear the answer is a resounding ***NO!!!!***

Are races out there at this moment moving a giant asteroid with our name on it into an orbit that will shunt our progress and send us hurtling back to the cave ages??? Are they chuckling to themselves as earth based scientists put together feeble rocket and jet propelled systems of warfare in hopes of fighting these people who have been space faring for possibly millions of years and have seen thousands of misguided species come and go like flashes in the proverbial pan?

Man is besieged by natural disasters, but his biggest disaster may very well be his own greed and self-serving interests. Are there some who have learned these lessons but are powerless in the current government schemes where the powerful are daily consuming more human rights along with the resources they consume for warfare and corporate profits?

Man is at the crossroads and that is why I selected that phrase for the title of my weekly radio show (*The James McCanney Science Hour – At the Corssroads*)and that is how I end every show. Because as we see each passing week and the ongoing march of man on a crash course to disaster, we in fact are at the serious crossroads on many, many issues. Clearly the leaders are not in step with the program and they are apparently of the idea that we can continue down this road unabated for the next 50 years. It simply will not last that long.

I often state that "time is our most important resource" and this is because we are trapped into the illusion that things will continue on forever as they are right now. Keeping the truth of the this simple fact from the public with a constant barrage of interruptions and diversions is the aim of the government sponsored disinformation crews that span nearly every topic known to man. Many of them have Ph.D.'s in disinformation ... or the art of turning a story around to say exactly the opposite and to get at least 95% of the public to believe it.

Surviving in outer space likewise has many facets, only one of which is the technical side of learning how to endure the rigors of space. When man conquered the old west it was because the pioneers as individuals set out en mass and learned by doing. The belief that we can pay huge amounts of money to an agency that then feeds this to rich CEOs sitting in offices in California and these hire thousands of engineers and scientists who likewise work in California or Texas laboratories to think of what we should do to be in space is absurd to the Nth degree. They expect that by this method somehow we are going to conquer space???? As a comedian once said ... GET SERIOUS !!!

I have stated that the Chinese are much better suited to go into space and endure as they live in a society where it is understood that every person must do their part. Also the Chinese have a surplus of people and they have always been good at copying and expanding on the innovation of others. Once the Chinese learn the art of moving large numbers of people into space the western cultures will only then realize that they had lost the "space race" before it ever started. This is because we did not change the culture of space along with the needs of space and have this directed by people who understand these principles rather that Presidents and CEO's who have political and financial agendas to follow.

Many will read this with their mouths open wondering what on earth I am talking about and imagining that good ole' western technology and innovation will prevail as it has in the past ... space is different ...

XX. SMALL, MEDIUM AND LARGE COMETS

I cannot imagine a more bizarre situation than that which exists today with the issue of comets and the adherence by astronomers to the obviously incorrect dirty snowball comet model. It becomes even more bizarre when one sees the amount of data that has to be hidden to prop up this charade. The high temperatures of comet nuclei and the photos prove that there are no ices or snow and even if you could pile large heaps of snow on one of these … the solid water would sublimate in a matter of hours and could certainly never last for days let alone years or longer … and most certainly not 4.5 billion years as traditional theory proclaims.

The large moons of Jupiter have icy sheaths that would create the largest comets one could imagine yet they orbit Jupiter totally exposed to the solar wind and radiation that supposedly creates comets according to the dirty snow ball comet model. How can such a contradiction be ignored?

The current chapter was necessary for two reasons … the first because mainstream astronomers still hold that all comets are small and that a giant comet might be 40 kilometers across which is the size of a small asteroid (comets can be planet sized or larger and there is no limitation on size with the Plasma Discharge Comet Model) … the second is to clarify the real issues based on the Plasma Discharge Comet Model and to identify what one might see and experience if any one of these would come by earth or through our solar system … the small, medium and large comets will act quite differently and affect earth differently even though the basic concept … the discharge of the solar capacitor is the same for all … it is a matter of scale.

I have stated specifically that the large comets may become planets if they meet specific conditions, but not all comets become planets and although this has been stated many times, it is good to reiterate it here for the point of clarification. The small comets act differently than the medium sized comets that may have a nucleus the size of our moon. The huge comets such as recounted by the ancients are another story … these are capable of discharging the solar capacitor all the way to Pluto or beyond. I truly hope we never see such a comet to prove a point, but the ancients saw and experienced them and Earth and the other planets hold the scars to prove that they have come by in the past.

The small comets that space probes have approached and photographed are the baby comets of the solar system. Even though their tales may be 100 million miles long, their overall energy would be considered local. From past experience with Comet Lee, it produced in conjunction with other electrical alignments a series of storms, which we considered dangerous and damaging on earth. When earth passed through the tail of Comet Halley in 1910 astronomers claimed that nothing happened to earth. But remember that we had no earth monitoring satellites and if large storms were generated in the Pacific Ocean or far out to sea none of this would have made the history books. I do recall reading accounts of people seeing atmospheric glowing during the passage of Comet Halley so I do question astronomers story that nothing happened. It would be interesting to see the same encounter today with the dozens of earth monitoring satellites all looking at earth and the comet is the encounter transpired.

In many cases it is impossible to tell the true size of the comet nucleus because it is shrouded in the coma which many times can be from 100,000 to many millions of miles in diameter. When Comet Hale-Bopp was first discovered astronomers said that its nucleus was over 1000 miles in diameter. Soon this was reduced to about a hundred miles and eventually down to about 40 miles in diameter. Clearly there was some hocus pocus going on what the data. The temperature of the nucleus of this comet was also measured using the very large array radio telescope and all we know is that the temperature was extremely high and that data is classified.

The first picture is of Comet Arend Roland in May 1957 with its bright sunlight spike that lasted for over seven days during its passage by earth. Remember that in 1957 astronomers were keenly aware of Velikovsky in his claim of electrical comets that lit up the sky. An excuse was made for why this comet had the extension in the sunlit direction ... astronomers claimed this was an optical illusion. That argument propagated through textbooks and journal articles for decades until I pointed out that the view of the extension could not possibly allow it to be in the tail direction as astronomers claimed (that is they claimed that you are seeing a thin type II tail which always points perfectly in the anti-sun direction). Only under a very brief and exclusive viewing conditions could such a claim be made, however the sunward spike of Arend Roland lasted for a period of seven days. In spite of this fact, never has there been a single professional astronomer who questioned this claim and actually looked at the orbit of Arend Roland until I finally pointed out the flaw in the standard argument.

In May of 2004 I organized a worldwide amateur astronomical viewing session of two comets, both of which would align with solar system planets and both which would at that very same time present perfect broadside views of the comets. My prediction was at least one of these comets would generate a sunward spike which is a predicted effect of the Plasma Discharge Comet Model. To my delight and surprise … all of the comets performed on queue as expected and we were blessed with a third comet called Comet Bradfield which added a third observable comet which produced the best sunward spike of all. Amateurs from around the world joined to look at the comets and I created a web page specifically designed to explain what to look for and where and when. I also offered a $1000 prize for the best photo, only to find that my e-mail was being blocked and the prize contestants were be notified and harassed. The entry pictures that did make it through were one day surgically removed from my web site and I was never able to contact anyone regarding this again. To add insult to injury, these agents began interfering with this process also by taking my web mail address and were sending out solicitations for pornographic sites using my e-mail address. These are your tax dollars at work, protecting NASA scientists. The two comets were named C/2002/T7 and C/2001/Q4.

The following two pictures show NASA artistic conceptions of a dirty snowball comet nucleus. One can see in both cases large amounts of snowing material sitting on what appears to be a loose composite collection of material with snow blasting off the comets surface allegedly to create the comet coma and tail.

Every time NASA comes out with a new comet project it is rather comical to see the artist conception with less and less snow on the nucleus until lately there appears to be none at all ... yet comets are still stated to be dirty snowballs ... the snowiest artists conception was before the Comet Halley flyby when it was believed that comets were pure white and nearly 100% snow .

The next two pictures are of the hot dry rocks that are the comet nuclei of comets Borrelly and Wild II.

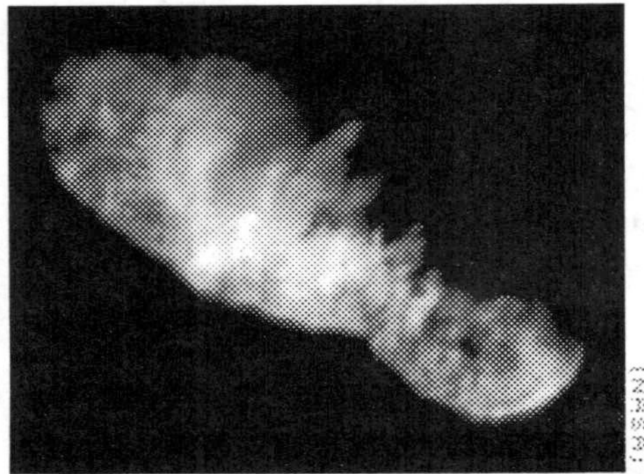

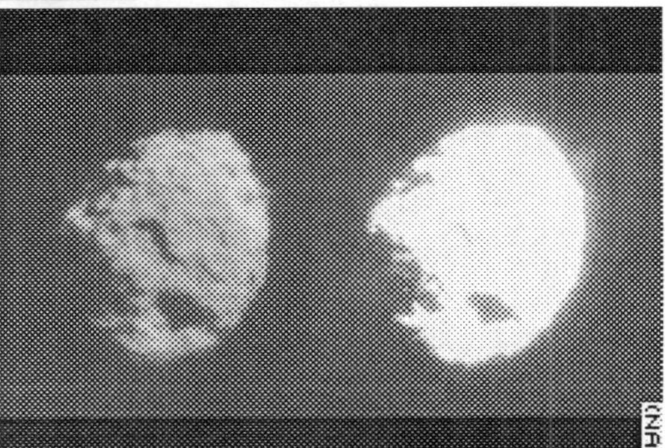

Although both are super-enhanced with computer imaging they have been measured to be the blackest objects in the solar system, blacker than a piece of charcoal and with extremely high temperatures. Rather than having me talk about the data results, I'll quote directly from the NASA news releases that talked about the discovery that comets have no water or ice on their surface and that the temperatures are hot enough to boil water at atmospheric temperatures ... yet scientists still maintain that these are dirty snowballs. Here is the news release quote from April 5, 2002 regarding Comet Borrelly ...

NASA Spacecraft Finds Comet Has Hot, Dry Surface
News release April 2, 2002

Comets are sometimes described as "dirty snowballs", but a close fly by of one of the NASA is Deep Space One spacecraft last fall detected no frozen water on its surface. "The spectrum suggest that the surface is hot and dry it is surprising that we saw no traces of water or ice," said ... the lead author for a report on the Borrelly flyby results appearing in the online edition of the journal Science.

.....

"Comet Borrelly is in the inner solar system right now, and it is hot, between 26 and 71°C (80 and 161°F), so anyone ice on the surface could change quickly to a gas" ... " as the components evaporate they leave behind a crust, like the crust left behind by dirty snow."

"Borrelly is unusually black for an object in the inner solar system. The comets surface is about as dark as a block of photocopy toner, possibly the darkest surface in the solar system."

"...Borrelly's old, mottled terrain with dark and very dark spots -- different shades of black -- are apparently inactive. Ground-based observations estimated that 90% of Borrelly's surface might be inactive, and the observations taken by deep space one show that this is indeed true."

Although astronomers have attempted to reconcile this information with a dirty snowball comet model full of fluffy white snow, the temperatures prove that there could never be any ice on this object or inside of it. The 161°F or even the conservative estimate of 80°F would not allow water ice or snow to exist even a split second in or near this nucleus. As already discussed, at this temperature within Earth's atmosphere water is nearly at the boiling point, however in outer space the boiling point of water is far below this temperature. If there were water inside the nucleus it would be exploding like a pressure cooker with a stopped cap and outlet. Astronomers see activity around the nucleus but this is due to material being attracted into the nucleus by electrical forces. The photo enhancements would be the equivalent of taking a picture of a blackboard and enhancing it to the point that it is white with white rays of light coming off of it. The black tarry surface was literally that, black hyrocarbons baked onto the surface by the heat of the electron beam that comes from the sunward side.

The Giotto spacecraft visiting Comet Halley in 1986 directly detected the electron beam to the sunward side of the comet nucleus. Literally every aspect of the plasma discharge model for comets has been confirmed. Literally every aspect of the dirty snowball comet model has been disproven by direct observation, yet these astronomers continue to sit in their government sponsored monopoly seats and pretend that they somehow know something. The point of this discussion on small comets is to point out that we had seen as early as 1957 enough evidence to scrap the dirty snowball comet model in its infancy. So for nearly half a decade incorrect theory has managed to dominate the scientific scene. One cannot imagine all the Ph.D.s that have been awarded within this time to people who bought this incorrect science hook line and sinker and have repeated it over and over again, never questioning any of the obvious flaws that are being pointing out here. The nucleus of comet Wild II, which is the second photo above, was though it also was directly measured to contain no water ice astronomers only inferred such by noting activity around the nucleus. It was stated also in the news release for this comet that no water was detected on the nucleus. This nucleus was obviously of a very dense rocky material pitted from many anguishing trips through the solar capacitor as it was gouged out by the electron beam coming from the sunward side of the comet nucleus.

In the summer of 2005 scientists hope to crash a car sized probe into a comet nucleus (Comet Tempel) in hopes of penetrating the surface and finding ice that has eluded them to date. When the probe crashes into the dry rocky surface and no water is found, what excuses will astronomers think of then? My guess is that they will detect water as the probe itself will be contaminated as it too will become a comet ... a plasma discharge, that is ... on its approach to the nucleus of Comet Tempel as it will discharge the solar capacitor. But no matter what the results one might rest assured that these astronomers will claim that it somehow supports the dirty snowball comet model ... as their careers and paychecks depend on it ... after all where would one go to get a job with a resume that stated that you had a Ph.D. in incorrect science.

The next two photos show a comet on the lower left side of the sun approaching the solar desk in the subsequent explosion as it passes by the upper left extension of the sun.

I have dozens of videos and pictures that show the same situation ... with many of the explosions from the sun resulting in major solar flares. Comets do affect the solar surface, and the solar surface is affected by its environment. A dirty snowball comet would not last 10 seconds in the solar environment that we see here. The solar environment next to the sun would be as follows. Imagine a fire hose with the liquid coming out of the nozzle at 600,000 km per hour ... it has a temperature of 6000 degrees and the nozzle is a 100 thousand miles in diameter. Now imagine a mile wide little ball of dust and snow in this environment ... how long do you think it would last ???

Then what are the chances that this would affect the sun and create a solar flare large enough to be seen from earth?

You do not have to be an astrophysicist to see how bizarre and out of touch these scientists are from reality.

The next photo is of the famous Comet Neat V1 that surprised astronomers and which caused the enormous solar flare seen in the photo. There is a long and complicated story that as this comet became visible, NASA scientists cut the feed of the SOHO cameras taking this shot, and did not release it for a few days. This comet was so large that it was visible from earth at sundown with the naked eye. People were walking out of office buildings on their way home from work and asking, " hey, what is that thing next to the sun?" ... NASA's answer was that this was just one of those little harmless ice balls no more than a mile wide. One can see that the nucleus of this is approaching the size of the sun and its tail is far larger than the sun's atmosphere. This I suspect was a medium sized nucleus with a diameter approximately the size of our Moon.

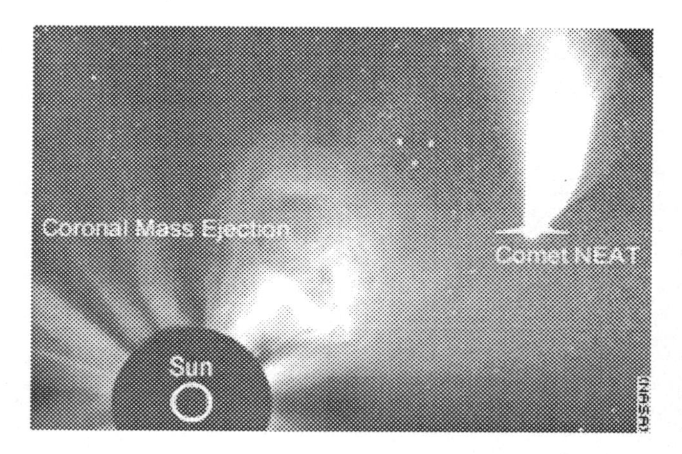

The next picture was taken by the Spitzer Infrared telescope of Comet P-29 (one of the oldest and best known small comets). Much to the surprise of astronomers as you look into the nucleus area ... rather than getting colder as you approach what they believed would be an icy nucleus, it got hotter and hotter and hotter, too hot for ice to exist.

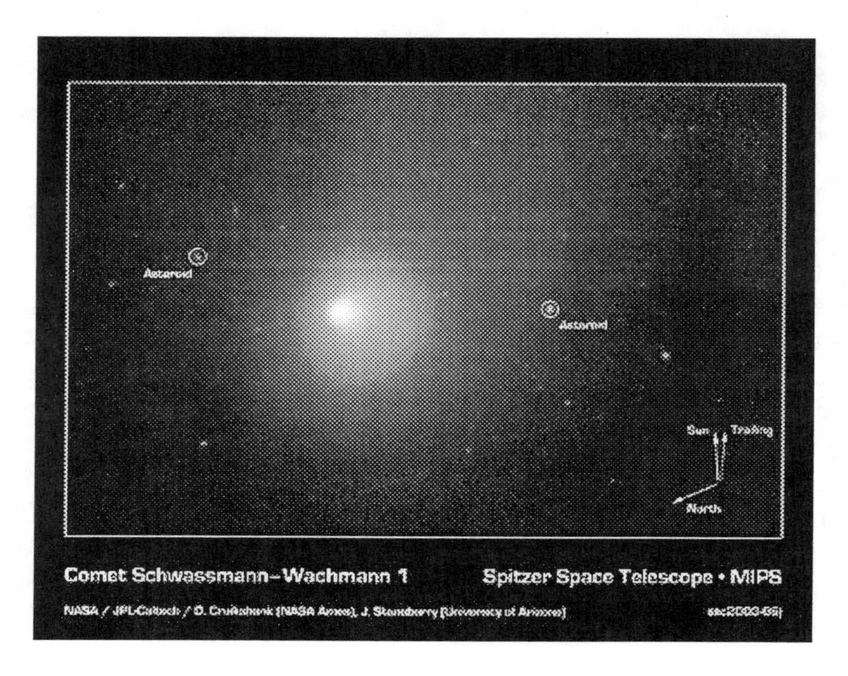

The final picture is of the weather in north America that was generated by comet Bradfield a few days after it created a large solar flare that affected our earth weather in April 2004. Once again I have file cabinets full of such weather reactions caused by comets as they affected the sun which in turn affected our weather ... proof of the Action at a Distance principle.

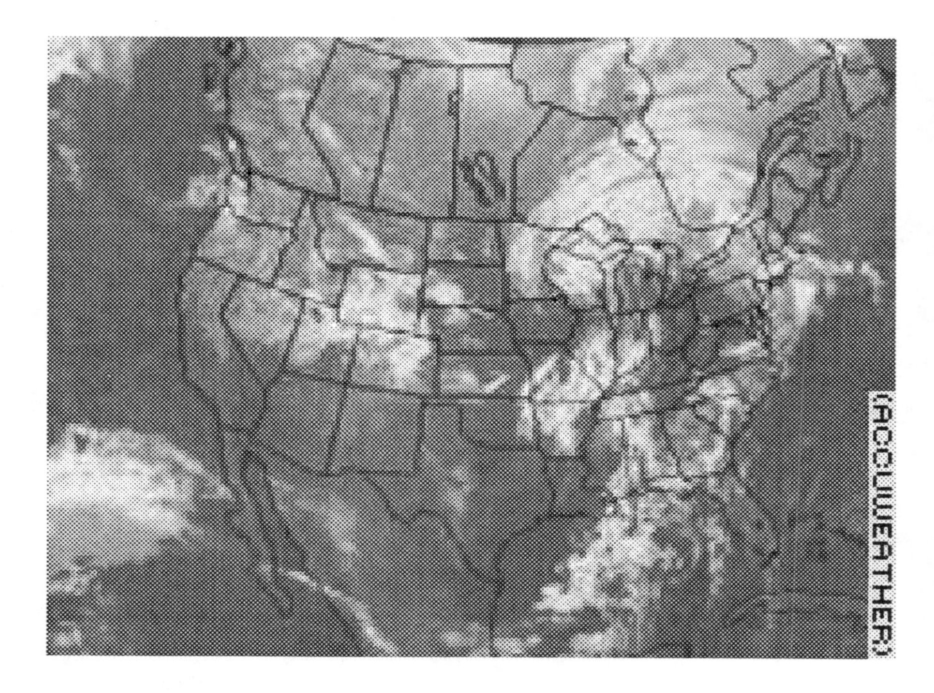

We have one very well observed medium-size comet that has come into the solar system in recent years and that was the comet Hale-Bopp. Hale-Bopp came in with the nucleus slightly smaller than our moon and after a period of six years of accumulating matter, and had its orbit reduced by tail drag from an original period of 4200 years to a final period of approximately 2600 years, the final size of the nucleus is estimated to be larger than our Moon ... Hale-Bopp is a new planetary member of our solar system. Its orbit is nearly perpendicular to that of the other planets, but on its next trip to the solar system it is expected by the plasma discharge comet model to reduce its orbit in half once again. One of my future projects is to gather the data on the final orbital parameters for Hale-Bopp and estimate whether it might have an encounter with Jupiter during a future orbit. Might this bring it into alignment with the rest of the planets? Might this reduce its orbit even further? Even if it does not encounter Jupiter on the next go around it will have its orbit reduced to approximately half of 2600 years or approximately 1300 years. On the next trip into the solar system this might be cut in half again. As you can see Hale-Bopp is a new member of our solar system ... a new planet and is forming from a comet ... a plasma discharge comet.

What would happen if earth passed near or within the coma of Hale-Bopp, a medium sized comet (not a baby comet like Halley's). This almost happened as Hale-Bopp passed through the ecliptic behind earth's orbit a mere 1 million miles from where earth was only a few months earlier. We literally dodged a bullet. From what I understand it would not have been a direct collision, but it would have been close enough to create severe electrical conditions, which would have included severe electrical storm such as hurricanes over land and water. But more than this, we would have been plunged into darkness as we passed through the cometary coma for a period of from five to 20 days robbing us of essential sunlight and sending earth into a deep freeze.

This could have been the beginning of the next ice age, but we missed. Hale-Bopp was visible for a period of over six years, which is highly unusual. Comets generally are only visible to the naked eye for a day or two or possibly a week at most. NASA claimed that it never took a single picture of Hale-Bopp with the Hubble space telescope. This was a lie and one has to wonder were they also lying about the size of the nucleus. The official claim was that Hale-Bopp had a nucleus approximately 40 miles in diameter. I know that the nucleus was at least or possibly larger than our Moon. This can be calculated using the original companion and its orbital period.

Hale-Bopp also pumped up the energy of the solar capacitor and returned it to the sun for over this period of six years. This caused the sun to miss its solar maximum and extended it far into the year 2001 and 2002 where it should have been heading into a solar minimum. Hale-Bopp was also responsible for severe weather in the 1990s when we had hurricanes and typhoons with record wind speeds and also had the jet stream dropping down to the Earth's surface ripping out large sections of land ... for example in China.

If we ever witnessed a really large comet, one with the nucleus the size of earth or larger, this could then discharge the entire solar capacitor from the sun all the way out to far beyond Pluto. The amount of energy stored in this capacitor is beyond human comprehension and the effect it would have on the sun would be that it would first cause tremendous explosions and then possibly the sun would enter into a cool state for a long period of time. Whatever the result, mankind would have a difficult time surviving on this planet. The ancients talked about such events and they survived ... barely.

This is the way of the solar system and nature in general. It is one of selective violence with intermittent periods of calm to allow the survivors to regain a semblance of peace and serenity. But this can be shadowed on a moments notice as we know from the experience with Comet Bradfield which was observed only three weeks before its closest approach to the sun. A close approach to Earth by one of the large comet nuclei would be a truly devastating event for earth and would cause us possibly to lose our atmosphere and burn earth's surface with unrelenting electrical discharges. Earth might recover and regenerate someday … but in the most severe case nothing would survive. It is truly the downfall of our species that astronomers are allowed to deny the past that is so essential to understanding and pursuing a future as a species.

XXI. THE FUTURE OF WEATHER CONTROL

In the bible it predicts that man will someday move mountains... however while growing up I always imagined this to the more of a figurative statement than anything based on reality. But now that I understand the importance of what I call "trigger mechanisms", mechanisms to unleash incredible amounts of energy stored in the universe, moving mountains does not seem like such a daunting task anymore.

It was the same with hurricanes, tornadoes and earth weather. When I first began imagining how one might possibly control this, the only thing we had even close to resembling this level of power was a nuclear bomb. And in fact there have been people who have suggested that we ignite atomic bombs in hurricanes or other storms in an attempt to dissipate their energy. I have since learned that this would not be a very good idea based on what I know about hurricanes and how they form. But nature has its own way of dealing with the storms and neutralizing them ... so it is from this realization that I finally determined the mechanism to control the storms.

There's also a joke amongst people that live in the Midwest United States as it seems tornadoes are always devastating trailer courts. The reality is that there is something actually to this since we now understand that tornadoes in fact are electrical discharges to ground. So what would be better suited to attract a tornado than a large array of metallic boxes put along the ground in a nice even rows and columns.

This leads one to the conclusion that there is a way to attract tornadoes to a given area so that we can conveniently dissipate their energy and do away with these monster storms. The second part of the "equation" is to take the electrical energy that is creating the destructive force and place it on the grid system to be used for electrical energy to power our country. There would be a double benefit ... reduction of storm damage and conversion to useful energy to reduce pollution caused by other energy sources. It is a little more complicated than this but the point is that we see in nature the mechanisms that we have to learn to use and begin to control severe weather systems.

The point is that the energy stored in our atmosphere, which comes from the ionosphere to ground vertical electric field, is coming down to earth in the form of these violent storms. So if we learn how to control and reduce the energy from these violent storms, we can then transform this energy into useful energy to drive our industrial lifestyle rather than burn fossil fuels. The simple solution is that we can take the energy from the storms, convert into useful energy and distribute amongst a grid system for use in areas where there are no storms. Did the ancients know about these forms of storm control and energy? I believe they did and there are many indications to suggest that they knew much more than we do to control the storms and utilize the energy. So in a sense they were possibly far more advanced than we ever have imagined in our so-called technologically advanced society.

An unmarked military "airliner" pumps out a "chem-trail"

In the above photo an unmarked military aircraft simulating a commercial jetliner sprays an unknown chemical composition into the atmosphere to perform unknown experiments on our atmosphere and the public. For many years NASA had an unknown secret project to control weather using chem trails. I have been invited to talk on many radio show is to discuss the various possibilities and implications of spraying chemicals into the atmosphere relative to weather control. It is believed that these spraying experiments are used in conjunction with other facilities and other Black Ops technologies. What the public must realize is the number of people in these operations who know about what is going on ... literally 10's of thousands of people ... and none are allowed to talk about what they are doing to the public in these experiments that were essentially outlawed after the World War II atomic bomb tests that used the public as human guinea pigs.

A few years ago the Russians approached the United Nations and international communities insisting that the weather control technologies be registered as a weapon of mass destruction, referring to the United States involvement with the radio array known as HAARP. The Russians believe that it would be possible to secretly affect the weather of another country and affect its ability to support the public, in other words this would be a weapon used against the public of another nation and not simply a weapon that could be used in military "theaters" against just military personnel with military tactics as defined by the Geneva Convention. It also violated the international convention on the use of outer space for military weapons.

It is truly unknown as this book goes to press what the future of weather control will be and how much has already been implemented in black ops programs within the various governments around the world. The truly unfortunate situation, as with all military weapons, is that the long-term effects are truly not known and people in these organizations are playing with fire next to literally a can of gasoline and the general public will be the long-term loser.

When the experiments dealing with weather control first began many decades ago, much of what we now know about the atmosphere and the electrical nature of our planet was literally not even conceived of at that time. So the people in those programs were literally shooting in the dark ... and they still are much in this same boat today. There are many patents on record producing ideas for the purpose of weather control, whether manipulation or the transmission of various effects around the globe. In all the ones that I have read, not a single one appears to understand what they are truly dealing with, what the levels of energy that are ready to be unleashed by nature when inexperienced government scientists pull the triggers on these enormous pent up energy sources.

In August of 2003, one short month after I released my Atlantis to Tesla book, a military experiment took place in the countryside outside of Ottawa Canada. These scientists set up a Tesla coil and were deriving energy from the Northeast power grid of both Canada and the United States to power the coil in an experiment to see if they could tap into the vertical electric field is pointed out in that book. Whenever I released information like the nature of the energy source for the Tesla Tower, I am always cautious not to include the key information so that people would go out of their backyards and perform some of these experiments, which can be quite dangerous. So it was with complete irresponsible management on the part of the Black Ops group(s) that performed this experiment … allowing it to be performed with the public as guinea pig. The end result was the Northeast power outage of August 2003.

The low rumbling of the Tesla tower could be heard over the countryside of the provinces and states of the Northeast that afternoon as the experiment proceeded. When they finally "drilled" electrically through to the ionosphere and tapped into the vertical electric field, an energy surge of unbelievable magnitude came passing down that column into the Northeast power grid and was sufficient to back up nine nuclear reactors on the north east grid system of the United States and enough to fry three nuclear reactors in the Ottawa area itself. The amount of energy that came down in probably a brief two to three seconds is beyond human comprehension.

There was untold damage to equipment such as computers, radios, appliances and even automobile alarm systems were triggered as the incredible surge of power came roaring through the northeastern United States. This is included in this chapter to illustrate the level of irresponsibility of people in these black ops programs and to also illustrate the amount of energy that is locked into the vertical electric field of earth … which is the same power source that powers our tremendous electrical storms, hurricanes, typhoons, tornadoes, water spots etc.

The simple result is that there is a natural control mechanism that occurs when the ionospheric connection occurs to cloud tops that power the large storms. By the same token we have to control the release of energy from the ionosphere to Tesla Towers to prevent serious damage to our grid system. There is also an understanding of the vast nature of the energy sources that are contained in our vertical electrical capacitor and that the "standard explanations" for the causes of such storms such as ocean water temperature are totally insufficient to produce the amount of power for example we measure in a hurricane … which is estimated to be the equivalent in a large hurricane to be more than all of the atomic bombs on earth. That is a huge amount of power and not by any stretch of the imagination provided by a small differential in sea water temperature … it would be like watching a car move down the street and imagining that the motion is provided by the exhaust coming out of the tail pipe while not recognizing that there is a powerful engine that is actually making the car go. In the case of the car it would be a simple matter of measuring the energy coming out of the tail pipe and one would quickly determine that there had to be some other very powerful source to make this 4000 pound machine move down the road at 75 miles per hour. The little stream of exhaust just would not be enough!!!

However with hurricanes and the other powerful storms the case is just the same. With tornadoes, which are claimed to be caused by atmospheric energy sources, once again one would have to take the entire daily allotment of solar light energy over the area of many thousands of square miles to accumulate the energy needed to create one F-3 tornado. Now take the situations where he have seen tornadoes over a mile wide running along the ground for over 50 miles, or the bands of 70 tornadoes that moved from western Texas all the way to the east coast of the US … the amount of energy here is staggering and there is simply not enough atmospheric energy to cause these storm systems. If you were able to accumulate this amount of energy from an atmospheric source, then the temperatures or the surrounding areas would have to be reduced tremendously and this does not happen (you do not get energy for nothing). And what of the storms that form at night with no solar light source at all?

Once again you have to look to other sources of energy and the only place to acquire this level of energy is from the vertical electric field, which is driven by the main source of power … the solar electric field and the solar capacitor. Remember that the solar capacitor holds far more energy than the daily dose of electrical energy that passes by us daily in the solar wind, which in turn is far greater than the quantity of solar light energy that meteorologists have imagined to be the only energy source for the cause of our weather.

It has also become apparent that one can direct the paths of hurricanes by a number of methods. The primary method would be to direct an energy beam through the edge of the hurricane eye, which would increase the ionization and therefore the current path along one edge of the hurricane eye. This would cause the hurricane to move in the direction of increased current flow. It is this characteristic elongation of the eye that we have been seeing lately in some of the hurricanes and typhoons and it appears that there may be storm manipulation occurring, although without corroborating data it would be impossible to say with 100% certainty. But also just from knowing the mentality of the people in the black ops groups, I would be very surprised if they were not doing this!!!

The second method of manipulating storm movement would be with grounding stations that simulate the various ways nature moves storms. I the case of hurricanes we see these storms changing directions as the leading edges interact with the shallow continental shelf "banks" that lie off shore of Florida and the Caribbean islands. If one were to simulate these conditions with grounding buoys as already noted above and do this so that one side of the storm eye is drained, then this would also affect the storm direction as well as its strength.

This is more than pure speculation as many times I have tracked hurricanes as they passed over the Bahamian banks or come through the channel between Cuba and the Yucatan in Mexico. One can track the turns as the edge of the eye connects to the banks off shore, or as the connection is lost as the eye moves out over deeper water.

Land storms such as tornadoes can similarly be generated or enhanced by manipulating the path to the ionosphere. One can attract tornadoes to a given area with arrays of grounded metal structures and this has given rise to the idea that one could set arrays of bunkers out in the open fields to the west of towns and cities in the plains of Oklahoma where the worst storms occur. As storm systems approached the bunkers, balloons or kites (very sturdily built of course) would fly into the storm to drain the electrical energy. This energy would have to be dissipate by some method … one method might eventually be to pass this energy to the electric power grid where it would be utilized by people in adjacent grids. I have talked about these systems and a future book will give details.

In 1998, long before anybody ever imagined that one might try to control their horrendous forces of a hurricane, tornado or atmospheric electricity, it had already become apparent to me that due to the understanding of how the storms formed and the mechanisms that powered them, it would be entirely possible to shunt their energy. A good deal of corroborating evidence was put together and proposal was actually presented to the United States Air Force, NOAA and the National Weather Service. There were no provisions at our request for remuneration, but simply the request that this be utilized to end the destruction that was occurring around the globe at that time. Already our weather had been increasingly severe over anything the world had measured before in the previous hundreds of years. As you will read about in the next chapter regarding my weather work with the Russians in the mid-1990s, they had already begun to realize that a global shift was underway and that this had nothing to do with man-made greenhouse gases, but was in fact a reality based on changing energy conditions in our solar system and interstellar space.

The proposal that was presented to these government agencies is included here in its entirety to show two things. The first is that it was in fact presented to these agencies and they did nothing. The second is to show the level of information that was available at that early date. All of a sudden in 2004 there was a flurry of activity to develop so-called weather and severe weather control devices: everything from dropping vast amounts of powder in a storm to dropping atomic bombs in a storm to attempt to divert their energies. It turns out that none of these are very good ideas. The simple reason being that they did not realize the true nature or source of energy that provides these storms with the tremendous power and damaging destructive energy.

Before reading this excerpt which came from the Millennium Group 1998 home page that contained my theoretical work as its core material, it is interesting to note that the names of the hurricanes in that year were named the same as the September 2004 entourage of hurricanes that have spawned in the Atlantic as this book goes to press. This is a most curious "coincidence" since the names of storms are not supposed to repeat (especially if they caused damage).

THE HURRICANE/TYPHOON SOLUTION

Practical Ideas To Avoid The Destruction Of Killing Storms

THE TRUTH IN SCIENCE TEAM:
JAMES M. McCANNEY, EARL CROCKETT
GARY D. GOODWIN, RAY WARD, A.N. DMITRIEV
[WOULD YOU CARE TO JOIN THE TEAM?]

In many past articles and for several years now, Members of The Millennium Group have given numerous proofs of the electrical nature of the universe in which we live. We have supported and given evidence of both Alfven's and Velikovsky's ideas concerning the sure existence of such currents throughout our solar system. These currents, in the form of charged particles or plasmas, flow from the greater galaxy and sun through the planets and their atmospheres. In most cases we have strongly urged authorities, such as NASA and other governmental agencies and representatives, to recognize these powers and their effects upon the inhabitants of this planet. Now in this brief abstract, we present one more proof and one more practical application of the research and work at The Millennium Group. In truth there are many, many applications of this area of research that can widen man's knowledge and experience and indeed save lives. The following abstract of ideas has been presented to the United States Air Force and other relevant agencies, in some degree of detail, without charge or expectation of remuneration. These ideas must be acknowledged if there will ever be an answer to the great losses that the human race has sustained. Meanwhile, after Georges has done his damage and Zeb has nearly destroyed the Phillipines, we have to wonder who's next and how long will the authorities take before they give our ideas a chance????

The following article appeared September 27th, 1998 at cnn.com:

Record-tying 4 hurricanes in Atlantic at once Karl joins Georges, Ivan and Jeanne in a first since 1892

September 26, 1998 Web posted at: 3:47 p.m. EDT (1947 GMT)

MIAMI (AP) -- For the first time in more than a century, four hurricanes have sprung out of the Atlantic at the same time. One has already wreaked havoc in the Caribbean and southern Florida, while another is expected to hit the Azores islands sometime Saturday. Hurricane Karl joined hurricanes Georges, Ivan and Jeanne on Friday, the first time since 1892 that the Atlantic Ocean has played host to four simultaneous hurricanes, said Michele Huber, a meteorologist at the National Hurricane Center. "Everything hit at the same time," Huber said. "This is definitely something beyond the ordinary." Of the four hurricanes, Georges so far is the most damaging, killing 300 people in the Caribbean before crashing over Key West and heading into the Gulf of Mexico toward the Gulf Coast. The next to pose trouble for land will be Ivan, which was racing on an easterly track toward the Azores. A still-growing Karl whirled out of a tropical storm that was born Wednesday in the central Atlantic. Karl was moving northeast near 10 mph (16 km/h), and a gradual increase in speed was expected. Jeanne was centered south-southwest of Lajes with 80-mph (130-km/h) winds. The three systems won't affect the United States, Huber said, and it appeared Karl and Jeanne will live and die at sea.

Anyone who watches the weather news, with any regularity, knows the devastation that hurricanes andf typhoons can do. Until last year, the fastest wind speed known to mankind was on one of the highest mountains in the world, Mt. Wilson in New Hampshire. Then last year at *sea level*, Super Typhoon Keith hit a sea level Pacific island at a wind speed of over 220 MPH!!!! Mind you this was at SEA LEVEL! We've seen dozens of hurricanes do billions of dollars worth of damage, not to mention the many lives lost. We saw Andrew obliterate Southern Florida, and before that Hugo... the list goes on and on. FEMA struggles to deal with the fall out and the government (US-> YOU AND ME!) pay the tax dollars to repair the damage. What if there were a way to lessen the damage? A way to save lives? The following is only an abstract that we have presented to a few of our government agencies.

That same person who watches the evening t.v. news, likely knows that when hurricanes hit the land, they lose their strength. Why is this? We know the current beliefs. And why do they gain strength over warm sea water?

Most of us have seen pictures of the beautiful Aurora Borealis. Their wonderful flashing, dancing lights incredibly lighting the northern skies. It is interesting to note, as an introduction to this abstract, that this phenomenon usually follows the coast line. Here is the crux to this matter:

The Aurora Borealis is the result of a current flow, dissipating through the earth's field. Sea water is less conductive than land. (see Tim Kelly's paper Observed Natural Events And Hypotheses Related To The Physics Of Fault-Free Earthquakes also see A.N.Dmitriev's paper

Electrogravidynamic Concept of Tornadoes). Great charges of plasma are introduced into the upper atmosphere of the earth where they must be dissipated. Some of these charges are dissipated through the common storm systems that we see circling the earth. The source of these charges can be readily seen and explained in a recent paper entitled VENUS, THE SUN, AND WHAT?.

The fact that land mass attracts the charge greater than the seas is readily seen in a recent study where lightening strikes were counted over land and compared to strikes over the water. This was a simple study by NASA where all they had to do was just count!

> **"Lightning likes land more than water, according to the first three months' of images of data from NASA's Lightning Imaging Sensor (LIS). It's not just that most lightning occurs over land. From December 1997 through January 1998, LIS saw that 90 percent of lightning was over land, a significant finding. Three months of Lightning Imaging Sensor data dramatically shows that most lightning occurs over land. Areas over sea match major circulation patterns that carry storms over water."!!!!**

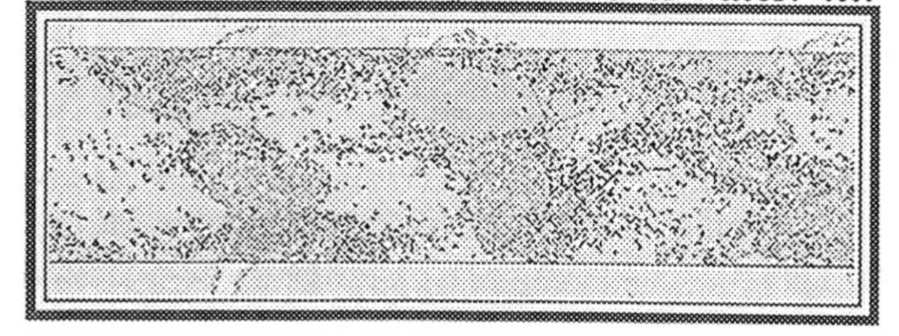

(You can see this report HERE.)

This system of charges coming to the Earth - coming through the atmosphere and searching for an area to discharge is easily seen in the recent discovery below.

(Some of the following images are taken from http://www-cmpo.mit.edu/~djboccip/papers/S95/Sprites.htmln excellent explanation of the phenomenon at hand.)

Over the last few years an interesting phenomenon has come to the attention of a number of researchers. It was noticed that over the *top* of storms, strange lights seemed to be emanating. Of course no one had ever seen these before except a few pilots and perhaps in mythology. So the researchers have associated these lights only with storms. That's of course the only time when they look for them! It's a bit of the "chicken and the old egg" story, but there does seem to be a rational story here. These are actual images of what are now called *Sprites*:

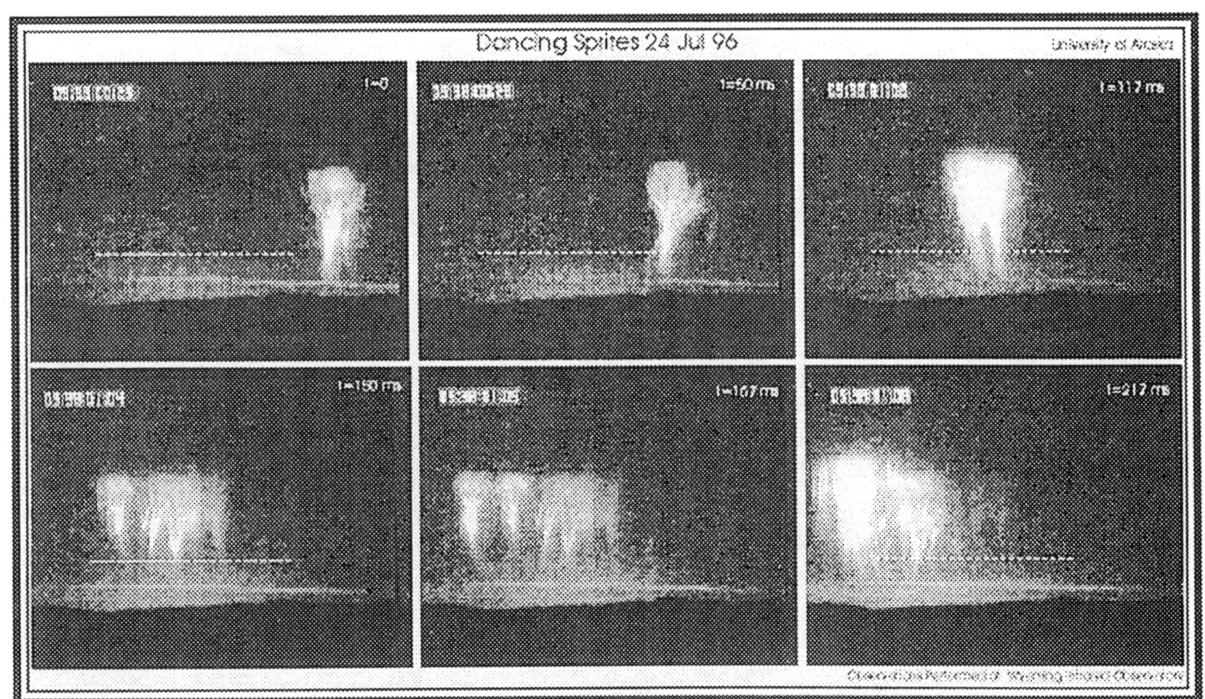

HERE is a depiction of the altitude of where these electrical events occur.

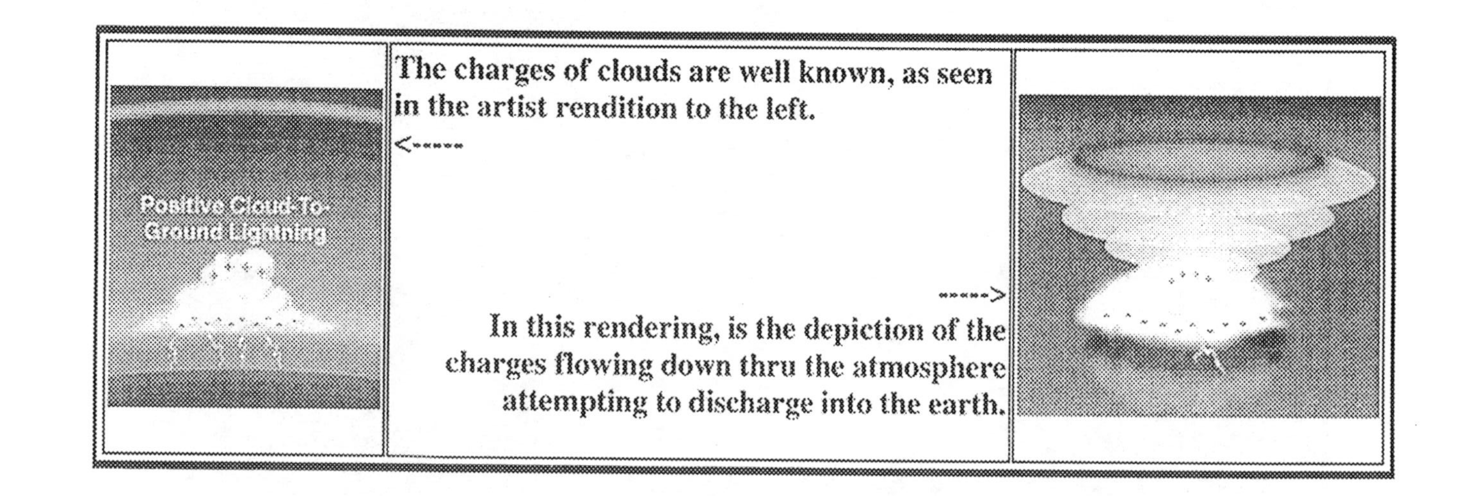

The charges of clouds are well known, as seen in the artist rendition to the left.

<------

------>

In this rendering, is the depiction of the charges flowing down thru the atmosphere attempting to discharge into the earth.

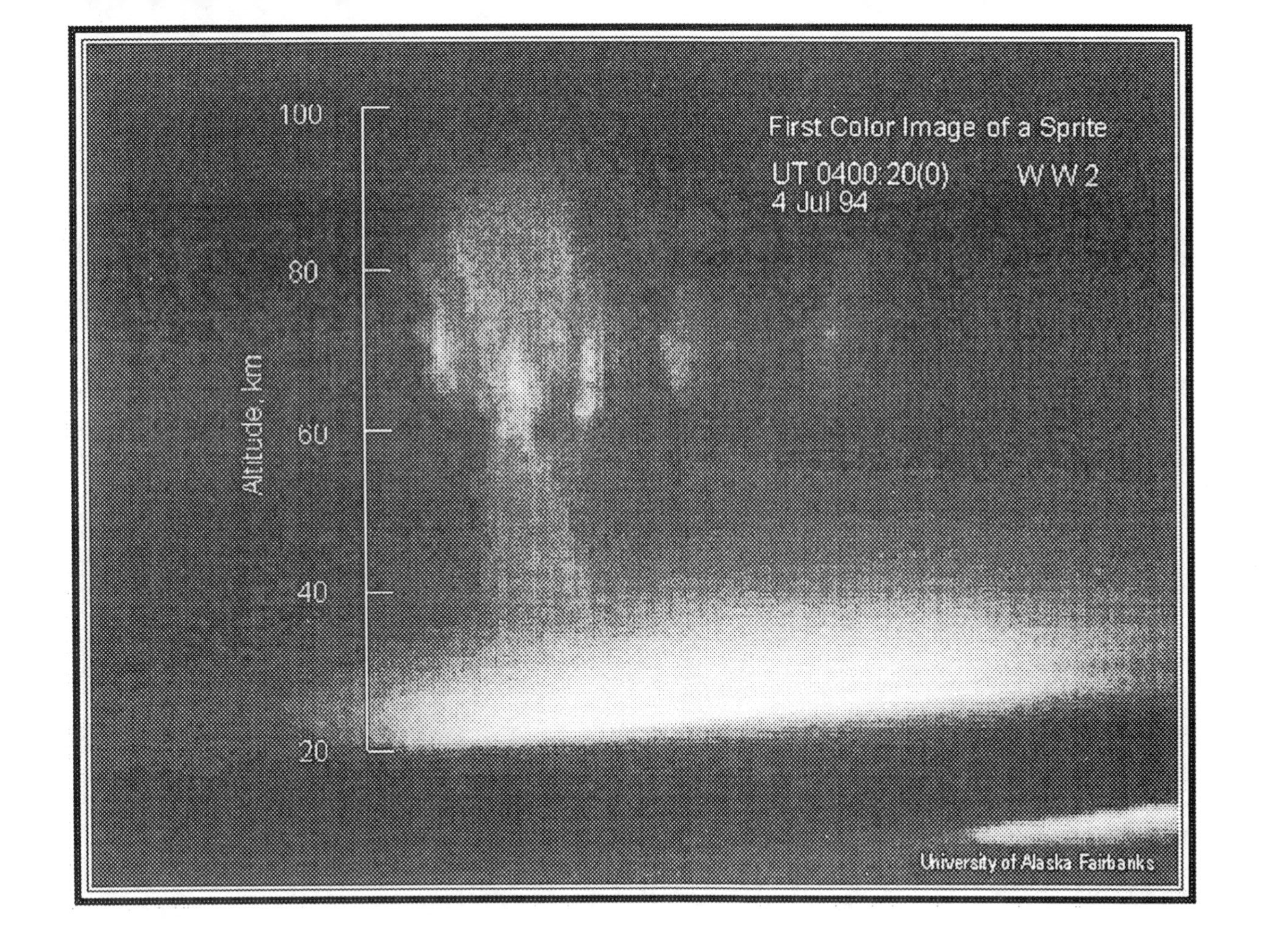
First Color Image of a Sprite
UT 0400:20(0)
W W 2
4 Jul 94
Altitude, km
100
80
60
40
20
University of Alaska Fairbanks

Sprites and Elves, as they are called got their name due to the eerie light shows that they put on and the fact that they seem to be difficult to see without the right equipment.

The Millennium Group has an answer to the problem that these charges create. The solution is a simple arrangement and order of devices to dispel the charge that is not being allowed to dispel over water. The Hurricane has the time to build up enough charge to create damaging circumstances when it finally reaches land. Let us remind the reader of the potential disastrous storm that lies out there waiting to destroy.

The proposal of the combination of devices and the entire explanation is available to those that are in position to utilize this knowledge. If you are a member of an organization that is in the position to use such theory, please contact us for detailed information. The conditions of release of this information are few. Please contact us HERE.

Associated links:
National Hurricane Center

Hurricanes98.com

Storm 98

XXII. RUSSIAN WEATHER WORK (Dr. ALEXEY DMITRIEV, et. al.)

In the mid-1990s, I had the great fortune of being introduced to a group of Russian scientists and this led to a fruitful collaboration that branched into a number of topics that ranged from my comet and Electrical Universe work to the physics of the Sun and the galactic wind that the solar system moves through and its changing attacks on earth weather. We dealt with the Tunguska event and the electromagnetic weather of earth ... we even discussed and combined research on the electromagnetic causes of human response to the positions of the planets (in other words, a true scientific basis for astrology).

The extent of this collaboration is not completely going to be made public as it became clear as we entered the current century that they were people who did not want me talking to the Russians any longer. My communications were cut off and I heard that the U. S. had infiltrated their study groups that were meeting regularly to discuss our progress. They were told directly that they should stop teaching my work in the University which they had been doing for some time in both undergraduate and graduate level classes. I heard also that they were offered money, as in funding from the West, if they ceased discussing my material.

The scientists always used to joke about their incomes and life status. They were housed in government housing projects near the University and the professor salary, that is the full professors, made approximately $75 a week, although of course all of their collective needs such as medicine etc. were paid for by the state. At one point they were trying to get money together to publish a book with my material in Russian, attempting to raise the money by pooling a little from each person's salary over the course of many months to accomplish that end. They had all papers translated but ultimately, to my knowledge, they were never able to actually publish their book.

Eventually I could tell that the people responding to my communications were not the Russians that I was used to talking to. Communications in both directions were being intercepted and for a number of years it became fruitless to attempt to contact them. They all lived in fear of what would happen to them and their careers if it were found out that they were communicating with me. Mind you this was not being imposed by their own government, but by the infiltration from the West. This was at the time when NASA was making inroads to use Russian launch vehicles and was launching on a very regular basis from the Central Russian launch pads, something not usually mentioned in the Western press. This included secret military payloads and God knows what else was lifted in the space for military from the Central Russian remote launch pads.

It was also during this time when I was collaborating with the Russians that a young American singer died in a strange unexplained air crash in San Diego Bay (October 12, 1997), as his plane allegedly ran out of gas just minutes after take off. That person's name was John Denver and few people knew that he was about to become the first private astronaut to go into space. He successfully negotiated and had been training with the Russians to become the first astronaut and his music at that time reflected his intent ("Fly Like an Eagle" and "all alone in the universe" "Looking for Space and I find out who I am" and "to try and reach the stars").

Denver was always far ahead of the curve … he was doing concerts in China in the 60's long before Nixon ever thought of "opening up China" … He was performing humanitarian work in Africa with starving nations and was an avid spokesman for the environment long before it was fashionable. His singing and guitar work were unrivalled … as noted by Paul of the 60's folk group Peter Paul and Mary, "not many people realized how good he was on the guitar". And after hang gliding in the Rockies with eagles, and flying a designer air craft … he turned his eyes towards space … apparently first approaching NASA and when they turned him down he went to Russia and was on the road to succeeding in fulfilling his dreams of being the first civilian in space. He died before that dream came true.

I have always believed and still believe to this day that John Denver was murdered by American interests associated with NASA and the government who did not want uninvited guests seeing what was going on over there in central Russia. My belief was increased when NASA stated later when a private American businessman negotiated and was about to go into space with the Russians … that he would not go. NASA raised all kinds of intents to block the private venture that cost $20 million US dollars but to no avail ... as the Russians had finally had enough of NASA and their bullyboy tactics.

The cause of Denver's air crash was very similar to the many unexplained small plane crashes that occurred with pilots who were taking part in the Mena Arkansas covert "government" operation during the Iran Contra scandal. Denver's Aircraft was designed by designer Burt Routan who off record was noted as saying that it would be impossible for that plane to do what it did the day with Denver on board. Immediately after the "accident" there was a national smear campaign in all the news media stating Denver was abusing alcohol and that the FAA was trying to pull his license. This all was more than highly unusual for the FAA to make such a public presence over a small private single passenger plane crash ... especially since major airlines such as Northwest Airlines at that same time had numerous pilots flying 747's with pilots who repeatedly were caught intoxicated in flight with hundreds of passengers on board and the FAA said nothing about that.

There was and still is a concerted effort within NASA and the US aerospace monopolies to prevent certain people from "participating" in any efforts to move into outer space. I saw this first hand at many points in my career as an independent scientist ... If you did not play their game in their ball park with their rules you were very much put into a squeeze play ... the only problem with me is they keep squeezing and I keep coming out ahead of them. And so this game continues even today as the FAA tries to protect NASA and the US aerospace giants from innovative entrepreneurs who wish to bring the public into space. Favoritism is given to those who play by the rules. Those who do not will find they are ten dozen ways that they will be prevented from succeeding.

This discussion all began due to the topic of my work with the Russians. The next topic is also something I learned from the Russians for the first time and began to realize it more and more as I learned the incredible amount of flight time the Russians had in space (for example their KOSMOS mini-shuttle that sat on the front of the larger launch vehicles as a piggy back rider with from 1 to 3 cosmonauts aboard made no less that 1600 flights from 1962 to 1976 when it was decommissioned). This was the smaller craft that road up into low earth orbit on the nose of the giant boosters with either manned, scientific or military payloads ... so there were many times more cosmonauts in the main rocket capsule. The mini KOSMOS was able to dock with their space stations and other craft and was versatile in that it could be glided back into earth's atmosphere to any location. Remember this was in the 60's while the US was building its Apollo moon program. The Russians during this entire time were launching nearly on a daily basis with essentially the same rocket designs they are still using today. They had the ability to keep men in space for long periods of time and had very much the capability at any time to boost their payloads to the moon or anywhere else they wanted.

It was during this time (in the mid 60's) that the Russians attempted a manned mission outside of the Van Allen belts. Their cosmonauts returned very dead from severe x-ray exposure. The Russians knew this and openly talked about it. They were amazed that the US citizens really thought that NASA had gone to the moon and "beaten the Russians". If you understand the immense capabilities that the Russians had throughout this entire period and maintained even after the "fall of Russia" in the Reagan era, you would realize that on any given day of the year they could have turned a space station moonward and AT LEAST sent a craft to circle the moon and return (not necessarily landing on it).

Dealing with the Russians taught me a lot ... but most of all it taught me what it is like to work with real scientists who are interested in science and not their egos or scientific vacations that are just some of the benefits of their richer American counterparts. It was also at this time that I began working on the very issue of how to get through the Van Allen Belts safely. I knew that the Russians had not succeeded and I know that NASA has an entire program with thousands of high level physicists working on it at the time this book goes to press call Living With A Star ... which is a nice name for "how on earth do we get through the Van Allen Belts????!!!!!!????!!!! I would liken this project in scope and importance to the Manhattan Project. .. at least in the eyes of NASA.

One, of course, has to ask the question ... if there was no problem in flying astronauts through the Van Allen Belts and to the moon in 1969 through 1976 in the Apollo Program, then what is the big deal about now? Maybe you are starting to see the contradiction here. Why was the Space Shuttle designed specifically for low earth orbit work only? Why did the Astronauts' eye brows begin to glow when they once went up to a few hundred mile orbit and why did an incredible electrical discharge nearly destroy one Shuttle as they let out a conducting tether (long thin wire) into what I know to be the non-uniform electric field or LEB (local electric battery) that exists just above the Shuttle's low earth orbit. Why were the Apollo rocket and Moon landing programs completely disassembled and all records destroyed (leaving nothing for kids or the rest of us to look at in the national archives at the Smithsonian Museum)?

So I set about the task of looking into the method to get through the Van Allen Belts. I finally came across the method and it is quite simple ... as I always say it is like baking bread that rises ... it is simple once you know how to do it ... but just think how many civilizations went though history and never learned how to make leavened bread?

So as this book goes to press at least, the USA has still not learned how to accomplish the one thing they need to get into space beyond low earth orbit. I will have nothing to do with the thieves and liars in NASA and I as yet have not found a good outlet to pass the concept to for the betterment of mankind. If they find out how to do this it will not be at my doing. Man is not ready yet to take his greed and war ridden civilization into space to destroy that as they have done to this beautiful planet.

The rest of this chapter will give a sampling of the communications that went back and forth during those years of working with the Russians which make obvious the exuberance shown by scientists in "the east" to the work I had done ... work that to this day has been totally suppressed in the west to protect outdated astronomical and astrophysical "axioms". You will see immediately that the Russians picked up very quickly on the importance of my work and were applying it to everything from earth weather, the cause of the destruction of the Tunguska Meteorite (prior to hitting the ground), tornadoes on the sun and the electrical connection of biological life to the movements of the members of the solar system. They interpreted the explosive events of the Shoemaker-Levy 9 comet as it hit Jupiter ... they had every possible instrument trained on Jupiter ... as NASA stated publicly that it had no intention of even looking as this would be a non-event ... since the harmless little snow balls would simply fall into Jupiter's vast atmosphere and by the time Jupiter turned around for us to see that part of its atmosphere, there would be nothing to see at all ... they now pretend as if they had never made those statements).

The pieces selected will include an early statement by the Russians regarding their first impressions of my work after translating and having their first study group meeting regarding my 1981 paper **The Nature and Origin of Comets and the Evolution of Celestial Bodies**. (It is incredibly amazing that we are still at the time at which this book is going to press in 2004, and we are still talking about government supported scientists in the USA holding on to the clearly incorrect dirty snowball comet model ... imagine where we would be in space science today in all fields if the past 25 years had not been spent in this ridiculous battle as opposed to moving forward into fertile ground).

The second is a clip from the Russians requesting me to clarifying some questions that they had following one of their meetings which included a question about the possibility of an intra-Mercurial planet, that is, a planet (or planets) that had been discovered by astronomers long ago to exist between Mercury and the sun, but later disappeared. That same piece will include the Russians statement that the fusion of the sun is not in its core, but in the upper surface of the sun, and their detection by way of measuring x-ray temperatures, that the sun had a cooler large planetary type core.

The next clip will be a portion of an e-mail for the Russians inviting me to come over and give a series of lectures at the University at Novosibirsk.

The next clip is a complete short paper referring to the Russians' work regarding detection and interpretation of data from the 1994 impact of 21 pieces of comet Schoemaker-Levy 9 crashing into Jupiter and their sentiments that this was an ELECTRICAL PLASMA event and in it they refer to my work, recognizing it for the correct explanation of the events of that comet impact and also stating as was the rumble across the entire worldwide scientific community that this was NOT a consequence of a miniscule dirty snowball. Is it not interesting that this data conclusively proved this to the worldwide scientific community and yet in 2004 NASA and its entourage of scientists still claim it is correct ... this extends beyond all absurdity.

The next will be a short paper entitled **PLANETOPHYSICAL STATE OF THE EARTH AND LIFE** by A. N. Dmitriev and Andrew Tetenov (translation by Eark Crockett who was one of the 3 musketeers of the original Millennium Group). This paper is quite long, and as you will see for the date written 1996, they were far ahead of its time in the realizations regarding the physical state of planet Earth. Due to the paper's length the long reference list is not included at then end.

The clips and communications with the Russians follow ... Note that the English is somewhat broken but the following is reproduced exactly as in the original communications ...

What follows is an early statement by the Russians regarding their first impressions of my work ...

Please, excuse us for so long silence. At first, partially it was because we took part in giant work with girl in discussion in preparing materials. Secondly, only interpreters translated your papers in their free time. Not long ago (last week) we held first close seminar, devoted your article "the nature and origin of comets and the evolution of celestial bodies". Under advising Dr. A. N. Dmitriev, about 10 members (well mathematically and physically educated, in nice Siberian scientific center) heard in discussed part one of this paper sentence by sentence. We are going to make four to five seminars more. Now we have the next questions on this part to you.

One) we considered, that this work is revolutionary in essence and gigantic step forward even because it involves in consideration great number of possibilities for behavior of celestial objects (for example electrical and magnetic forces), and new method revolutionary ways (especially your idea about attracting material into comet nucleus). Facts and references are very interesting too.

Two) when discussing we didn't understand properly your first charge mechanism. Maybe it will be clear with next parts; the second charging process seems to be clear. You state, that moving in plasma, the heterogeneous (varying?) electric field, and object obtains negative (net) charge. Why? If we consider only action of electrical field in there should be only redistribution of charges on surface of given object. If plasma plays some role, but then we didn't catch it or understand from your text. (Where do the positive charge go and how?). Please, make more precise it for us.

Three) You know, we consider, that the comet nuclei are not frequently asteroidal solid bodies. They could be plasmic formations (objects) or vacuum domains as Dr. Dmitriev think. You write: "it is particularly hard to imagine a sun grazing ice ball passing through 1,000,000° solar Corona (not to mention passing through the solar Roche limit on highly eccentric orbit), and passing to the outside again relatively unaffected"

four) An mechanism of formation of ion nebula cloud around our solar system is not well-known by us.

From Vladimir N. Vlasov, Dr. Alexey N. Dmitriev
and Dr. Andrew Tetenov

The following is a clip from the Russians requesting me to clarifying some questions ....

Dear Earl (questions for Jim) Maybe, you did not understand Alexey's question. It means the following: there are indications in different sources at the existence of planets in the solar system which are closer to the sun than Mercury. They are sometimes called intra-mercurial planets. Alexey discussed this question in his book <u>The Science of the New Quality of Solar System</u> *(my translation of the book's name is bad). In the end of last century there were mentions that some astronomers observed some planet near the sun but later it "disappeared". Possibly, it is not seen covered by Corona. Here we have else to speak about one more myth of modern science: this is thermonuclear model of the sun, which is as good as snowball comet model. There are x-ray photos of the sun showing that it is solid part is twice smaller than what we see. The model of the sun discussed in Dmitriev's paper views a sun is a solid planet surrounded by a hot plasmosphere at a distance from it. Outer part of plasma sphere is hotter than interior. So there may be planets inside the plasmosphere. Our friend Roman Gromov from Nuclear Physics Institute Are made estimates of their period based on Titus -Bode rule in it gave about 35 days for one of these planets. This question is open and is of great interest for us.*

Next, do you remember a number of communications concerning small snow meteors in upper atmosphere discovered by Louis Frank? Can you find any detailed information on that topic? I've got two AP communications from your mails on that question. Maybe, there is a possibility to find some additional information on this question?

Closest 4 or 5 days I will stay in G-A, (and therefore without internet). Frosts keep still, and don't weaken (-34 C here and about --40 in Novosibirsk).

Does El-Nino Grow these days?

From Dr. Andrew Tetenov

The next clip will be a portion of an e-mail for the Russians inviting me to come over and give a series of lectures at the University at Novosibirsk.

FIRST ... MY EMAIL TO THE STAFF AT NOVOSIBIRSK

Re: plan lecture series and visit

Dear Vladimir and friends: I have been encouraged by many colleagues here to visit you and the group of supporters of my work in Russia and if possible give a series of lectures and work with you and the groups there to define experiments and other projects. Additionally I have a great deal of new and exciting work. If this would be of interest please respond. I have waited too long for Western scientists to recognize the value and extent of my work. Say hello to all of my friends there. Awaiting your response.

Sincerely;

James McCanney

THEIR RESPONSE INITIATING THE LECTURE SERIES

Dear James!

Of course, we will be glad to see you here and to help you in giving lectures, for instance in our State University. I'm not sure that our possibilities and forces will be enough for your projects, but in any case we can work together! And I'll resend your message to all my friends and I will keep consulting with them. Please, get some details if it is suitable now and we will be able to talk with you about realizing your project.

With Best Wishes

Vladimir

The next clip is a Russian paper for detection and interpretation of data from the 1994 impact of 21 pieces of comet Schoemaker-Levy 9 crashing into Jupiter and their sentiments that ***this was an energetic ELECTRICAL PLASMA event, and NOT a dirty snowball*** ...

The Powerful Events on Jupiter in July 1994

By A.N. Dmitriev
"Modern Problems of Natural and Physical Sciences"
Novosibirsk State University
1996

The after effects of the explosion of self-luminous formations on Jupiter in July 1994 are considered to be a result of the relaxation of a swarm of plasmoids generated in the Solar System region of maximal energetic and material heterogeneity. [Note to Dmitriev: Can you name this region?] A cosmophysical formation widely known as "Shoemaker-Levy 9 Comet" is still far from having a reliable, single meaning, interpretation. And, the indefiniteness of an explanatory definition has tended to increase proportionally with the arrival of new information.

Current cometary theory versions of the July 1994 explosions on Jupiter [1,2,] lack credibility, as far as they go, because of their inability to explain the observed reactive forces; especially in the area of electromagnetics [3]. The application of the plasmic nature model of self-luminous formations, (currently in an advancing state of development) [4,5], however, moves the problem into an arena of much more plausible answers concerning the true nature and eventual consequences of the observed massive explosions. The huge amount of data that has been provided by surface, as well as satellite and interplanetary probes, (Galileo, Ulysses, and Voyager) regarding the Jupiter/SL-9 events is difficult, if not impossible to coordinate with luminous "cometary fragment", solid body, models. The observed chemical composition, and an input matter of less than 10,000 ton [3]) does not translate, or equate, to a composition of "dirty ice". Questions regarding the power mechanisms, and the sequence of explosions, are hard to answer using standard "dirty snowball" theory. The consequences of the series of "weak" and "strong" effects resulting from the impacts on Jupiter, are natural occurring events when the plasma model of comets is applied. Observations of the electromagnetic relaxation of the local electromagnetic field imply the equivalent of a short circuit between the planetary surface, and Jupiter's surrounding plasma (composed primarily of S02) by way of the comet's multiple nuclei. [4,8] [Alexey: I got help from McCanney on this sentence]

The electrical charged and magnetized clots of plasma made a vertical cut in the electromagnetic frame of Jupiter, and injected energy and matter into the top atmosphere which was 3 to 4 times greater than the expected "ice and dust" chemical concentration of energy [6]; it was typical, however, of a plasma composition which exhibits an absence of water, and a small quantity of dust . As in the case of the 1908 "Tungusska meteorite" in Siberia, the massive forces unleashed on Jupiter by S-L9 resulted in an unusual breach of the physical vacuum homogeneity [7] via the anisotropy of interplanetary space. This leads to a number of natural consequences resulting in differing energy-saturation and chemical composition objectives. The injection of energy and matter by S-L 9's "string of pearls" plasma queue, has created a new and excited energetic state on Jupiter that is reflected in a number of new developments which include: A reflective light echo from Jupiter's moons , a variation in decimeter radiation readings, an excited and unusual state of seismic activities, an increase in the radiation belts, an excited "glimmering Aurora", a detection of flashes of X-ray's and ultraviolet radiation, an excitation of the auroral process in the Northern Hemisphere, and a decreasing luminosity of Io's plasma torus.[3].

We would like to emphasize that due to the magnetic conjugation between Earth and Jupiter, that a number of the processes occurring on the giant planet do, in fact, influence the state of Earth's magnetosphere. This magnetoconjugation is proven by the actual coincidence of their dipole axes, as well as the matching of the parameters and location of their non-dipole magnetic fields. There are four world magnetic anomalies (quadro-poles) on both Earth and Jupiter. It is then possible to reasonably hypothesize that the present alteration of Earth's magnetic fields by the extension of its of polar slits, and the vertical redistribution of ozone layers, is closely connected with powerful developments resulting from Jupiter's encounter with Shoemaker-Levy 9.

Literature

1. Churyumov K.I. Once more about collision comet with Jupiter. // The Earth and The Universe. -1994.- No.1.- p.83-85 (rus).

2. Ciel et Espase & Paris. - 09.1994.- p.17-23

3. Fortov V.E., Gnedin Y.I., Ivanov A.V. and others. Collision comet Shoemaker-Levy 9 with Jupiter. // Achievements of the physical sciences.- 1996 -v.166, No.4 -p.391-422. (rus)

4. Dmitriev A.N. Earth's echoes on powerful processes in Jupiter's system. // MIKA news - Novosibirsk, 1994. - v.1 - p.16-21.(rus).

5. Dmitriev A.N. Les consequences terrestres des evementes sur Jupiter. // Energie Sante. - Paris, 29 - 1995 -p.16- 22.

6. Dmitriev A.N., Zhuravlev V.K. Tungusska phenomenon 1908 as a kind of Solar-Earth two-way connection. - Novosibirsk, - Institute of Geology and Geophysics, Siberian branch of Academy of Sciences in USSR, 1984. - p.143
(rus).

7. Dmitriev A.N., Dyatlov V.L. Model of heterogeneous physical vacuum and natural self-luminous formations. - Novosibirsk, 1995. - p.35 (preprint / Rus. Academy of Sciences, Siberian branch, Institute of mathematics - No.16.) (rus).

8. Conversations with James McCanney 1/15/98. Addition to original paper.

The next clip will be a paper entitled **PLANETOPHYSICAL STATE OF THE EARTH AND LIFE** by A. N. Dmitriev and Andrew Tetenov (translation by Eark Crockett who was one of the 3 musketeers of the original Millennium Group). This paper is quite long, and as you will see for the date written 1996, they were far ahead of their time in the realizations regarding the physical state of planet Earth. Clearly the Russians, who were climatologists, atmospheric Physicists and with a large cast of supporting scientists from every field of study, were already tuned to the changing earth conditions in the early to mid 1990's and they recognized that it was due to causes from outside of our planet (***not due to manmade greenhouse gasses***). That is why they welcomed my work with open arms, as it finally gave them a sound scientific basis for what they were measuring. Due to the paper's length the long reference list is not included at then end.

PLANETOPHYSICAL STATE OF THE EARTH AND LIFE.

By DR. ALEXEY N. DMITRIEV*

Published in Russian, IICA Transactions, Volume 4, 1997

*Professor of Geology and Mineralogy, and Chief Scientific Member,
United Institute of Geology, Geophysics, and Mineralogy, Siberian Department,
Russian Academy of Sciences.
Expert on Global Ecology, and Fast -Processing Earth Events.

Russian to English Translation and Editing:
by A. N. Dmitriev, Andrew Tetenov, and Earl L. Crockett

INTRODUCTION

Current, in process, geological, geophysical, and climatical alterations of the Earth are becoming more, and more, irreversible. At the present time researchers are revealing some of the causes which are leading to a general reorganization of the electro-magnetosphere (the electromagnetic skeleton) of our planet, and of it's climatic machinery. A greater number of specialists in climatology, geophysics, planetophysics, and heliophysics are tending towards a cosmic causative sequence version for what is happening. Indeed, events of the last decade give strong evidence of unusually significant heliospheric and planetophysic transformations [1,2]. Given the quality, quantity, and scale of these transformations we may say that:

The climatic and biosphere processes here on Earth (through a tightly connected feedback system) are directly impacted by, and linked back to, the general overall transformational processes taking place in our Solar System. We must begin to organize our attention and thinking to understand that climatic changes on Earth are only one part, or link, in a whole chain of events taking place in our Heliosphere.

These deep physical processes, these new qualities of our physical and geological environment, will impose special adaptive challenges and requirements for all life forms on Earth. Considering the problems of adaptation our biosphere will have with these new physical conditions on Earth, we need to distinguish the general tendency and nature of the changes. As we will show below, **these tendencies may be traced in the direction of planet energy capacity growth (capacitance), which is leading to a highly excited or charged state of some of Earth's systems**. The most intense transformations are taking place in the planetary gas-plasma envelopes to which the productive possibilities of our biosphere are timed. Currently this new scenario of excess energy run-off is being formed, and observed, in the ionosphere by plasma generation, in the magnetosphere by magnetic storms, and in the atmosphere by cyclones. This high-energy atmospheric phenomena, which was rare in the past , is now becoming more frequent, intense, and changed in it's nature. The material composition of the gas-plasma envelope is also being transformed.

It is quite natural for the whole biota of the Earth to be subjected to these changing conditions of the electromagnetic field, and to the significant deep alterations of Earth's climatic machinery. These fundamental processes of change create a demand within all of Earth's life organisms for new forms of adaptation. **The natural development of these new forms may lead to a total global revision of the range of species, and life, on Earth** . New deeper qualities of life itself may come forth, bringing the new physical state of the Earth to an equilibrium with the new organismic possibilities of development, reproduction, and perfection. In this sense **it is evident that we are faced with a problem of the adaptation of humanity to this new state of the Earth**; an Earth whose biospheric qualities are varying, and non-uniformly distributed. Therefore the current period of transformation is transient, and the transition of life's representatives to the future may take place only after a deep evaluation of what it will take to comply with these new Earthly biospheric conditions. Each living representative on Earth will be getting a thorough "examination", or "quality control inspection", to determine it's ability to comply with these new conditions. **These evolutionary challenges always require effort, or striving, be it individual organisms, species, or communities.** Therefore, it is not only the climate that is becoming new, but we as human beings are experiencing a global change in the vital processes of living organisms, or life itself; which is yet another link in the total process. We cannot treat such things separately, or individually.

1.0 TRANSFORMATION OF THE SOLAR SYSTEM

We will list the recent large-scale events in the Solar System in order to fully understand, and comprehend, the PlanetoPhysical transformations taking place. This development of events, as it has become clear in the last few years, is being caused by material and energetic non-uniformity's in anisotropic interstellar space [2,3,4]. In it's travel through interstellar space, the Heliosphere travels in the direction of the Solar Apex in the Hercules Constellation. On it's way it has met (1960's) non-homogeneities of matter and energy containing ions of Hydrogen, Helium, and Hydroxyl in addition to other elements and combinations. This kind of interstellar space dispersed plasma is presented by magnetized strip structures and striations. The Heliosphere [solar system] transition through this structure has led to an increase of the shock wave in front of the Solar System from 3 to 4 AU, to 40 AU, or more. [1 AU, the distance from Earth to the Sun is approximately 93 million miles]. This shock wave thickening has caused the formation of a collusive plasma in a parietal layer, which has led to a plasma overdraft around the Solar System, and then to it's breakthrough into interplanetary domains [5,6]. **This breakthrough constitutes a kind of matter and energy donation made by interplanetary space to our Solar System .**

In response to this **"donation of energy/matter"**, we have observed a number of large scale events :

- A series of large PlanetoPhysical transformations.

- A change in the quality of interplanetary space in the direction of an increase in it's interplanetary and solar-planetary transmitting properties.

- The appearance of new states and activity regimes of the Sun.

1.1 A Series of Large PlanetoPhysical Transformations.

The following processes are taking place on the distant planets of our Solar System. But they are, essentially speaking, running the whole System.

Here are examples of these events:

1.1.1 A growth of dark spots on Pluto [7].

1.1.2 Reporting of auroras on Saturn [8].

1.1.3 Reporting of Uranus and Neptune polar shifts (They are magnetically conjugate planets), and the abrupt large- scale growth of Uranus' magnetosphere intensity.

1.1.4 A change in light intensity and light spot dynamics on Neptune [9,10].

1.1.5 The doubling of the magnetic field intensity on Jupiter (by 1992 data), and a series of new states and processes observed on this planet as an aftermath of a series of explosions in July 1994 [caused by "Comet" SL-9] [12]. That is, a relaxation of a plasmoid train [13,14] which excited the Jovian magnetosphere, thus inducing excessive plasma generation [12] and it's release in the same manner as Solar coronal holes [15] inducing an appearance of radiation belt brightening in decimeter band (13.2 and 36 cm), and the appearance of large auroral anomalies and a change of the Jupiter - Io system of currents [12, 14].

Update Note From A.N.D Nov. 1997:
A stream of ionized hydrogen, oxygen, nitrogen, etc. is being directed to Jupiter from the volcanic areas of Io through a one million amperes flux tube. It is affecting the character of Jupiter's magnetic process and intensifying it's plasma genesis.{Z.I. Vselennaya "Earth and Universe" N3, 1997 plo-9 by NASA data}

1.1.6 A series of Martian atmosphere transformations increasing it's biosphere quality. In particularly, a cloudy growth in the equator area and an unusual growth of ozone concentration[16].

1.1.7 A first stage atmosphere generation on the Moon; where a growing natrium atmosphere is detected that reaches 9,000 km in height. [17].

1.1.8 Significant physical, chemical and optical changes observed on Venus; an inversion of dark and light spots detected for the first time, and a sharp decrease of sulfur-containing gases in it's atmosphere [16].

1. 2 A Change in the Quality of Interplanetary Space in the Direction of an Increase in It's Interplanetary and Solar-Planetary Transmitting Properties.

When speaking of new energetic and material qualities of interplanetary space, we must first point out the increase of the interplanetary domains energetic charge, and level of material saturation. This change of the typical mean state of interplanetary space has two main causes:

1.2.1 The supply/inflow of matter from interstellar space.(Radiation material, ionized elements, and combinations.) [19,20,21].

1.2.2 The after effects of Solar Cycle 22 activity, especially as a result of fast coronal mass ejection's [CME's] of magnetized solar plasmas. [22].

It is natural for both interstellar matter and intraheliospheric mass redistribution's to create new structural units and processes in the interplanetary domains. They are mostly observed in the structured formation of extended systems of magnetic plasma clouds [23], and an increased frequency of the generation of shock waves; and their resulting effects [24].

A reporting already exists of two new populations of cosmic particles that were not expected to be found in the Van Allen radiation belts [25]; particularly an injection of a greater than 50 MeV dense electron sheaf into the inner magnetosphere during times of abrupt magnetic storms [CME's], and the emergence of a new belt consisting of ionic elements proper for the composition of stars . This newly changed quality of interplanetary space not only performs the function of a planetary interaction transmission mechanism, but it (this is most important) exerts stimulating and programming action upon the Solar activity both in it's maximal and minimal phases. The seismic effectiveness of the solar wind is also being observed [26,27].

1.3 The Appearance of New States and Activity Regimes of the Sun.

As far as the stellarphysical state of the Sun is concerned, we must first note the fact that significant modifications have occurred in the existing behavioral model of the central object of our solar system. This conclusion comes from observations and reportings of unusual forms, energetic powers, and activities in the Sun's functions [20,21], as well as modifications in it's basic fundamental properties [28]. Since the end of the Maunder minimum, a progressive growth of the Sun's general activity has been observed. This growth first revealed itself most definitely in the 22nd cycle; which posed a real problem for heliophysicists who were attempting to revise their main explanatory scenarios:

1.3.1 Concerning the velocity of reaching super-flash maximums.

1.3.2 Concerning the emissive power of separate flashes.

1.3.3 Concerning the energy of solar cosmic rays, etc.

Moreover, the Ulysses spacecraft, traversing high heliospheric latitudes, recorded the absence of the magnetic dipole, which drastically changed the general model of heliomagnetism, and further complicated the magnetologist's analytic presentations. The most important heliospheric role of coronal holes has now become clear; to regulate the magnetic saturation of interplanetary space. [28,30]. It turns out, that they generate all large geomagnetic storms, and that the ejection's with a southerly directed magnetic field are geo-effective [22]. Besides this there are already good reasons favoring the solar winds effects upon Earth's atmospheric zone's circulation, and lithospheric dynamics [31].

The 23rd cycle was initiated by a short series of sunspots in August 1995 [32], which allows us to even predict the solar activity maximum in 1999. What is also remarkable, is that a series of class C flares has already happened in July 1996 . The specificity and energy of this cycle was discussed even at the end of the 1980's. [23]. The increased frequency of X-Ray flux flares in the very beginning of this cycle provided evidence of the large-scale events to come; especially in relation to a growth in frequency of super-flashes. The situation has become extremely serious due to the growth in the transmitting qualities of the interplanetary environment [2 3, 24] and the growth of Jupiter's systems heliospheric function; with Jupiter having the possibility of being shrouded by a plasmosphere extending over Io's orbit [13].

As a whole, all of the reporting and observation facilities give evidence to a growth in the velocity, quality, quantity, and energetic power of our Solar System's Heliospheric processes.

[Note to Alexey and Andrew]
[Do you think we should place an update of recent sun activity here? I'm thinking particularly about the April 7, 1997 CME, the Sept. 1997 events, and the very dramatic X-2 and X-9.4 xray flux events of Nov.4 and Nov.6, 1997?]

2.0 THE EARTH REORGANIZATION PROCESSES

The recorded and documented observations of all geophysical (planetary environmental) processes, and the clearly significant and progressive modifications in all reported solar-terrestrial physical science relationships, combined with the integral effects of the antropohenedus activity in our Solar System's Heliosphere, [33,34], **causes us to conclude that a global reorganization and transformation of the Earth's physical and environmental qualities is taking place now; before our very eyes**. This current rearrangement constitutes one more in a long line of cosmo-historic events of significant Solar System evolutionary transformations which are caused by the periodic modification, and amplification, of the Heliospheric-Planetary-Sun processes. In the case of our own planet these new events have placed an intense pressure on the geophysical environment; causing new qualities to be observed in the natural processes here on Earth; **causes and effects which have already produced hybrid processes throughout the planets of our Solar System**; where the combining of effects on natural matter and energy characteristics have been observed and reported.

We shall now speak to the global, regional, and local processes.

2.1 The Geomagnetic Field Inversion.

Keeping clearly in mind the known significant role of the magnetic field on human life, and all biological processes, we need to outline the general features of this changing state of the Earth's geomagnetic field. We have to remind ourselves of the many spacecraft's and satellites that have registered the growth of heliospheric magnetic saturation in recent years [11,18,35]. The natural response of the Earth to this increased saturation level reveals itself in it's dipole intensity, it's magnet "c" poles localization, and in it's electromagnetic field resonance processes[36]. Earth is number one among all of the planets in the Solar System with respect to it's specific ability regarding the magnetization of matter [6]. Specific magnetization is magnetic field intensity divided by mass. Count it for each planet, and you will find that Earth has the greatest.

In recent years we have seen a growth of interest by geophysicists and magnetologists, in general, to geomagnetic processes [37-40], and specifically, to the travel of Earth's magnetic poles [41,42]. They are particularly interested in observing the facts surrounding the directed, or vectored, travel of the Northern magnetic pole (which is located in the Southern Hemisphere). In the last 100 years this magnetic pole has traveled almost 900 km towards, and into, the Indian ocean. This significant shift by the magnetic poles began in 1885. The most recent data about the state of the Arctic (Southern) magnetic pole (which is moving towards the Eastern Siberian world magnetic anomaly by way of the Arctic Ocean) reveals that this pole "traveled" more than 120 km during the ten year period 1973 through 1984, and 150 km during the same period, 1984 through 1994. This estimated data has been confirmed by direct measurement (L. Newwitt. The Arctic pole coordinates are now 78.3 deg. North and 104.0 deg. West) [42].

We must emphasize that this documented polar shift acceleration (3 km per year average over 10 years), and it's travel along the geo-historic magnetic poles inversion corridor (the corridor having been established by the analysis of more than 400 paleoinversion sites) necessarily **leads us to the conclusion that the currently observed polar travel acceleration is not just a shift or digression from the norm, but is in fact an inversion of the magnetic poles; in full process.** It is now seen that the acceleration of polar travel may grow to a rate of up to 200 km per year. This means that a polar inversion may happen far more rapidly than is currently supposed by most investigators of Geotechnical phenomenon.

We must also emphasize the significant growth of the recognized world magnetic anomalies (Canadian, East-Siberian, Brazilian, and Antarctic) in the Earth's magnetic reorganization. Their significance is due to the fact that these world anomalies constitute a magnetic source that is almost independent from Earth's main magnetic field. The intensity of these world magnetic anomalies usually substantially exceeds all of the residual non-dipole component; which is obtained by the subtraction of the dipole component from the total magnetic field of the Earth.[48]. It is the inversion of the magnetic fields process which is causing the various transformations of Earth's geophysical processes and the present state of the polar magnetosphere.

We also have to take into account the factual growth of the polar cusp's angle (i.e. The polar slots in the magnetosphere; North and South), which in the middle 1990's reached 45 degrees (by IZMIRAN data). [Note: The cusp angle was about 6 degrees most of the time. It varies depending on the situation. In the last five years, however, it has danced between 25 and 46 degrees.] The increasing and immense amounts of matter and energy radiating from the Sun's Solar Wind, and Interplanetary Space, by means previously discussed, has began to rush into these widened slots in the polar regions **causing the Earth's crust, the oceans, and the polar ice caps to warm** [27].

Our study of geomagnetic field paleoinversions, and their after effects, has lead us to the unambiguous, and straight forth, conclusion that these present processes being observed are following precisely the same scenarios as those of their distant ancestors. And additional signs of the inversion of the magnetic field are becoming more intense in frequency and scale. For example: In the last 25 million years the frequency of magnetic inversions was twice in half a million years while the frequency of inversions for the last 1 million years is 8 to 14 inversions in a million years [43], or one inversion each 71 to 125 thousand years. What is essential here is that during prior periods of maximum frequency of inversions there has also been a corresponding decrease in the level of oceans world-wide (10 to 150 meters) from contraction caused by the wide development of crustal folding processes. Periods of lessor frequency of geomagnetic field inversions reveals sharp increases of the world ocean level due to the priority of expansion and stretching processes in the crust. [43-44]. Therefore, the level of World's oceans depends on the global characteristic of the contraction and expansion processes in force at the time.

The current phase of growth of geomagnetic inversions frequency may not lead to an increase in oceanic volume from polar warming, but to a decrease of ocean levels. Frequent conversions mean stretching and expansion, rare inversions mean contraction. Planetary processes, as a rule, run in complex and dynamic ways that require the combining and joining of all forces and fields into a picture of the whole. Therefore, along with the consideration of hydrospheric redistribution **there are developing events which indicate a sudden and sharp breaking of the Earth's meteorological machinery.**

2.2 Climate Transformations.

Since public attention is so closely focused on the symptoms of major alterations, or breakdowns, in the climatic machinery, and the resulting and sometimes severe biospheric effects, we shall consider these climatic transformations in detail. Thus, while not claiming to characterize the climatic and biospheric transition period exhaustively, we will give a series of brief recent communications regarding the temperature, hydrological cycle, and the material composition of the Earth's atmosphere.

The temperature regime of any given phase of climatic reorganization is characterized by contrasts, and instabilities. **The widely quoted, and believed, "Greenhouse Effect" scenario for total climatic changes is by far the weakest explanation, or link, in accounting for this reorganization**. It has already been observed that the growth in the concentration of CO2 has stopped, and that the methane content in the atmosphere has began to decrease [45] while the temperature imbalance, and the common global pressure field dissolution has proceeded to grow.

There were reports of a global temperature maximum in 1994, and the almost uninterrupted existence of an "El-Nino" like hydrological effect. Satellite air surface layer temperature tracking [49,50] allowed the detection of a 0.22 degrees C global temperature variation (within a typical specific time period of about 30 days) that correlated with recorded middle frequency magnetic oscillations. **The Earth's temperature regime is becoming more, and more, dependent on external influences**. The representative regulating processes, or basis, of these general climatic rearrangements are:

2.2.1. A new ozone layer distribution.

2.2.2. Radiation material [plasma] inflows and discharges through the polar regions, and through the world magnetic anomaly locations.

2.2.3. Growth of the direct ionospheric effects on the relationship between the Earth's meteorological (weather), magnetic, and temperature fields.

There is a growing probability that we are moving into a rapid temperature instability period similar to the one that took place 10,000 years ago. This not so ancient major instability was revealed by the analysis of ice drilling core samples in Greenland [51]. The analysis of these core samples established:

2.2.4. **That annual temperatures increased by 7 degrees centigrade.**

2.2.5. **That precipitation grew in the range of 3 to 4 times.**

2.2.6. **That the mass of dust material increased by a factor of 100.**

Such high-speed transformations of the global climatic mechanism parameters, and it's effects on Earth's physical and biospheric qualities has not been rigorously studied by the reigning scientific community; so far. But, researchers are now insisting more, and more, that the Earth's temperature increases are dependent upon, and directly linked to, space-terrestrial interactions [52,53]; be it Earth-Sun, Earth-Solar System, and/or Earth-Interstellar.

At the present time there is no lack of new evidence regarding temperature inversion variations in the hydrosphere [oceans]. In the Eastern Mediterranean there have been recordings of a temperature inversion in depths greater than two kilometers from a ratio of 13.3 to 13.5 degrees centigrade to a new ratio of 13.8 to 13.5; along with a growth in salinity of 0.02% since 1987. The growth of salinity in the Aegean Sea has stopped, and the salt water outflow from the Mediterranean Basin to the Atlantic has diminished. Neither of these processes, or their causes, has been satisfactorily explained. It has already been established that evaporation growth in the equatorial regions leads to a water density growth causing the denser water to immediately submerge in depth. Ultimately this would force the Gulfstream to reverse it's flow. A probability of this event happening is confirmed by other signs as well as multiparameter numeric models [53]. Therefore the most highly probable scenario for the European Continent is a sharp and sudden cooling. Elsewhere, the Siberian region has been experiencing a stable temperature increase [58] along with reports from the Novosibirsk Klyuchi Observatory of a constant growth of up to 30 nanoteslas per year of the vertical component of the magnetic field. This growth rate increases significantly as the Eastern Siberian magnetic anomaly is approached.

2.3 Vertical and Horizontal Ozone Content Redistribution.

Vertical and horizontal ozone content redistribution is the main indicator, and active agent, of general climatic transformations on Earth. And, evidence exists that ozone concentrations also have a strong influence upon Earth's biospheric processes. Widespread models for "ozone holes" being in the stratosphere [7 to 10 miles above Earth] (Antarctic and Siberian) are receiving serious confirmation from reports of vertical ozone redistribution, and it's growth in the troposphere [below 7 miles]. It is now clear that the decrease in our atmosphere's total ozone content is caused by technogeneous [industrial, human designed, pollution], and that the total ozone content in general has serious effects upon the energy distribution processes within Earth's gas-plasma [atmospheric] envelopes [54].

Stratospheric, tropospheric, and surface layer ozone's are now being studied. Photodissociation [the process by which a chemical combination breaks up into simpler constituents] of ozone, controls the oxidizing activities within the troposphere. This has created a special atmospheric, physio-chemical, circumstance by which the usual tropospheric concentrations, and lifetimes, of carbon monoxide, methane, and other hydrocarbon gases are modified and changed. **So, with the established fact that a statistically significant rise in the ozone concentrations has taken place in the tropospheric layers between 5 and 7 miles, and with the addition, and full knowledge, of ozone's oxidizing properties, we must conclude that a basic and fundamental correction of the gas composition and physical state of Earth's atmosphere has already begun.**

There are continuing reports of diminishing regional stratosphere ozone concentrations [25 to 49% or more above Siberia (57)], and of global decreases of ozone content in altitudes of 20-26 miles; with the maximal decrease of 7% being at 24 miles [55]. At the same time, there is no direct evidence of a growth of UV radiation at the ground surface [58]. There are, however, a growing number of "ozone alerts" in large European cities. For example, in 1994 there were 1800 "ozone alerts" in Paris. In addition, remarkably high concentrations of surface layer ozone were registered in the Siberian Region. There were ozone concentration splashes in Novosibirsk that exceeded 50 times the normal level. We must remember that ozone smell is noticeable in concentrations of 100 mkg/m3; i.e. at 2 to 10 times the normal level.

The most serious concern of aeronomists comes from the detection of H02 that is being produced at an altitude of 11 miles by a completely unknown source or mechanism. This source of HO2 was discovered as a result of the investigation of OH/HO2 ratios in the interval between 4.35 and 21.70 miles in the upper troposphere and stratosphere. This significant growth of HO2, over the course of time, will create a dependence on this substance for the ozone transfer and redistribution process in the lower stratosphere.

The submission of ozone's dynamic regime and space distribution to the above unknown source of HO2, signifies a transition of Earth's atmosphere to a new physico-chemical process. This is very important because non-uniformity's in the Earth's ozone concentrations can, and will, cause an abrupt growth in temperature gradients, which in turn do lead to the increase of air mass movement velocities, and to irregularities of moisture circulation patterns. Temperature gradient changes, and alterations, over the entire planet would create new thermodynamic conditions for entire regions; especially when the hydrospheres [oceans] begin to participate in the new thermal non-equilibrium. The study [53] insists on that conclusion, **and the considering of a possible abrupt cooling of the European and North American Continents**. The probability of such a scenario increases when you take into account the ten year idleness of the North Atlantic hydrothermal pump. With this in mind, the creation of a global, ecology-oriented, climate map which might reveal these global catastrophes becomes critically important.

3.0 THE ARRIVAL OF NEW CONDITIONS AND CONSEQUENCES.

Considering the totality and sequential relationship of transient background and newly formed processes brought about by the above stated cosmogenic and anthropogenic PlanetoPhysical transformations and alterations of our weather and climatic systems, we find it reasonable to divide matters into their manifest (explicit) and non-manifest (implicit) influences upon Earth's environment.

3.1 The Manifest or Explicit Consequences.

The classes or categories of effects brought about by the Earth's current stage of reorganization are very diverse. Most often, however, they tend to the transient high-energy type of event. Based on the results of the Yokohama Conference (Fall 1994), they can be called "significant catastrophes". There are nine types of "significant catastrophes":

Catastrophes By Type: For the period of 1963-1993

	Number	$ Damage (Billions)	Deaths
Flooding	76	162	202,000
Hurricanes	73		153,000
Drought	53	167	
Frost	24		
Storms	24		
Epidemics		100	133,000
Earthquakes		20	102,000
Starvation		18	
Landslides			54,000

In addition, we must point out the abrupt growth of meteorological/weather catastrophes in recent years. In the Atlantic region alone there were 19 cyclones in 1994; 11 of which became hurricanes. This is a 100 year record [60]. The current year, 1996, is especially laden with reports of flooding and other types of meteocatastrophes. The dynamic growth of significant catastrophes shows a major increase in the rate of production since 1973. And in general, the number of catastrophes has grown by 410% between 1963 and 1993. Special attention must be focused on the growing number and variety of catastrophes, and to their consequences.

Years	Damage >1% of gross national product.		Casualties>1% of population		> 100 deaths.	
	total	Annual	total	annual	total	annual
1963-1967	16	3.2	39	7.8	89	17.8
1968-1972	15	3.0	54	10.8	98	19.6
1973-1977	31	6.2	56	11.2	95	19
1978-1982	55	11.0	99	19.8	138	27.6
1983-1987	58	11.6	116	23.2	153	30.6
1988-1992	66	13.2	139	27.8	205	41.0
	241	8.0	503	16.8	778	25.5

One must keep in mind that the growing complexity of climatic and weather patterns signals a transformation tending towards a new state, or as Academician Kondratyev says, it is acquiring all of the features of moving in the direction of climatic chaos. In reality this transition state of our climatic machinery is placing new requirements upon Earth's entire biosphere; which does include the human species. In particular, there are reports from Antarctica that show a dramatic reaction by vegetation to the recent changes in climate; there were 700 species found growing in 1964 and 17,500 in 1990 [61]. This increase in Earth's vegetative cover provides evidence of the biosphere's reaction to the ongoing process of climatic rearrangement.

The overall pattern of the generation and movement of cyclones has also changed. For example, the number of cyclones moving to Russia from the West has grown 2.5 times during the last 10 years. Increased ocean levels caused by the off loading of ice from the polar regions will lead to sharp changes in coast lines, a redistribution of land and sea relationships, and to the activation of significant geodynamic processes. This is the main characteristic of those processes leading to a new climatic and biospheric order.

3.2 The Non-Manifest or Implicit Consequences

Implicit consequences are those processes which are below the threshold of usual human perception, and are therefore not brought to our common attention. Instrument recordings, and even direct observations, of these phenomena throughout Earth's electromagnetic field provides evidence that an immense transformation of Earth's environment is taking place. This situation is aggravated by the fact that in the 1990's anthropogeneous (human) power production/usage increased to (1-9)E+26 ergs/per year which means it reached the conservative energetic production/usage values of our planet. For example, Earth's annual energy consumption is comprised of (1-9)E+26 ergs for earthquakes, (1-9)E+24 for geomagnetic storms, and (1-9)E+28 for heat emission [54].

There already are technogeneous effects upon the functional state of Earth's electromagnetic skeleton being registered and recorded. A seven-day technogeneous cycle for geomagnetic field dynamic parameter variations was revealed in 1985 [62,63]. This cycle has affected many of the short cycles in Solar-terrestrial relationships. More than 30% of middle magnetosphere disturbances are caused by power production, transmission, and consumption. The Van Allen radiation belt has abruptly lowered above the East Coast of the US from 300 km to 10 km. This process is associated with electricity transmission from the Great Lakes to the South along a magnetic meridian, and usage of the ionosphere-resonance frequency (60Hz) of energy consumption [63]. There is also a registered coherence between the gutter qualities of the Brazilian magnetic anomaly, and the "Hydro-Quebec" power production system. Combined techno-natural electromagnetic processes in megalopolises are very complex and as yet unstudied. A 1996 study of mortality from cardiovascular diseases in St. Petersburg, Russia uncovered a direct connection between the city's power consumption and mortality .

Moreover, the increase in the frequency, and scope, of **natural self-luminous formations** in the atmosphere and geospace forces us to wake up and take notice [64,65,66]. The processes of generation, and the existence of such formations, spreading all over the Earth, represents a remarkable physical phenomenon. What is most unusual about these natural self-

luminous formations is that while they have distinct features of well-known physical
processes, they are in entirely unusual combinations, and are accompanied by process features which cannot be explained on the basis of existing physical knowledge. Thus, features of intense electromagnetic processes are being found in the space inside and near these natural self-luminous objects. These features include:

3.2.1. Intense electromagnetic emissions ranging from the micrometer wave band through the visible diapason, to television, and radio wavelengths.

3.2.2. Electric and magnetic field changes such as electric breakdowns, and the magnetization of rocks and technical objects.

3.2.3. Destructive electrical discharges.

3.2.4. Gravitation effects such as levitation.

3.2.5. Others.

All of the qualities of this class of phenomena are requiring the development of new branches of modern physics; particularly the creation of a "non-homogeneous physical vacuum model". [67]. An advancement of the sciences in this direction would allow us to reveal the true nature of these objects, which are acting apparently, and latently, upon our geological-geophysical and biospheric environment, and on human life [68].

Therefore, we must first take into account all of the newly developed processes and states of our geological-geophysical environment. These processes, for the most part, manifest themselves in the hard-to-register, and observe, qualities of the Earth's electromagnetic skeleton. This data also concerns the geophysical and climatic meanings of Solar-terrestrial and planetary-terrestrial interactions. This is especially true of Jupiter which is magnetically conjugate to our planet. The totality of these planet-transforming processes develops precipitately, ubiquitously, and diversely. That is why a call for training politicians to understand these global relations between the totality of natural and anthropogeneous activities becomes so important [69].

A critical need now exists for a study laying out the problems associated with Earth's current transformational processes, and the effects it will have on global demographic dynamics.[70]. The sharp rise of our technogeneous systems to being destructive on a planetary as well as a cosmic scale, **has now placed the future survival of our technocratic civilization in question** [33,7]. And the principle of Natures supremacy [72] over that of humanities current integral technogeneous and psychogenic activities and results, becomes more, and more, apparently formed.

CONCLUSIONS:

The situation that has been formed here in our Heliosphere is of **external, Interstellar, cosmic space origin**, and is herein assumed to be caused by the underlying fundamental auto-oscillation, space-physical, processes of continuous creation that has shaped, and continues to evolve our Universe. The present excited state of our Heliosphere is directed to the whole, or entire, organism that makes up the Solar System; the Sun, Planets, Moons, Comets, and Asteroids, as well as the plasmas, and/or electromagnetic mediums, and structures, of Interplanetary Space. The response to these Interstellar energy and matter donations has been, and continues to be, a series of newly observed energetic processes and formations on all of the Planets; between the Planets and their Moons, and the Planets and the Sun.

Earth's ability to adapt to these external actions and donations is aggravated, made more difficult, by the technogeneous alterations we have made to the natural quality, or state, of our geological-geophysical environment. **Our Planet Earth is now in the process of a dramatic transformation**; by altering the electromagnetic skeleton through a shift of the geomagnetic field poles, and through compositional changes in the ozone and hydrogen saturation levels of it's gas-plasma envelopes. These changes in the Earth's physical state are being accompanied by resultant climatic/atmospheric, and biospheric, adaptation processes. These processes are becoming more and more intense, and frequent, as evidenced by the real time increase in "non-periodic transient events"; ie., catastrophes. There are reasons favoring, or pointing to, the fact that a growth in the ethical, or spiritual quality, of humanity would decrease the number and intensity of complex catastrophes. It has become vitally important that a world chart be prepared setting forth the favorable, and the catastrophic, regions on Earth taking into account the quality of the geologic-geophysical environment, the variety and intensity of cosmic influences, and the real level of spiritual-ethical development of the people occupying those areas.

It is reasonable to point out that our Planet will soon be experiencing these new conditions of growing energy signifying the transition into a new state and quality of Space-Earth relationship. The living organisms of those regions of Earth having the major "inlets", or attractions, for cosmic influences will be taking the lead in evolving life's appropriate reactions, or processes, to these new conditions. These zones of vertical commutations and energy transfers are already becoming the heart, or hotbeds, for the search for new systems of adaptation and mutual transformation. The general list of these zones includes the polar regions, the eastern continental extremities of the equatorial regions [Caribbean, Madagascar, Philippines, Yellow Sea, etc.], and the inner continental zones tending to folding and uplifting [Himalayas, Pamir-Hindukush, Altay-Sayan systems, etc.]

The most significant of these areas are the helio-sensitive zones which have intense responses to geoeffective solar activities [Note #1]; responses that include the very dramatic and unusual production of non-homogeneous vacuum, or ether, domain structures. These structures, or objects, then interact with the heliosensitive zones producing deep and powerful effects upon the environment such as the alteration of seismic activities, and chemical compositions. Because these non-homogeneous vacuum domain objects display not-of-this-physical-world characteristics such as "liquid light" and "non-Newtonian movement" it is difficult not to describe their manifestations as being "interworld processes". It is important to note that those heliosensitive zones that exhibit middle and large scale processes are also those that are closely associated with these "interworld processes" produced by physical vacuum homogeneity disturbances.

Such disturbances cause, and create, energy and matter transfer processes between the ether media and our three-dimensional world. The multitude of such phenomena, which is rich in it's quality and variety, is already growing quickly. Hundreds of thousands of these natural self-luminous formations are exerting a increasing influence upon Earth's geophysic fields and biosphere. **We suggest that the presence of these formations is the mainstream precedent to the transformation of Earth**; an Earth which becomes more and more subject to the transitional physical processes which exist within the border of ightening in decimeter band (13.and **Update N All of this places humanity, and each one of us,**

squarely in front of a very difficult and topical problem; the creation of a revolutionary advancement in knowledge which will require a transformation of our thinking and being equal to this never-before-seen phenomena now presencing itself in our world. There is no other path to the future than a profound internal experiential perception and knowledge of the events now underway in the natural environment that surrounds us. It is only through this understanding that humanity will achieve balance with the renewing flow of the PlanetoPhysical States and Processes.

End Paper

Note #1:
1. Since the Earth is a large very highly organized organism, each of its structural units or territories such as, mountain systems, rivers, tectonic faults, ore deposits, oil fields etc. plays a certain functional role in it's life, and in it's connections with the outer world. For example, iron ore deposits support the climate stability because they perform the connection between the electrical activity in the atmosphere, and the electrical activity beneath the Earth's surface.

2. Nowadays we all know the works of Tschizhevsky who discovered, and proved in the 1920's, that deep and various connections exist between Solar activity and various life processes. Using vast historical and statistical material he showed that Solar activity acts as an accelerator and moderator upon the whole biosphere, which manifests in the frequency and quantity of : births, deaths , harvests, epidemics, heart attacks, emergencies, bank crashes, catastrophes, suicides, populations growths and decreases, etc, etc.

3. Since different zones of Earth have different functions in the Earth organism, their response to Solar activity is also different. For example, the polar regions are first to react to Solar disturbances, which we know well in the form of magnetic storms, auroras, and nowadays, in ocean warming at the 75 degree North latitudes. We also know other places which demonstrate intense reactions to different kinds of solar activity; that's what we call *heliosensitive zones*. Such reactions include local electromagnetic disturbances, low-latitude auroras, and specific changes in the pattern of magnetic field variations on the short term scale. There are also long-term reactions in the state of the biosphere. One of our colleagues, Ildar Mingazov, found, in studying the distribution and frequency of different

types of diseases in various regions, that the intensity of disease frequency in correlation with solar activity varies between regions , and is maximal for heliosensitive zones (for example, cardiovascular diseases).

4. These heliosensitive zones are also remarkable for the high frequency and density of the self-luminous formations appearing in these zones, and that their frequencies is dependent on the state of the Solar activity. Therefore we cannot say that Solar activity is dependent on these zones and luminous phenomena occurring there, but that these phenomena most often appear in these zones and in connection with solar activity.
(Note by: Andrew Tetenov)

References

1. Vasil'yeva G.Ya.,Kuznetsov D.A., Shpitalnaya A.A. On the question of galactic factors' influence upon Solar activity. "Solar Data", 1972, , N9, p. 99- 106 (in Russian).

2. Kurt V. G. Interstellar medium and it's interaction with stars. Zemlya i Vselennaya (Earth and Universe), 1994,N5, p.3-10. (in Russian).

3. Parker E.. Space magnetic fields (their formation and manifestations). -Ì.: Ìèð, ÷.2-ÿ, 1982, 469ñ.

4. Zakoldaev Yu.A., Shpitalnaya A.A., Efimov A.A. Cyclic pattern and evolution of geology processes as a consequence of Sun's circulation in anisotropy interstellar space. // New ideas in interaction of sciences on Earth and Universe (Internat. conference transactions). Sanct-Peterburg., 1996. - p. 23-24.

5. Kruzhevskii B.M.,Petrov V.M, Shestopalov I P. On radiation conditions forecasting in interstellar space. / Kosmicheskiye Issledovaniya (Space research), v. 31, no. 6, - 1993. - p. 89-103.

6. Dmitriev A.N. Mahatmas and the Science of new quality of Solar System. Tomsk. Human Sciences Institute, "Natural Sciences" series, 1995.

7. Science News, 1994. 144. 334.

APPENDIX 1
From Exodus to Voyager II
The Velikovsky Connection

I wrote the following text with drawing in 1982. It is reproduced here exactly as I wrote it in 1982 to give you a feeling for how my material and sentiments have remained the same over the past decades. It also shows how predictable would be the astronomical community migration of ideas to become slowly what I had been saying all along … what I have since come to call "the creeping crud" (the term I created for the constant migration of traditional astronomical beliefs to adopt my work but without recognition).

Read the following with the understanding that this was written in 1982, however it could be equally as valid today as then … except for some noted improvements in understanding that of course have occurred since that time. Notice how my weather work was already well formed in this writing and the understanding that of the electrical nature of weather, storms and the relation of the Electrical Universe to the physical earth (e.g. in triggering earthquakes and volcanoes as well as mountain formation and other geological effects caused by the passage of a large foreign celestial object).

From Exodus to Voyager II
The Velikovsky Connection
J.M. McCanney (1982)

Darkness engulfed a land of poisoned water and fiery rains. Reddish-blue fingers of auroral death performed satanic dance among the clouds. The decimated slave nation sealed their doors, covered chimneys and prayed their god to avenge 200 years of Egyptian bondage. Desperate to end the plagues wrought over his empire, Pharaoh searched the alleys for the slave profit Moses to deliver his surrender, "Go, take your people, all is ruined".

Fleeing into the wasteland, the multitude packed only the next day's bread. The air reeked of ozone as they reached the Red Sea. Pillars of swirling electrical smoke plumed skyward. Deafening strokes of cosmic lightning thundered like marching hooves along the Sinai. And now, besieged by armies from behind, with a raging comet in their path, a doomed nation's cries awakened as a miraculous wall of water arose to devour the Sphinx's pride. The waters were moved and the throngs escaped over what was once the sea bottom.

Studying at Columbia University in 1946, Immanuel Velikovsky began to unravel the tales of destruction handed down from cultures of ancient lands. His goal was to search for and hopefully establish a single world wide event with the goal to establish a time line for chronology of world history based on correlated events from around the globe. He was a rare man, educated and science, psychology, law, ancient languages and history. His father had been the curator of the Museum of Natural History in Israel. He grew up reading ancient texts in the oldest area of western history.

Treating ancient scripts as a psychoanalyst would a traumatized patient, the patterns began to emerge. Ancient calendars had been revised with the birth of a new celestial god. The other gods made war and the new planet (Venus) formed from a comet, ravaging earth on two separate occasions. All mankind stood in awe as the comet's snakelike protrusion lashed out at Mars, lifting off its oceans and atmosphere, changing the once blue water planet into the dry red hulk we see today.

As the same comet passed Earth years later on its ravaging path through the solar system, earth's rotational poles were shifted by as much as 30 degrees. Previous tropical regions were shifted north. Mastodons were flash frozen in what is now called Siberia with fresh tropical plants undigested in their throats, while the old north polar cap (what we call today the Laurentian Ice Shield) melted to form the Great Lakes and forge out the upper Mississippi River Valley. Other areas of the earth were dramatically altered and glaciers formed as earth was plunged into an ice age.

Worlds in Collision (1950) , Earth In Upheaval (1955) and Ages in Chaos were embraced by millions in hardcover, going through countless printings and were translated into 14 languages. His astounding results contradicted beliefs in every major area of traditional western knowledge.

Academia was outraged. None could accept the notion that instant geological catastrophe could encompass the earth, wiping out civilizations, creating new mountain ranges, changing shorelines or ensnaring whole nations in noxious brimstone; with all is taking place not in billions of years but in days and even hours, and only a few thousand years ago.

Scientists leveled a boycott on McMillan press forcing it to relinquish publishing rights to these books and Velikovsky was banned from speaking at Princeton for conducting his "pseudo-science". The "crazy old man" had to be stopped. It was a young aspiring astronomer named Carl Sagan who led the onslaught, bringing the 76-year-old Velikovsky to face an Inquisition of traditional scientists at the 1974 meeting of the American Association for the Advancement of Science (AAAS). The outcome was predictable, "Velikovsky had been proven wrong".

That was in 1974, before we had sent sophisticated satellites to Venus, to Jupiter and Saturn. Subsequently, some of Velikovsky's illusions have been verified; "Horned" comets, radio noise from Jupiter, Venus' high temperature and a host of other predictions based on statements made by the ancients of what they had seen in the heavens. Modern science had never seen a giant comet, and in fact to this day modern scientists deny that giant comets and the effects that they produce could possibly exist.

At the time, it was easy for traditional scientists to point out all the mistakes Velikovsky had made, while never realizing their own. The arrogant space scientists could not imagine that the theories they based their results on could possibly be wrong. However, as space concepts rapidly adjusted to a wealth of new data, it soon became apparent that the only mistake Velikovsky made was in adopting the astronomical theories of the 1950s in his attempt to reconcile humanistic and geological findings with "science". It is now clear that a radically different theory for comet behavior and solar system formation support Velikovsky's hypothesis of Venus, the great comet, becoming a planet and in the time frame as stated by the ancients. ***But more than this, the scientists that attacked Velikovsky did not catch the subtle point that he was not studying or attempting to portray new theories of astronomy, but was studying ancient calendars and chronology of world history!***

The list of books that one must study to envision the scope and complexity of the subject is extensive and diverse, and these have literally never been read by the harshest critics. It has become apparent that Astronomers simply made a cursory reading of Velikovsky's material and since it did not agree with their wisdom of the day, they dismissed this work out of hand without the slightest consideration to look for possible solutions ... or to search for errors in their own primitive theories.

To mention just a few of the books one must read to begin studying this complex area of study ... THE OCCULT, Colin Wilson's life long study of the origins of magic and religion, agrees with Velikovsky's interpretation of the great deluge which was not simply 40 days of rain but also a tidal bulge of the Earth's oceans. This definitely implies a close gravitational encounter with a large celestial body. Wilson's arguments were similarly based on historical and geological records.

In America's Ancient Civilizations, A. Hyatt Verrill's accounts of the pre-Maya (Cocle) and pre-Inca cultures of Central and South America paints the same picture with the "plumed serpent god that ruled the sky" - Quetzalcoatl - carrying the ocean on his back, with his heart becoming a planet Venus. These early tribes were quite different from their successors and their massive stone cities of that prior era met sudden and violent downfalls.

Louis Ginzberg's The Legends of the Jews, describes in great detail the devastated Israelite nation wandering in the desert laced by the comets fury. Burning naptha rains blistered the skin and fiery brimstones crashing in from above smashed trees. During the three-day walk to the Red Sea they tell of high winds, the trembling earth, a world thrown into darkness and finally they speak of the "pillar of cloud with its pillar of fire" that blazed in the sky to light their journey, accompanying them for the next 40 years.

But we're told by traditional astronomers that the solar system originated 4.5 billion years ago and very little has happened since, that comets are harmless little balls of ice that sublimate when near the sun, having nothing to do with the origin of the planets. Mounting evidence indicates that none of these statements are true.

There has been a great deal of politics in ***the interpretation of data*** from space probes, and today the government controlled media has presented only the party platform of NASA and related scientists. As stated recently by one English physicist, "with its axiomatic starting points, it makes one wonder if Astronomy even qualifies as a science". A thorough and objective look at the technical literature shows that there are many anomalous observations, which are being ignored until "proper explanations can be found".

In Venus' atmosphere for instance, the high concentration of Argon 36, an element found only in the primitive solar system (the byproduct of a short half-life radioactive element), and the dark side luminosity are without explanation, while the much advertised greenhouse effect has been rejected by Russian scientists who have collected a good deal of data at Venus' surface. More fundamental than the unexpected high surface temperature, no one has shown why or from where Venus, assumed to be Earth's twin, obtained an atmosphere a hundred times denser than earths.

Only a few short years ago NASA scientists proclaimed that Jupiter and Saturn were expected to be composed of frozen balls of hydrogen. On a close approach we find both to be hot star-like objects. Scientists believe that comets are composed of ices also, but we have never witnessed the comet at close range.

[Recall, this article was written in 1982...in 2004 as this book goes to press, this "prediction" was born out since we have now visited 3 comets at close range and in fact their nuclei are seen to be hot dry rocks with no ice or snow]

Scientists did not believe that electric fields could exist in space and have maintained that gravity explains all the movements of the cosmos. But as Voyager I and II passed Saturn, a small star in its own right, and its ring system ... they were discovered to abound with phenomena not explained by gravitational or magnetic fields alone. Electrical discharges billions of times more powerful than lightning bolts on Earth snapped among the rings, causing rotating spokes and expanding 20,000 km in the space, forming in a matter of minutes and vanishing just as quickly.

Only electromagnetic noise, the radiation given off by electrical discharges, has been recorded to date. No spacecraft has ever carried a static electric field sensing probe because scientists did not expect to find such fields. So we must search the data for the apparent side effects. For example, Kepler's Laws of celestial mechanics specify that objects subject to gravitational attraction will move in circular or elliptical orbits around the central star. An object is said to wonder if after calculating the "Keplarian orbit", including well-known planetary attractions, a deviant motion is detected. The wanderings of the planet Neptune have never been explained. Comets are known to wonder in their orbits and our moon and the asteroid moon Phobos of Mars have been known to wonder in their orbits since the 19th-century when detailed measurements were first made. The Voyageur Saturn rendezvous reaffirmed that gravity is not alone in the cosmos when Saturn's smallest moons were found to greatly affect charged particles and even the metal spacecraft in their vicinity.

Traditional theory regarding galaxy and star system formation depends on the spontaneous and rapid gravitational collapse of gas and dust clouds that we see permeating outer space, but astronomers observe that the huge "megallanic" clouds (those clouds with no central core object) are not collapsing at the rate expected, in fact, they're not collapsing at all. Traditional astronomical theory claims that small proto-planets must have formed from the collapse of the early solar nebula, and then quickly conglomerated to form the planets, moons and asteroids an estimated 4.5 billion years ago. But if cosmic clouds 10 times the mass of our sun cannot collapse, then how did the hot little planets form and by what process did the alleged frozen comets separate out of the nebular cloud? There is much speculation concerning these questions, but these are just theories with no substantiation ... and as with all data that are collected, the topic is open to interpretation.

The "red shift", the measuring stick of astronomers, is also under controversy. The Big Bang theory of the universe rests entirely on the validity of the Red shift interpretation, which scientists have used for the past 50 years to indicate that all matter in the universe is moving away from us. However, associated quasars and galaxies emit distinct red shifts and our sun exhibits an anomalous red shift at its edge. Neither observation is accounted for by the standard explanations of special and general relativity. Is the universe truly expanding or are we observing red shifted photons moving through electric fields that surround stars?

The theory of plate tectonics has its share of unexplained phenomena also. Venus has no tectonic boundaries as does earth, yet is has fully developed mountain ranges. Tectonic theorists have never identified the energy source which creates the Herculean forces that supposedly move entire continents around the globe. How can such a fundamental question be ignored?

As early as 1978 investigations led me to understand how gravitational and electric fields combine to create the characteristic comet shape around the charged asteroidal nucleus and how, if the comets were large enough, planets and moons could form by "capture processes" involving this new type of comet. It showed comets to be attracting the dust and ions in the tail area by electrical forces millions of times stronger than gravitational forces alone. The comets were building up matter and not melting away as explained by the popular iceball comet model, and the nucleus was now predicted to be composed of a hot dry rocky material. If the comet nucleus were massive enough (e.g. it had sufficient gravity to hold the material it was gathering) it would continue to grow.

Most importantly, anomalous observations could now be explained by a new understanding of the importance of electric fields in the cosmos. In addition, the new theory explains in great detail the observations of the ancients as they watched the comet Venus being captured by Jupiter to become the planet we know today. My estimate is that the entire process from capture to final planet took approximately 600 years.

In short, Velikovsly was correct in his interpretations of the ancient texts, and as already noted, his only mistake was in adopting the incorrect astronomical theories of the 1950's that were still in vogue in 1974 when Astronomers "proved him wrong". We see today that it was in fact the astronomers who were totally wrong.

To illustrate how a planet is born from a large comet, a hypothetical example can be devised by combining the concepts of the "Plasma Discharge Comet Model" comet theory with historical records as deduced from ancient texts.

[The diagram on the next page was drawn to accompany this article in 1982 and is still as valid today as it was then ... the second drawing was included recently to give the example of "capture" of a large comet moving through the solar system after being captured by a larger planet like Jupiter ... the comet then wanders through the solar system encountering planets which changes its course and it is also influenced by the comet "tail drag" which causes the orbit to spiral ever inwards while also circularizing the orbit until it becomes a stable planetary orbit]

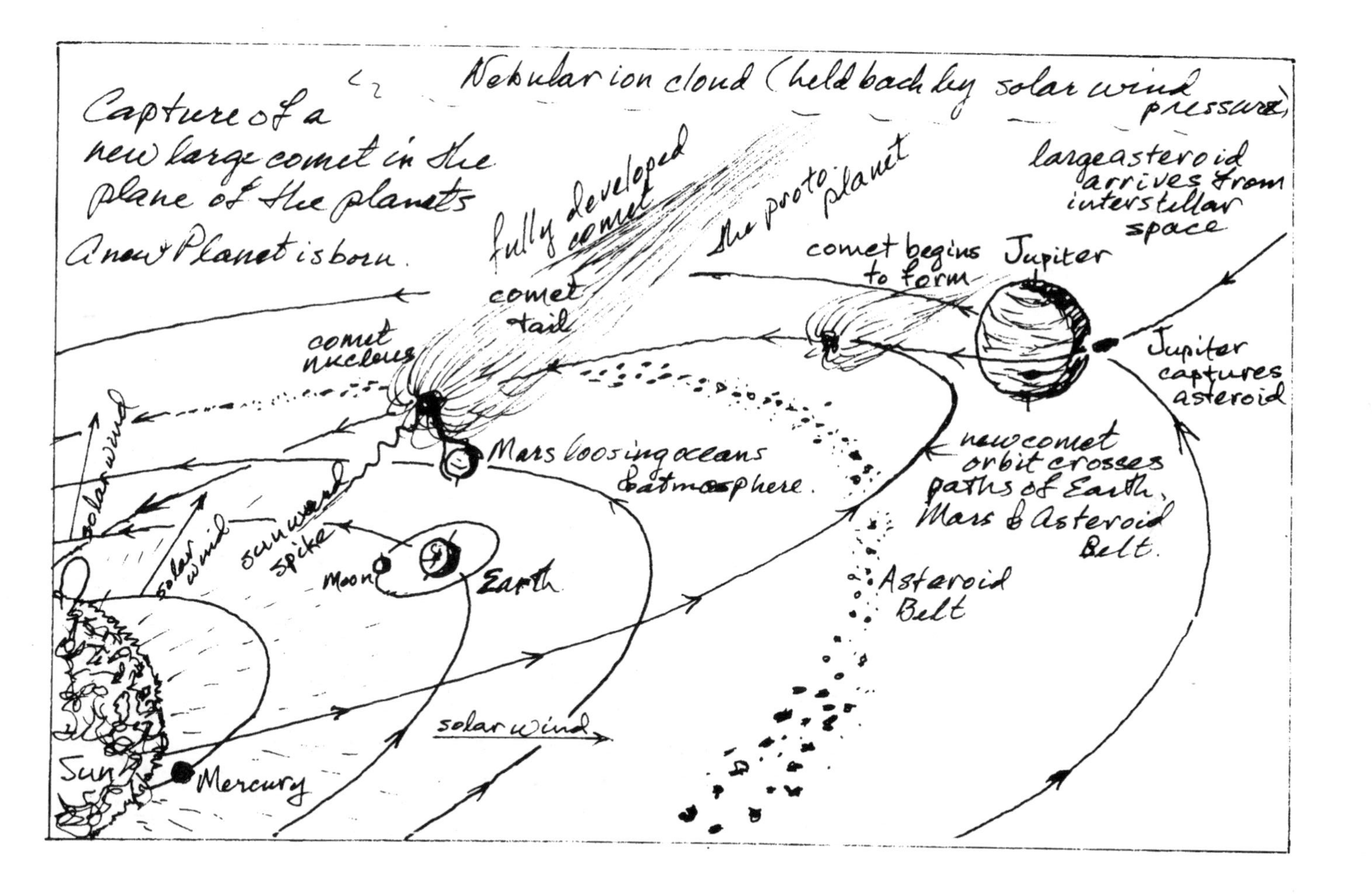
Capture of a
new large comet in the
plane of the planets
A new Planet is born.
Nebular ion cloud (held back by solar wind
pressure)
fully developed
comet
the proto-
planet
large asteroid
arrives from
interstellar
space
comet begins
to form
Jupiter
comet
tail
comet
nucleus
Jupiter
captures
asteroid
Mars loosing oceans
& atmosphere.
new comet
orbit crosses
paths of Earth,
Mars & Asteroid
Belt.
solar wind
sunward
spike
Moon
Earth
solar
wind
Asteroid
Belt
Sun
Mercury
solar wind

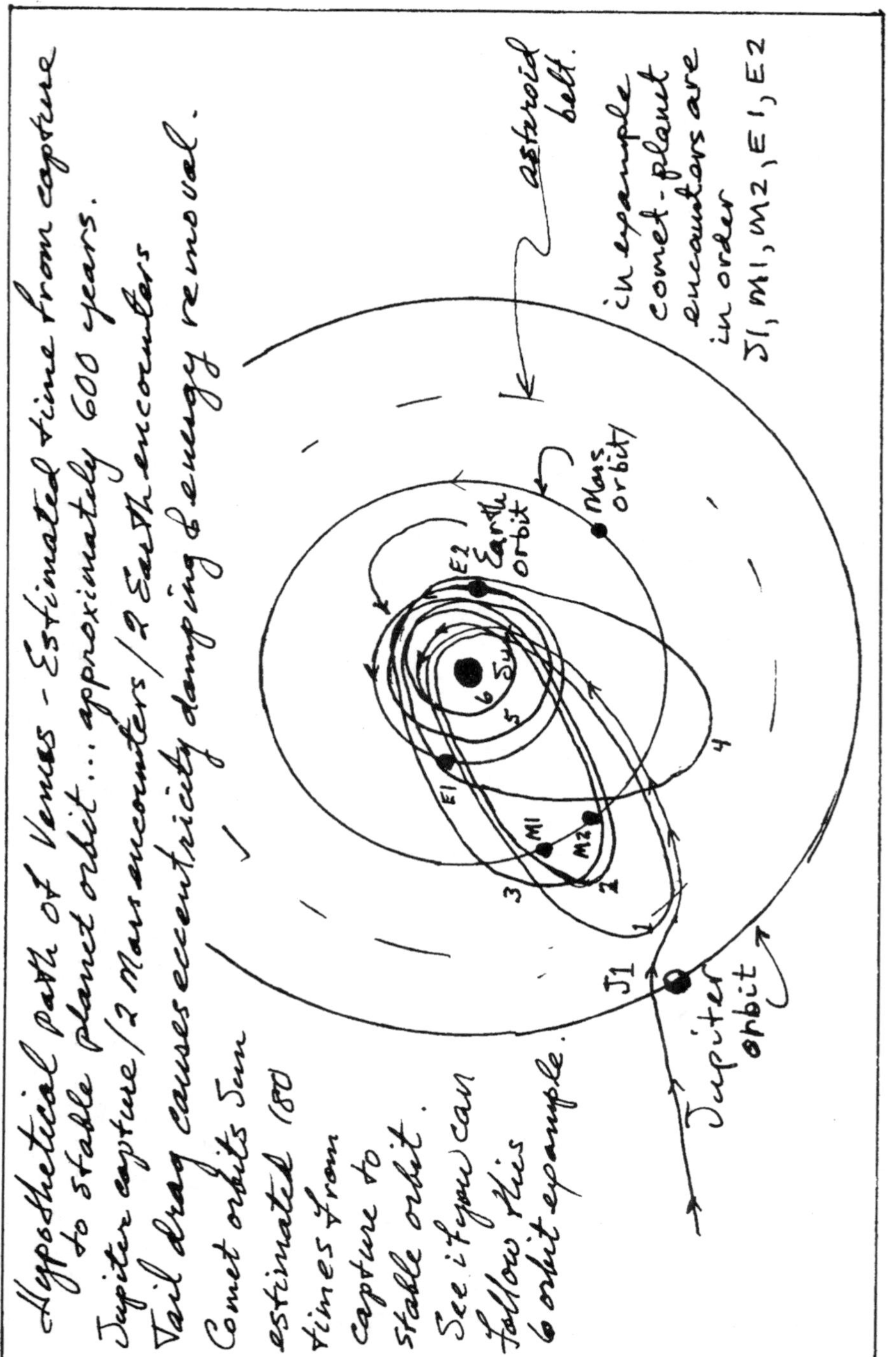

Hypothetical path of Venus - Estimated time from capture to stable planet orbit... approximately 600 years.

Jupiter capture / 2 Mars encounters / 2 Earth encounters

Tail drag causes eccentricity damping & energy removal.

Comet orbits Sun estimated 180 times from capture to stable orbit.

See if you can follow this 6 orbit example.

J1

1

2

3

4

5

6

M1

M2

E1

E2

Sun

Earth orbit

Mars orbit

Jupiter orbit

asteroid belt.

in example comet-planet encounters are in order J1, M1, M2, E1, E2

[Note on the drawing of the previous page that it is estimated that the orbital path of Venus took at least 600 years from the time it was captured to the time it settled into a relatively stable circular orbit that we see today ... the diagram shows only 6 hypothetical orbits to allow you to follow the path with a pencil and see if you can envision the capture by Jupiter, 2 encounters with Mars and the 2 encounters with earth before obtaining a stable near circular orbit ...and now to continue with the original text of <u>From Exodus to Voyager II – The Velikovsky Connection</u>]

Our hypothetical story begins cerca 2000 B.C. when an unusually large asteroidal body, 1200 km in diameter, approaches the far reaches of our solar system after traveling 35 light-years through interstellar space. Its origin was either a stellar Nova (called a Nova remnant) or possibly the remnants from a tremendous cataclysmic collision of celestial bodies that occurred in the unknown times of the distant past in some distant star system. Its composition is dense crystallized metallic rock and contains radioactive material with a large inherent magnetic field. Left unaffected, it would have passed 360 million kilometers from the sun. But Jupiter's position in its orbit brings them on a near collision course. The massive gas planet captures the future comet nucleus by the well known "energy transfer" effect of celestial mechanics used in reverse to hurl the Voyager spacecraft to the far reaches of the solar system. Comets like Lexell (1770) and comet Brooks II (1886) underwent similar orbital changes when they encountered Jupiter, their new orbits passing between Jupiter and passing very near the sun.

From earth, the ancient pre-Maya, Chinese, Babylonian, and Egyptian astronomers could see Jupiter brightening as the asteroid penetrated its radiation belts, igniting the charging process just as modern astronomers have observed with comets Brooks and Bielas. "Venus was born of Jupiter" (Athena was born of Zeus) as the newly captured comet flared out its new tail and ignited into brightness as it moved away from Jupiter to begin traversing the inner solar system. She continued to be visible in the day and night sky for the next 600 years as an immense comet. By chance its orbit lay in the plane of the planets (the ecliptic) and twice every seven years, crossed the orbits of Jupiter, Mars, earth and the asteroid belt.

Again this is not different from small comets seen today, 50% of which move very close to the ecliptic. Jupiter, Saturn, Uranus, and

Neptune all have families of captured comets that are well documented in today's astronomical literature.

Inca, Mayan, and other American natives began worshiping Quetzalcoatl, the plumed serpent of the sky with his long extended tongue, making human sacrifices to appease the monsters anger when he drew near. They developed rituals by which they would paint blood over the door of their houses, close their doors and remained in hiding on a certain night every 54 years. If they emerged the next day and the comet had not destroyed the earth, they would rebuild their temple cities (actually putting a new layer on top of the existing temple cities) in honor of Quetzalcoatl who did not destroy the world. The most dominant deity in all of meso-american culture was Quetzalcoatl ... the plumed serpent of the night sky whose heart (the huge comet nucleus) eventually became the planet Venus.

The solar wind of protons and electrons, which is constantly blown off by our sun, holds back the sparse cloud of positively charged gasses and dust found beyond the orbit of Jupiter.

[Note that when this was written in 1982, the current sentiment amongst astrophysicists was that the outer boundary of the sun, known as the heliopause, would be found around the orbit of Jupiter ... since then satellites have passed the planet Pluto and still have not encountered the end of the solar wind and the influence of our sun].

This giant cloud of positively charged material that surrounds the sun creates a giant cosmic capacitor with the negatively charged sun in its center.

[Note that the IRAS and other satellites have discovered hundreds of other stars in our vicinity of interstellar space that harbor these same clouds of dust and gasses]

Already charged to a high negative voltage from its encounter with the region near Jupiter's radiation belts, the asteroid (the proto Venus comet nucleus) enters the inner solar system, breaking the normal flow of solar wind and initiating the discharge of the solar capacitor. Positive ions and dust drain into the comet nucleus under electrical forces millions of times greater than gravitational forces alone, becoming visible from earth as the huge flowing comet tail. Additionally this comet is very large and its tail lights up like a giant neon tube as the immense electrical currents pass through the comet tail and surrounding clouds of hydrogen and other gasses.

The existence of the predicted mysterious charging processes were confirmed by the Voyager I and II satellites studying Jupiter and Saturn in the early 1980's and it is now certain that traditional astronomers did not understand these essential facts when they discredited Velikovsky many years earlier.

Electrons streaming out from the sun formed the other half of the discharge, manifesting in a twisting snakelike spike pointing towards the sun. The 6000-year-old rock painting of a comet found near Green River, Utah speaks for our native ancestors. **[this is the picture that was eventually used for the cover of the <u>Planet X, Comets and Earth Changes</u> book]** The ancient artist drew the comet twice, once with a huge comet nucleus visible and once without. Similar sunward spikes have been observed in comets Arend Roland (1957), Kahoutek (1973) and others as they neared the sun.

[Note that in May of 2004 I proposed a definitive test to prove that the comet "spikes" were truly sunward (and not optical illusions as stated by traditional astronomers) with a series of small comets passing near earth ... all 3 comets had clear broadside views allowing for clear viewing of the spikes as they could only be sunward given the geometry of the viewing angle ... all 3 clearly formed the visible comet spikes and proved conclusively that the standard "optical illusion" argument was incorrect and that all comets in fact have this sunward extension that is predicted and explained by the "Plasma Discharge Comet Model" electron beam ... It also explains the sunward side x-rays predicted by this model in 1979 and finally observed in 1996]

The comet is the ultimate nuclear linear accelerator, smashing atoms and electrons at energies only recently attainable by man. As a large comet nucleus builds up layers, this produces and stores up the long-lived radioactive elements whose decay will internally heat the planet for eons to come. This is the source of Argon 36 we see in Venus today.

Ancient astronomers knew the art of determining celestial orbits, but this new member did not obey the rules. Meandering wildly through the solar system, it was that named "the lawless one". Comets of our day similarly wander in their orbits; comet Encke always returning a few days early while Halley's is always a little late. The Plasma Discharge Comet Model explains this wandering is due to the drag the tail exerts on the Comet nucleus (this is also called energy disposal and eccentricity dampening).

Venus, the comet, used its electrical charge to gather a meteor stream by a force known in elementary physics texts as the "induced electric dipole force". Acting on pieces of space debris containing metals (meteoroids) this attractive force can be enormous at short range compared to gravitational forces. A huge comet can be likened to a cosmic vacuum cleaner, with the larger comets easily drawing in objects the size of railroad cars. The metal spacecraft attempting a close approach of a comet will meet the same fate and demands a properly designed spacecraft to insure a successful flyby.

The ancients watched as ever-present Venus began to dominate their lives. She had as many as seven separate tails at one time, stretching from horizon to horizon; explosive brightening appeared as celestial skyrockets. Her enormous sunward spike looked like a coiled Cobra, striking and lashing at everything she passed.

Then finally the inevitable happened. The comet emerged from behind the sun on a near collision course with Earth. With the comet tail blocking its light, the sun slowly dimmed, the comet nucleus becoming larger and larger in the daytime sky. Aurora's in earth's upper atmosphere increased until smooth snakelike discharges bolted between Venus and Earth. Hydrocarbons from the comet tail in the form of oil (the burning naptha spoken of by the ancients) mixed with burning volcanic ash and fell from the heavens. (For this reason we do not have to fight a war in the Middle East to secure oil, it is found everywhere on earth as geologists are beginning to find out). The stars "seemed to fall from the sky" as Earth encountered the comet's meteor stream and Earth was lowered into a stifling darkness. On the day of the close encounter, the gravitational wave of Venus (now nearly as large as Earth) shook the mountains, moved the seas and irreversibly altered the face of the Earth. The few people who did survive emerged to see the Moon's face running red with volcanic flows and so the legends have been passed on from every part of the globe.

From the ancient legends that are passed on, it appears that the second passage of Venus by Earth was the one that was far more devastating than the first passage. We know from the Mayan legends that this time between passages was approximately 54 years. However, this may have been 54 of the years chronology based on the previous Earth year, which we are told was only 360 days long. What is clear is that the year, the day and calendars in general were forced to change during this tragic time. Calendars did not solidify until long after these devastating events had slipped from the memory of man.

Hundreds of years earlier the ancients recorded their horror at watching the same huge comet as it passed near Mars ... ripping off its blue oceans and atmosphere and leaving the red deserted hulk of a planet we see today.

One cannot help but notice the similarity between these descriptions in the biblical tradition as told by Daniel and the many ancient texts leading up to our modern world. The tale is reiterated once again in Christ's message to this his apostles of the end day prophecies, "the sun will darken, the Moon will turn to blood, the stars will seem to fall from the heavens, and the powers of the heavens will be shaken; the mountains will tremble and every island will be moved from its place ... but of that day knoweth no man ... as in the days before the flood" Matthew (24:29-39). Clearly, the knowledge of these events and their power upon the Earth were well known to the ancients.

Mayan priest cults immediately began a new calendar based on Venus' first encounter and they re-occupied the cultural centers of Tulum, Palenque and Chichen Itza. It was 54 years later that the final close encounter with Earth occurred, giving rise to their belief that every 54 years Venus would again threaten mankind and they must rebuild their temple cities. Their legends also claim that the end of the world will be heralded by the arrival of a great comet.

Venus' elliptical orbit was changed to pass completely to the inside of Earth's orbit due to its multiple energy exchanges with Earth. Close range tidal forces in Venus' molten interior caused the new planet to always show the same side to Earth, a modern astronomical enigma. Slowly Venus' new elliptical orbit became circular from the continual drag of the comet tail. The comet tail reduced in size over time as Venus' orbit became circular. This effect ... the "tail drag" that causes the comet to work towards a circular orbit ... has been the key to understanding one of the most difficult analytical problems facing Velikovsky's hypothesis.

The problem was this: how could the highly elliptical orbit of a massive comet quickly changed to a near circular orbit. Traditional astronomy offered no explanation, so theorists "proved" Velikovsky's story to be impossible. It is now known that the tail drag performs this function. Within no the more than a hundred years after the final Earth encounter, Venus settled into approximately the orbit it maintains today. It cooled rapidly from an incandescent state by heat loss from its volcanoes, many of which are still active today.

Celestial evolution is similar to biological systems we have come to know on Earth. Of the countless celestial "seeds" blown off by the stellar Nova, or massive celestial collision, only a few will be captured by twin star systems and only a very few of these will become major comets which might develop into planets or large moons. The majority of comets are small and are evolving into asteroids and small moons that litter the solar system.

Statistical surveys show three results: the majority of comet orbits lay very near the asteroid belt; there are many more smaller celestial objects than large; Jupiter, Saturn, Uranus and Neptune all have associated "families of comets" indicating that the giant gas planets are indeed capturing comets into the solar system all the time. The ability of solar systems to capture comet nuclei coming from all directions in space and organize them quickly into neat circular orbits is a restatement of the quantum hypothesis. Because of the electrical nature of this central star and its stellar capacitor, theory now indicates that "Newtonian Space" is "quantized" ... just like the atom and subatomic space.

Nature's way is one of selective violence. This is to assure the constant mixing of the elements necessary for life, as with hurricanes or forest fires. Modern biologists have only recently become convinced that Earth wide catastrophes have led to numerous mass extinctions, the case of the dinosaurs being the most widely publicized. One theory suggests that a large asteroid punctured the Earth's mantle producing the volcanic island of Iceland with after effects terminating 75% of all life on Earth 65 million years ago. The problem with many of these asteroid extinction theories is that they do not address the other known factors that occurred around the same time such as magnetic reversals, mountain building all over the Earth and other major Earth wide devastation.

Biologists also see cases of gradual change in certain species during the long interim periods between the sudden mass extinctions. The picture that is emerging suggests a dual nature to evolution: it proceeds both by slow, long-term adaptation, however the more radical changes to the species occur during times of high stress or mass extinctions.

The search for the missing link has ended. Anthropologists have shown that human evolutionary changes coincide with the sudden reversals of the Earth's magnetic field, which generally accompany mass extinctions and brief periods of mountain building. The close encounter (not necessarily a collision) with a massive highly charged comet is suspected to be the cause.

Many recent articles by traditional theorists have reaffirmed their position that "the solar system was created all at one time 4.5 billion years ago and nothing has happened since". "Uniformitarianism" with a modern twist of celestial catastrophism is now well entrenched in all the academic disciplines, and today these groups hold the reins of the media. But as the data are analyzed, the hard facts are emerging. The records of sudden radical change have left their impact on the Earth. Man must look to celestial events to explain them, and low and behold the name of Velikovsky returns.

Literally every modern scientist that has recently "discovered" celestial catastrophism, including none other than Carl Sagan (who wrote in his book condemning Velikovsky that celestial catastrophies were theoretically impossible), has also had to explain why they arrived at Velikovsky's same conclusions, yet avoid the dignity of a reference to this monumental work by silently referring to the bogus 1974 AAAS Inquisition of Velikovsky. Basically they "proved" him wrong with incorrect astronomical theories and then proceeded to borrow wholesale his conclusions and work. I suspect this will continue into the future until history looks back with 20-20 vision to judge this incredible injustice.

The new comet model imposes important new directions on a view of life in the universe. We observed that 75% of all-stars exist in double star systems with many of the remaining 24.9% (which stand alone) giving evidence of smaller unlit companions. The sun -- Jupiter system is a smaller than average twin star, with Jupiter being the unlit companion. Celestial mechanics requires a twin star for the energy transfer to proceed, which captures comet nuclei into the inner solar system (any of the planets in fact can produce the same capture effect). Therefore, the vast majority of stars in the heavens are continually adopting new members, which will evolve into planets and moons, and some are given the essential atmosphere and internal heat that will assure the development of biological life systems. In some of the larger star systems, there could easily be many biologically active planets.

Earth too was once a comet. The oldest Earth rocks date back only 3.8 billion years, so a billion years elapsed from when the sun was formed to when Earth blazed across the sky and saw its fiery birth as young planet. That Earth's center has an extremely dense odd shaped core, the original cometary seed nucleus of our planet. This is how solar systems are formed.

The evolving planet cools from the super hot "nuclear stage", to the "chemical stage" (Venus present condition) with the onset of the "biological evolution stage" at temperatures below 200°F. Primitive "intelligent molecules" form in the random mixing of this primordial soup in the presence of extremely active electrical lightning and high-pressure conditions. Life will someday evolve on Venus and primitive or even advancesd forms of life may have existed on Mars before it lost its atmosphere to Venus only a few thousand years ago. Evolution seems to allow for an infinite variety of species, so plant and animal life on other worlds will certainly reflect this diversity. It would appear that a species would have to evolve on a given planet to make use of the environmental resources of that planet.

At this point, creationists would claim necessity of a divine intervention, but it seems that this designer works by a more wondrous plan. The solar system is a very dynamic place and its true history is becoming clear. When Athen's great statesman Solon visited Egypt in 572 B.C. to inquire about the ancient priest cults' knowledge of the flood, the historians told him of the great Deluge, the distruction of Atlantis, and that five different catastrophes had plagued their development in the previous 10,000 years. There is scientific basis now for believing that statement.

The spacecraft that Russia the European Space Agency and Japan have designed to examined Halley's comet have followed the NASA designed orbiter and are expecting to find a docile melting ice ball. The delicate craft however will encounter strong electrical forces and be hurled uncontrollably in around the comet nucleus.

[Note that this prediction in this 1982 writing was vividly confirmed as the French Giotto space craft passed close to the sunward side of Comet Halley in 1986 and was almost completely destroyed as it was thrown off course and all of its sensors went off

scale ... it measured directly they predicted sunward electron beam]

A Voyageur type of craft would be better suited with the addition of an electric field sensing probe and a device to measure directly the direction of the comet tail material movement. It should follow the well-documented comet Encke, which has a period of 3.3 years as opposed and Halley's comet which only appears every 76 years.

At stake is more than just verifying a theory. If Man is to endure for any length of time on this planet, he must understand the behavior of comets and how to control them, as with the Apollo asteroids which occasionally collide with Earth. The scientists who understand this have been handcuffed by NASA and other scientist's reluctance to admit the failure of long-held theories. We cannot predict when another major comet will be perturbed into the inner solar system, but it can be said with certainty that ***... it will happen again.***

Continental Shelves that Influence Tropical Storms